A NEW HISTORY OF
STEREOTYPING

The Power of The Printing Press is Far Mightier Than The Power of Arms. 1740

A NEW HISTORY OF
STEREOTYPING

by

GEORGE A. KUBLER, LL.D.

NEW YORK, N. Y.

1941

PRINTED FROM SILVERTYPE PLATES
PRODUCED BY THE
SILVERTONE STEREOTYPING PROCESS

Printed Letterpress in the United States of America
J. J. Little & Ives Company, New York

 199

FOREWORD

In 1927 I compiled "A Short History of Stereotyping," of which an edition of 6,000 copies was printed. The major part of these copies was donated to individual stereotypers in the United States, and the remainder of the edition was sent, upon special requests only, to schools of journalism, trade schools, public libraries and printing craft clubs throughout the world. In the course of the past ten years I have received a great many requests for copies of the little volume; however, none are left and thus to my great regret I have not been in a position to comply with these requests.

More than a decade has passed by since the book was published, and vast has been the number of new inventions and improvements in operating methods and of all kinds of innovations that have appeared during this span of time. Furthermore, research into the history of stereotyping has been continued and many new interesting facts have been unearthed. In the light of all these events the fourteen year old book may be regarded as antiquated, and for all the reasons cited I have undertaken the task of revising and augmenting the contents of the 1927 "Short History of Stereotyping."

In the preface of every one of the books I have published on this historical subject, I have stressed the fact, which I now repeat in respect to the present volume, that in writing the records I am writing solely as a compiler of historical facts. This present book is intended primarily for the erudition of stereotypers practicing their trade in newspaper plants or in job shops, and also for all other persons who may be interested in the history of the art.

I have added a few additional chapters to this volume that were not contained in the former book, and also, on request, have given a more detailed recital of the history of writing; I have furthermore gone to greater lengths than before in recording early American newspaper history; in doing this I have quoted passages from "The History of American Journalism," by James M. Lee, and "Printing in the Americas," by J. C. Oswald. Also passages from E. S. Watson's "History of Newspaper Syndicates" and from an article by the late W. Bullen in the "Inland Printer" of 1922. I also wish to express my thanks to Alexander Bradie for his aid in correcting the proofs and preparing the index.

As on former occasions, I again repeat that if this book will serve only one purpose, namely to instill in the American stereotyper the conviction that stereotyping is an *art* born thru centuries of hard, unceasing toil and research on the part of eminent men, and that in doing his daily bit he is carrying on the traditions of a craft and thus take additional pride in his daily task, I will feel most amply repaid for the time and labor I have spent in gathering and compiling the material contained in this book.

GEO. A. KUBLER

New York City
August, 1941

CONTENTS

A NEW HISTORY OF
STEREOTYPING

CHAPTER ONE

WRITING AND PRINTING

THERE ARE, IN the history of human intellect, three fundamental stages, and each one presents a tremendous advance over the preceding stage: Speaking, Writing, Printing. Through the gradual progress made by means of speaking, writing and printing, man became more and more qualified for that which is his particular privilege and which is the fundamental condition of his superiority, namely for the communication of thought.

Before entering upon the recording of historical data pertaining to the art of stereotyping, a short compilation dealing with the materials and implements used for writing throughout the ages will doubtless be of interest to the reader, as will a short recording of the history of the art of printing.

It is well nigh impossible to enumerate all the materials and objects which since the dawn of history have served for the reception of written and engraved figures and characters, designed for communication between human beings. At one time or another almost everything possessed of a surface adapted for the reception of written symbols has been used, either by necessity or often even when the necessity did not exist.

The most ancient samples of writing were found in Mesopotamia. These were the Chaldean tile tablets, dating back to several thousand years before Christ. These tablets contain a great mass of commercial and legal documents, such as bills, receipts, contracts, and so forth. They also have brought to us the knowledge of an entire literature. Herodotus, the Greek historian, mentions a letter engraven on plates of stone, which Themistocles, the Athenian general, sent to the Ionians over 500 years before the birth of Christ. Lead, however, and similar metals being less difficult to write upon, and more simple and convenient, afterwards superseded the use of such unwieldy substances as brick and stone.

Many centuries ago, an ancient book was discovered entirely composed of lead. Not only were the two pieces that formed the cover, and the leaves, six in number, of lead, but also the stick

[1]

inserted through the rings to hold the leaves together, as well as the hinges and the nails. It contained pictures of Egyptian idols. There were the Roman military diplomas, which were written on two bronze tablets. These were bound together through rings on the long sides, then wrapped in wires and the ends of same were kept together with wax, in which the seals of the witnesses were pressed. Lead and silver tablets with inscriptions were very often placed in the graves with the corpses. Even today stone tablets are used in the form of school slates. Another method was the pressure of engraved seals or signets into gold.

At an early period of their history, Greeks and Romans appear to have commonly used ordinary boards. These boards were written upon just as they were planed. Later on these planed boards were covered with wax. These wax tablets were carried in small bags, attached to the girdle with a string and took the place of today's notebooks. The general use of such wax tablets continued until 1500 A.D., and even up to 1783 such tablets were used in salt mines and monasteries.

The Arabians used the shoulder bones of sheep, on which they recorded remarkable events, carving them with a knife, and after tying them together with a string they hung these chronicles up in their cabinets. In the library of Ptolemy, which is said to have contained 700,000 rolls, were the works of the Greek poet, Homer, written in golden letters on the skins of serpents. Thus stone, metal, wood, ivory, bones, skins, tiles and many other materials were used for writing. The use of planed boards, and boards covered with wax, were in some measure superseded by that of the leaves of the palm, olive, poplar and other trees. A record of this custom may still be found in the word "leaf", which we continue to apply to sheets of paper, when sewed up in the form of a book. The mode of preparation, after cutting the leaves into strips of the length and width required, was simply to soak them for a short time in boiling water, after which they were rubbed backwards and forwards over a smooth piece of wood to make them pliable, and then carefully dried. Bark cloth, formed from the bark of a small tree or shrub, called the paper mulberry, which grew wild in the southern provinces of China, Burma and in India, was also used for writing purposes.

Before the art of paper making was known to the Chinese, they appear to have cut pieces of silk to such sizes as they wished to make their books, and thereupon painted the letters with pencils, the silk first being steeped in a kind of a size to prevent the color from running. But such material was liable to decay, and various animal substances of a more durable nature were afterwards employed. Skins were principally used, after being tanned, but bones and even entrails were also made use of for the purpose. The transition from these mostly stiff and rigid writing materials to others of a more flexible nature and permitting of a more extended use, was effected through the adoption of parchment, papyrus and paper. Hitherto all of these different writing materials could not be employed in the making of books in the present sense of the word, because they were not flexible and pliable, and durability was missing and their volume was too great when tied together.

Papyrus, from which the term "paper" is derived, is the name of a historical plant, once extensively used by the Egyptians for making various articles of utility, such as baskets, shoes, cordage and the like. This plant, once so useful, and for ages in Egypt so commercially valuable, has totally disappeared and is unknown to modern botanists.

With respect to the period at which the ancients began to make a writing substance of the papyrus, or of its originator, nothing definite is known.

Papyrus was described as a flag or bulrush, with a triangular stem that could hardly be spanned, and which grew to a height of ten feet, or even considerably more, in the immense marshes occupying a large part of the surface of Lower Egypt, a leafless wood, as it were, a forest without branches, the bare stem being surmounted only by a head of long, thin, straight fibres. The epidermis, or skin, being removed, the spongy part was cut into thin slices, which were steeped in the waters of the Nile, or in water slightly imbued with gums. Two layers were placed one above another, carefully arranged in opposite directions, that is, lengthwise and crosswise, which, after being dried, were finally smoothed and brought to a fit surface for receiving writing by being rubbed with a tooth or piece of polished ivory. The durability of this writing material is one of its best qualities. It can, in some instances, be rolled and unrolled after a lapse of many centuries without detriment to it.

So great was the importance of this manufacture at some periods that Firmus, who raised the standard of revolt in Egypt against Emperor Aurelianus, boasted he would maintain an army solely from the profits of his paper trade. The Egyptian paper factories, which were highly taxed under the reign of Tiberius, were very well installed, and during that period were already run on the principle of systematized distribution of different kinds of work. Thus there existed the Glutinatores (derived from the word "gluteum" meaning glue), who were pasters or gluers, then Malleatores (derived from "malleum" meaning hammer), who attended to the hammering. The ancient Egyptians called the papyrus plant "natit", but the Greeks named it "papyrus" after the word "papuro", meaning royal or regal. For the inner bark of the papyrus plant the word "byblos" was used by the Greek poet, Homer, and later on by the Greek historian, Herodotus, and from this word the term "byblon" was coined designating a written roll. From this Greek appellation the Romans constructed the word "biblium" meaning book, and finally the designation "biblia sacra", i.e., holy books, and from this our word "bible" was born. The papyrus paper industry automatically ceased to exist when, during the days of the Crusades, the Arabians brought Chinese hand-made paper to Europe.

The invention of parchment has this historical background: Eumenes, King of Pergamus (197-158 B.C.) appears to have endeavored to form a library which should surpass that of King Ptolemy Philadelphus at Alexandria, which is reported to have contained over seven hundred thousand volumes. In doing so, Eumenes so enraged the Egyptian ruler, Ptolemy, that he immediately prohibited any further exportation from Egypt of papyrus, which by that time was coming into very general use and thus effactually put a stop to Eumenes' emulation in that particular. It may be, however, that this prohibition was not solely occasioned by jealousy, but by Ptolemy's fear that his dominions, which were so much improved in arts, sciences and civilization, since the discovery and adoption of the papyrus, would be again reduced to a state of ignorance for the want of it. The plant sometimes failed in unfavorable weather, while the supply invariably proved unequal to the demand. The people of Pergamus, therefore, were obliged to devise other means, and the manufacture of parchment was the result. The manufactured article was brought on the market under the name "Charta Pergamena", i.e., pergamus paper, and later on was designated as parchment.

In the manufacture of parchment only sheep, goat and calves' hides were used, never donkey hides. The latter were used for making drums, and pigskins were used only for book binding. The preliminary steps in the manufacture were somewhat like those used in tanning—cleaning of the hair and flesh sides of the hides, then a thinning through scraping and rubbing with pumice stone. The

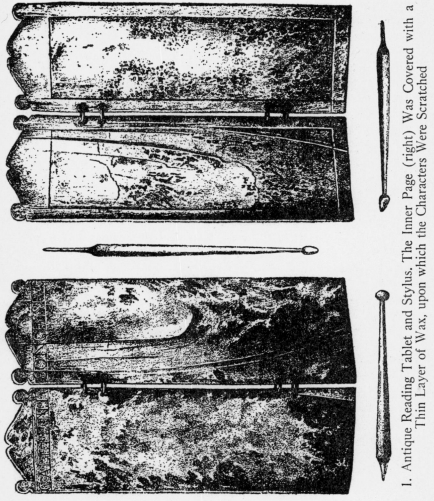

1. Antique Reading Tablet and Stylus. The Inner Page (right) Was Covered with a Thin Layer of Wax, upon which the Characters Were Scratched

2. Book Production in Rome

finest parchment was made from the skins of unborn lambs and were designated as virgin parchment. The rolls of parchment were read in the following manner: One began to read by unfolding, and continued to read and to unfold until at last one arrived at the stick to which the parchment roll was attached. Then it was turned around and one continued to read the parchment on the other side of the roll, folding it up gradually until the reading was completed.

The materials used to make paper were consecutively cotton, flax, then linen, rags and finally woodpulp. Paper is a Chinese invention made under the reign of Emperor Han-Ho-Ti, by the secretary of agriculture Tsai-Luen in the year 95 A.D. The Chinese made paper from vegetable matter reduced to pulp and carried it to a high degree of perfection. They employed the barks of trees, especially the mulberry tree, and occasionally from other substances, such as hemp, wheat or rice straw. The most ancient manuscript on cotton paper seems to have been written in 1050, and in the 12th century Egyptian papyrus seems to have gone into disuse.

The next step in the perfection of paper making was the use of rags, the paper being called rag paper. It was invented in the Seventh Century A.D. The historical background of the invention of paper is as follows:

The war between two neighboring Turkestan Princes, one of which called upon the Emperor of China for aid, caused the Governor Zijad ibn Sahib of Samarkand to start a war against this Turkestan Prince. In the month of July, 851 A.D., this prince was defeated, his army was forced over the Chinese frontier, and many prisoners, among them Chinese, were brought to Samarkand. Among these Chinese were papermakers. Since the raw materials used in China for paper making were not extant in sufficient quantities in Samarkand, and since there was no raw flax, this plant not being cultivated there, these papermakers took the fibres from used textiles, woven goods, i.e., from rags. From Samarkand the Arabians who had adopted this new method of paper making, introduced it via Puchara and Persia to Bagdad, where in the year 794 rag paper making was taken up. When the Arabs wandered from East to West, rag paper making came to Spain, where the first European paper mill was established in Jativa near Valencia (1154). Then it was introduced in Italy, from where it wandered north to Germany, where in the year 1290 the first Central European paper factory was opened.

In Nuremberg a paper factory was established by Ulmann

Stromer, who wrote the first work ever published on the art of paper making. Stromer seems to have employed a great number of persons, all of whom were obliged to take an oath that they would not teach any one the art of paper making, or make it on their own account. A short time afterwards, when anxious to increase the means of its production, he met with such strong opposition from those he employed, who would not consent to any enlargement of the mill, that it became at length necessary to bring them before magistrates, by whom they were imprisoned, after which they submitted by renewing their oaths. Two or three centuries later, we find the Dutch in like manner, extremely jealous with respect to the manufacture of paper, prohibiting the exportation of molds, under no less severe penalty than that of death.

From the fifteenth century to the year 1800 many improvements in the manufacture of paper from rags were made. For centuries paper had been made in sheets by hand. In 1799 the first paper making machine was invented and demonstrated by a Frenchman, Louis Roberts, a native of the little city of Essonne. The machine made paper in an endless roll. This invention cheapened the price of paper immensely and rendered the use of same possible to hundreds of purposes hitherto prohibitive.

In 1845 a German, named Gottlieb Keller, invented the method of making paper with wood pulp. During the eighteenth century a great amount of paper was consumed and a great dearth of rags started. This, together with the resulting increase in rag prices, brought on Keller's idea of a substitute for rags in the art of paper making. Keller had observed the work of the wasps, making their nests from wooden splinters. Examining the nests he found that they were like paper and he got the idea that one might use the fibres of wood to make paper. Although Keller had no knowledge at all of the art of paper making, he experimented in defibering of wood and finally hit upon a method of defibering wood with an ordinary grindstone. He tried boiling the resulting shavings, taking a small part of the putty-like mass out of the pot and spraying it on a table cloth. After the textile had absorbed all the dampness, a cohering flat cake remained, which proved to Keller that this material could be turned into paper. After years of patient experimenting and labor, he finally in 1845 sent a batch of his ground wood pulp to a paper factory; there this pulp was mixed with rag pulp and paper was first made from wood fibres. The invention of so-called "cellulose" or wood pulp treated chemically, was made

[8]

shortly afterwards, as was the manufacture of paper from straw and jute.

The instruments employed by the ancients to write with, and those employed in the Middle Ages, varied according to the nature of the materials on which they wrote. They may be divided into two kinds: those which acted immediately, and those which acted by the assistance of fluids. Of the first kind were the wedge and the chisel, for inscriptions on stone, wood and metal, and the stylus for wax tablets.

At first, the bare wood was engraved with an iron stylus; overlaying the wood with wax was a subsequent invention. The stylus was sometimes made of iron, sometimes of gold, silver, brass, ivory, or even of wood. The iron styluses were dangerous weapons, and were, therefore, prohibited by the Romans. The historian, Suetonius, relates that Julius Caesar seized the arm of Cassius, one of his murderers, and pierced it with his stylus. He also tells us that Emperor Caligula excited the people to massacre a Roman Senator with their styluses; and the Emperor Claudius was so afraid of being assassinated that he would scarcely permit the librarii, or public writers, to enter his presence without the cases which contained their styluses being first taken from them. The stylus was pointed at one end to form the letters, the other being flat, for the purpose of erasing them by flattening the wax. The stylus with which the letters were engraved was usually worn in the girdle as a prominent ornament of dress. As the stylus was too sharp for writing on parchment and Egyptian papyrus paper, and moreover, was not adapted for holding or conveying a fluid, a species of reed was employed, split on one end as our modern pens are, called calamus. Persons of rank and fortune often wrote with a calamus of silver.

From ancient authors, as well as from drawings on manuscripts, we learn that they used a sponge to cleanse the reed, and to rub out such letters as were written by mistake. Also a knife for mending the reed; pumice for a similar purpose, or to smooth the parchment; compasses for measuring the distances of the lines; scissors for cutting the paper; a puncher to point out the beginning and the end of each line; a rule to draw lines, and to divide sheets into columns; a glass containing sand for blotting and another glass filled with water, probably to mix with the ink.

The Chinese used pencils made of hairs for their writing. In the Seventh Century quills of geese appeared, afterwards quills of swans, pelicans, peacocks, crows and other birds came into use. Such quills remained in use until the year 1796, when Alois Senefelder of Prague invented the steel pen. He first used it to write upon his lithographic stones, and made his pen from a piece of hardened steel, from a watch spring. A short time thereafter steel writing pens were made on a manufacturing scale in the steel mills of England. The first mill for making steel pens exclusively was established in Birmingham in 1820, and in 1826 Josiah Mason, the owner, invented and put into operation specially constructed steel pen manufacturing machines. Up to ten years ago, the old-time Egyptian calamus, or reed pen, was in exclusive use among the Mohammedan peoples of the Orient, the name for the calamus in Arabic being "kelam".

The Boustrophedonic (ox-plowing) order of writing alternately from right to left was originated by a Greek scribe who saw an ox plowing and liked the motion. Later a left-handed Greek changed to our modern direction of writing, left to right only.

The composition and color of the ink used by the ancients were various. Lamp black, or black taken from burnt ivory and soot, from baths and furnaces, according to the historian Plinius, formed the basis of ink. The black liquor of the cuttle fish is said also to have been used for ink. From old manuscripts, from an ink stand found in Herculaneum, in which the ink appears like a thick oil, it is certain that the ink then made was more opaque, as well as encaustic, than that used now in modern days. Black ink was the first in use; afterwards inks of other colors were used. Gold ink was used by various nations. Silver ink was also common in most countries. One kind of ink, called the sacred encauster, was set apart for the sole use of the emperors.

In Rome, copies of books, records, speeches, etc., were readily, rapidly and cheaply multiplied by slaves, who were educated to serve as copyists or scribes. Thus the books of those early days were called manuscripts, from manus, the hand, and scribere, to write.

A word about booksellers: The booksellers hired the number of copyists they deemed necessary for the writing of certain books, 1,500 or more. A reader, or prompter, dictated, or read, in a loud voice word for word that which was to be copied, and thus the number of copies was quickly produced, enough to cover the expenses of the number of copies that were necessary to meet the demand. The Greeks alone composed over 3,000 tragedies and

Harvesting Papyrus

Papyrus Sheet

3.

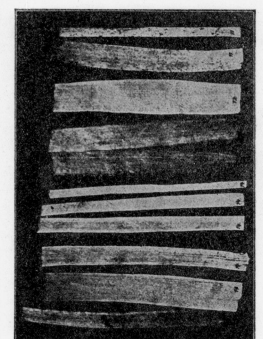

Papyrus Strips

[11]

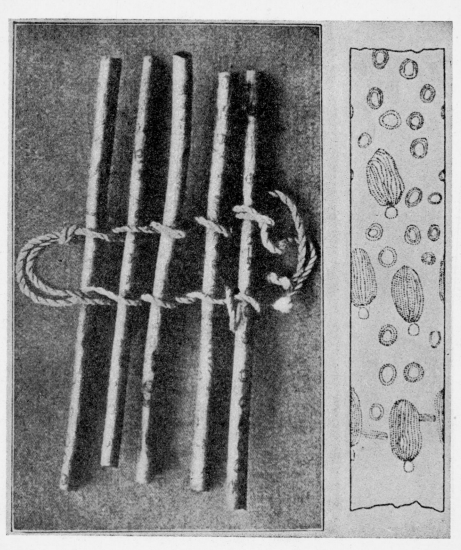

4. African Messenger Sticks
A Stick Unrolled

comedies, of which only 44 in the original state and in Roman imitations, have been conserved for posterity.

Ancient books were not commonly disposed in a square form, but were *rolled* up. Hence the word "volume," signifying a roll.

Writing of books by hand continued to be the only method practiced throughout centuries until the great migration of peoples was ended. The surging, driving ahead, the clashing together of the many different European peoples with the assaulting, onward storming tribes out of the East lasted for several centuries, and out of this turmoil there emerged a new European state formation. In this epoch of brutal might and endless battling, culture and scientific pursuit found but isolated havens of refuge. The remnants of learning and erudition took flight to the monasteries. Even the art of reading and writing, in the early Middle Ages, was known only to the clergy. The monks, almost exclusively, undertook the reproduction and multiplication of all spiritual and worldly statutes, bibles and other manuscripts; it was they who wrote the public documents.

The monks did not content themselves with simply copying; they developed it to an applied art. Some did the writing (scriptures), others compared and corrected the scripts and provided manuscripts with headings (rubricatores), and set them out in columns. Those possessing artistic skill painted initial letters (illuminatores), marginal adornments and miniatures (miniatores). The results of all this painstaking labor were pieces of veritable fine art, which were often bound in satin with covers of gold and silver, studded with precious stones. Cloth, linen, silk, parchment and vellum were used to write upon. Vellum, the skin of very young or abortive calves, was exquisitely stained in tints of rose, purple, yellow, blue and green. King Henry the Second was influenced to enact a law that of every work published in France one copy should be written on vellum and sent to the Royal Library, and this kingly order laid the basis of the splendid collection of vellum books in the Library of Paris. Books in those times were scarce and costly. Only the rich, the monasteries and the universities had libraries. The Countess of Anjou bought a book of Homilies, paying for it two hundred sheep, five quarters of wheat and the same quantity of rye and millet. The Cathedral of Notre Dame in Strasbourg was famed for its splendid collection of five hundred volumes. In Oxford, books were put in the pews or studies and chained to them.

The invention of stereotyping was one of the advance steps in the art of printing. It, therefore, seems that a few words dealing with the origin and development of the art of printing, before entering upon the data pertaining to stereotyping proper, will be of interest.

Printing is the art of reproducing a written thought, set up with the aid of movable, mechanically multiplied types, applying ink to this set up form of types, and making therefrom an indefinite number of impressions on a press.

It is difficult to state at what period the germ of the art of printing did not exist; some forms of printing were practiced at the most remote periods of antiquity. Cicero, the great Roman philosopher, has passages in one of his works from which the hint of printing was taken. He orders the type to be made of metal and calls them formae literarum, the very words used centuries afterward to describe them.

Coining money, by making copies of an original in gold, silver, copper or other metals, was also practiced by the Greeks and Romans several centuries before the Christian era. The Romans were acquainted with the art of printing. Agesilaus, king of Sparta, by strategem to animate his soldiers to battle, wrote upon his hand "nike", Greek for victory, and then by pressure imprinted the same word upon the liver of the slain victim, and the letters thus impressed became in the eye and imagination of the superstitious multitude a pledge of military success. We also learn of a Sultan who, on signing an edict, dipped his whole hand in blood, and then impressed the paper. The children of the Romans were taught spelling with the help of small tablets having elevated letters, which they combined in words.

Before its invention in China in the eleventh century, printing with the aid of a pigment was not known to have been applied to literary purposes. The Chinese were the first to impress upon paper, or similar substances, the reversed transcript of engraved characters, through the conjoint aid of ink and pressure. Each page was very neatly written on thin transparent paper, then glued face downward upon a smooth block of wood. The plain or white parts were cut away with most wonderful rapidity, and the drawing left in relief. Both sides of the block were similarly operated upon. The engraved wood was then properly arranged upon a frame, and the artist, with a large brush, covered the whole surface with a very thin ink; he then laid very lightly over it a sheet of paper, then

[14]

passed a large brush over it, lightly, yet so surely that the paper was pressed upon the raised figures, and upon no other part. One man printed ten thousand sheets in one day! The Daimond Sutra, printed in China by Wang Chieh, now on exhibition at the British Museum in London, is the oldest book known, the date is given as May 11th, 868. It consists of six sheets of text and one shorter sheet with a wood-cut, all sheets pasted together so as to form one continuous roll 16 (!) feet long by one foot wide. Each sheet is 2½ feet long by one foot wide, indicating the large size of the wooden blocks used. However, the printing of the Chinese appears never to have advanced beyond the style of wood-block books.

Block printing: The next step towards the invention of printing was the impressing of plates made out of one single block of wood upon which was engraved in relief the matter one proposed to print. In our days this would be designated as a wood-cut. Towards the end of the fourteenth century, the wood of the linden and of the beech tree was used, the matter carved with a sharp instrument in longitudinal sections; images of the Saints and playing cards were the first products made from such wooden plates. Great were the inconveniences experienced in the employment of these wooden plates, engraved in one single piece. It was necessary to make as many of these wood-cuts as the book had pages, engrave as many letters as there were in the copy, none could serve elsewhere than in the plates wherein it was fixed or engraved. The letters were without uniformity and the mistakes made by the engraver could be eliminated only by inserting in a solid block smaller wooden strips, which very rarely had the same stability as the full block of wood. These wood-cuts were alternately wetted with pigment and dried again, became bent and cracked, and were not of long service. In due time and through long practice, the wood engravers advanced to the stage where they carved entire books, primers which were called "donates." Donatus was a Latin grammarian.

Printing from these wood-cuts was not accomplished with a press; the paper was placed upon the form, the latter blackened with an earthy color, and then through application of a soft dabber the paper was printed against the picture or text. The back of the paper could not be used; these prints were all one-sided and a sheet printed only on one side was called Anopisthographic. In order to bind these loose leafs into book-form, two pages were printed side by side on one sheet of paper. This sheet was folded in the middle and the inner blank margins formed the back of the book. Even long after the invention of the art of printing, this kind of printing from wood-cuts remained in practice, and took the place of modern stereotyping. The wooden tablets for such pamphlets, of which several editions might be required, were preserved and used when needed. By the middle of the fifteenth century the art of reproduction was thus far advanced, and as intellectual life flourished, the craving for art and for the products of classical literature became more pronounced. Momentous questions pertaining to matters of the Church were the order of the day and awaited their solution. The time for the discovery of the art of printing was ripe, and it was, as soon as it became a necessity, not long in arriving.

From printing from movable, one-piece wood-cuts to the idea of printing with movable letters is indeed only one step; if one visualizes the printing block cut up in single letters, it becomes evident that one can assemble these letters to one's liking in other ways and thereby form a new text. The principle of the printing art does not consist only in the idea of assembling carved letters together, but in manufacturing metal letters mechanically, casting them in matrices, and to mechanically multiply with the aid of a press and ink the form set up with these letters. In one word, the invention of printing is bound up with the inventions of type casting, type setting, building of presses, press printing and printing ink. The invention of printing therefore was not simply a happy inspiration but the result of long search, laborious drudgery and oppressive worries.

Many are the cities who claimed for their sons the honor of having invented the art of printing. The Dutch city of Haarlem put forward Laurentius Koster, Schlettstadt in Alsace claimed the honor for its son, Johannes Mental; Peter Schoeffer of Gernsheim in the Palatinate, Pampilio Castaldi of Feltri, Italy, and Johannes Fust of Mainz on the Rhine, were convinced that they were the first discoverers of the art, but if casting and assembling of movable types are considered as the basic principle of the invention, then the honor goes to Johannes Gutenberg of Mainz, Germany.

Gutenberg arrived at his goal in the year 1452. His reflections, leading to his invention, seem to have been the following:

There are in the alphabet twenty-six letters, and the same letters are used over and over to spell many thousands of words. In a page of words portions of the alphabet are employed numbers of times; after printing has been accomplished with the solid

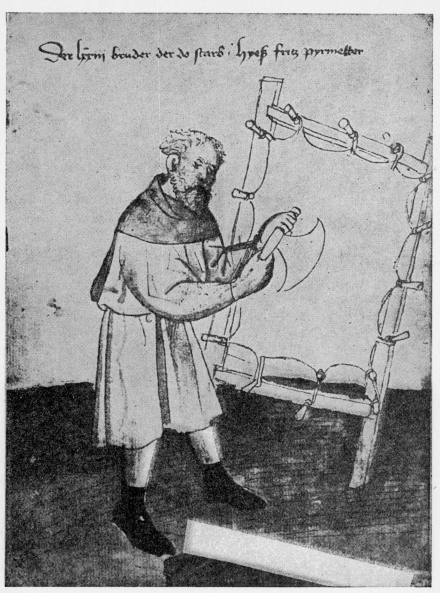

Der hirn bruder der do starb, hieß fritz pyrmetter

5. A Parchment Maker. A. D. 1420

[17]

6. A Scriptorium Showing a Scriber at Work. At His Right Is an Armorarium, or Book Cabinet. Conveniently Placed Are His Working Tools and Metals. (From Madan)

wooden block the carved letters are lost. If, instead of engraving the whole page on a solid wooden block, small movable blocks were used for engraving each letter, then the same letters could be used any number of times. The letters would have to be carved in wood with small handles to them so that they could be taken up and placed together as if one were spelling. The result of this reasoning was the birth of movable type—the keystone of the art of printing. Out of a piece of hard wood, Gutenberg sawed some thousand tiny blocks, a few inches long and very narrow. At one end he cut a letter in relief, and bored a hole through the other. After having thus furnished himself with a number of the letters of the alphabet, he placed whole words together, arranged them in lines on a string, until they formed a page; then he bound them together with wire and so prevented them from falling apart. Gutenberg then blackened his wooden type with ink and taking up the whole together, he pressed it upon a sheet of paper. It was the Lord's Prayer with which he made his first attempt at printing with movable types.

Instead of holding the type together with cord and wire, Gutenberg's next step was the invention of a frame with wedges to keep the type in place. Thereupon he constructed the press to imprint with; it was a simple wine-press, a common screw press. Ink softened the wooden type, injured the shapes of the letters and necessitated frequent renewal. Gutenberg first tried a method of hardening the wooden letters, but did not succeed. Then he and his associate Schoeffer experimented with lead. This, however, was too soft and would not bear sufficient pressure to print. They then tried iron but this metal pierced the paper. At last they hit upon a mixture of regulus of antimony and lead. This material proved to be of requisite softness and strength. As to ink, common writing ink would not answer, being so liquid as to spot the paper with blots. Finally, a mixture of linseed oil and lamp-black or soot was tried and found to be the right thing. The ink was applied to the type by a dabber, a ball of sheepskin stuffed with wool. It had the appearance of a huge mushroom.

Wearying of monotonous cutting of type, Gutenberg and Schoeffer began to make casts of type in molds of plaster. A new mold was required for each letter. Schoeffer thereupon cut impresses for the whole alphabet, cut punches and cast type with them.

Gutenberg's first important work was the printing of the entire Bible. Making one hundred Bibles took six men six years, working all day. His Bible was begun in 1450 and finished at the end of 1455, printed from cut metal types, not cast as we have them at the present day. Each single letter had to be engraved. Three hundred impressions were made on the press per day working it continuously. This Gutenberg Bible consisted of two volumes, the first had 324, the second 317 pages. The size is almost 12 inches high and 8 inches wide, printed in double columns. The initial letters in the parchment copies are in gold and various colors, in the paper copies they are painted in blue and red. Each page, with the exception of the first ten pages contains 42 lines, hence the designation of these Bibles as 42-line Bibles. Only 31 of them are known to be left, ten on parchment and 21 on paper. It is interesting to note that quite recently an American book collector paid $106,000 for one original copy of a Gutenberg Bible. Gutenberg's last important work was the "Katholikon", a Latin dictionary and grammar, finished in 1460.

As a contemporary of Gutenberg wrote, "Nothing yet invented by man, ever made such inroads on ignorance as this invention will effect. No more hoarding of libraries which kings and prelates and priests alone may read. The common people will also have their books."

The first publishers designated their profession as ars impressonia, i.e., the art of impression, and also they used the term chalcographic, i.e., metal writing. Towards the close of the 15th Century the term typographia, i.e., writing with type, was adopted. In the beginning the printers adhered to and copied closely the form, etc., of existing written books, mostly adopting the folio size and using parchment instead of paper. The octavo size of books came into use at the end of the 15th Century. The place and the year and name of printer of the imprints were not especially mentioned; later on they were shown as a postscript on a separate sheet. Titles appeared about 1476; before that year the titles were included in the first printed lines of the books. The leaves were without running title, direction-word, number of pages or divisions in paragraphs. The character was an old Gothic designed to imitate the handwriting of the era; no punctuation marks except colon and full point.

In order that the art of printing might not be divulged, Gutenberg administered an oath of secrecy to all the printers he employed. This was strictly adhered to until the year 1462, when following up a mighty strife between Diether, Archbishop of Isenburgh, and

Archbishop Adolphus of Nassau, the latter stormed and pillaged Mainz. The city was fired and the printing establishment of Gutenberg was laid in ruins. Gutenberg's printing franchise was revoked. Through the consternation occasioned by this event, the workmen believed that their oath of fidelity was no longer binding, they fled to other cities and to other countries, and there exercised their profession and instructed others in the art of printing. The end of the 15th Century saw this art exercised in the greater part of Europe. Among the many celebrated printers in Europe who carried on Gutenberg's invention and brought it to a high degree of perfection were:

Philippus de Lavagna, Milano, 1469.

Antonius Koberger, Nuremberg, 1473. His plant was equipped with 24 presses and employed over 100 men. He printed 19 Bibles and 2,000 other works; he was known as the "King of Printers". His "Book of Chronicles" contains over 2,000 wood cuts.

William Caxton, London, 1476.

Aldus Manutius, Venice. His books were designated as "Aldines".

Stephanus Etienne, Paris, 1532.

Christopher Plantin, Antwerp, 1555. This firm, Plantin-Moretus, is still operating and is the founder of the celebrated Museum of Printing in Antwerp.

Louis Elzevir, Leyden, 1580. He specialized in the printing of small size books, known as "Elzevirs".

Giambattista Bodoni, Italy, 1766.

John Baskerville, London, 1770.

Mrs. Glover, the widow of the Reverend Jesse Glover, non-conformist minister, brought the first printing press to America in 1638. In 1639 the first book was printed in the U. S. A., the "Bay-Psalm-Book".

At the close of the 15th Century over 1,000 printing plants were in operation in 250 different localities.

The term incunabulae or cradle impressions is used to designate books, printed during the period that began on the day the art of printing was invented and ending with the year 1500, thus approximately the span of time between 1440 to 1500. About 16,299 works were printed in that period, and as the usual edition was about 300 copies, about five million books were printed in these sixty years.

CHAPTER TWO

INVENTION OF STEREOTYPING

In the year 1795 the celebrated French printer and typefounder, Firmin Didot of Paris, coined the name "stereotype" for printing from solid lead plates.

"Stereo" in Greek means rigid, solid, and the Greek word "typos" means type, letter, character. Hence the combined word stereotype means a rigid, solid plate made of types. Stereotyping is the method of making of type metal perfect facsimiles of the faces of pages composed of movable type.

If we have reason to be surprised at the quick steps by which printing with movable types was perfected, we have more cause to wonder why, with the acquisition of movable types, the art became stationary. The transition from founding single letters to founding whole pages was so invitingly obvious, that the circumstance of it not having been attempted, may be imputed rather to a want of enterprise, than to any ignorance of the perfect practicability of the art. The art of printing from movable types was invented in 1452, and it was not until 1701 that the first attempts at stereotyping were made in Europe.

Printing from stereotypes is, in one respect, the reverse of printing from movable types. As described previously, the first books were made from solid wooden blocks, each of which formed a page. Then came typography (meaning writing, "graphein", from type "typos") the assembling of letters into words and pages, in which these pages were composed of numbers of separate types. There followed the period of the invention of stereotyping, in which pages again were formed by single blocks, i.e., where printed pages were solidified or made rigid in one plate. The distinction between the two is, that whereas the antique blocks were of wood, the later ones were of metal; and that while the one kind consisted of originals that were separately engraved, the other consisted of mechanically produced copies and were cast in a mold. The disadvantages of printing certain works with the aid of movable types which led to stereotyping were the following: It was necessary before redistributing types, that the total number of copies of which the edition was to consist, be printed at one single time and at once. Then again there was a great disadvantage in advancing capital for large editions, thus tying up considerable funds in standing type, and pages preserved in this manner were liable to become incorrect through letters being misplaced or dropping out. There also was always an element of danger involved through making mistakes in the new form, thereby causing offense and annoyance in books of a religious nature, or grave errors in technical, dramatic and classical works. Another danger was the jumbling of types ("pi") caused in the transportation of forms from one establishment to another. Before the art of stereotyping was invented, the forms of such works had to remain intact, and in some cases, for instance the Bible, thousands of pounds of metal types were stored away.

These many inconveniences led to experiments to overcome them; stereotyping was the ultimate result.

A Chinese Pioneer

It appears that the first attempt known to exercise a crude sort of stereotyping was made in China; however, the method used was later lost and never introduced in Europe. In the year 1041 a Chinese blacksmith, named Pi-Sheng, invented a method of printing with plates, called "ho-pan", or with plates formed of movable types—this name being still preserved to designate the plates used in the Government Printing Office in Pekin. The method employed by Pi-Sheng is interesting. He made a paste of fine glutinous earth, forming regular plates of the thickness of a Chinese piece of money called "tsien", and engraved upon them the characters most in use, making a type for each character. He then baked these types by the heat of a fire in order to harden them. He then placed upon the table a plate of iron, and covered it with a coat of very fusible mastic, composed of resin, wax and lime. When he wished to print, he took an iron frame sub-divided by narrow perpendicular bars of the same metal—the Chinese writing from above downward. This frame was placed upon the iron plate, and the types were then arranged upon it, pressed closely together. Each frame thus filled with type formed one plate or page. The plate being heated at the fire sufficiently to soften the mastic, a smooth piece of wood serving as a planer was then placed upon the composition, and the type was fixed into the mastic by pressure. By using two of these forms

7. Paper Mill of the 16th Century

8. Paper Mill. 1762

alternately the impression of each page was produced with great rapidity. When the printing from a plate was completed, it was heated again to soften the mastic, and the types were brushed by hand, detaching them from each other and freeing them easily from the mastic. When Pi-Sheng died, so says the Chinese chronicler, his friends, who inherited his type, preserved them as very precious, but discontinued the practice with them. Pi-Sheng had no successor and in the course of time the invention was lost.

THE OLDEST STEREOTYPE MATRIX *

In illustration No. 17, is shown a picture representing an exceedingly interesting curiosity, which years ago was acquired by Junius Spencer Morgan as a relief-impression and at the present time is preserved in the archives of the New York Public Library.

It represents the coronation, by the Holy Trinity, of the Virgin Mary, and as recorded in Matthew III, 16 and Mark I, 10, the Holy Ghost circling in the center overhead in the form of a dove. The inscription reads: SANCTA * TRINITAS * UNUS * DEUS *.

The original was most likely an altar chest (shrine) produced about the beginning of the 14th Century. Using this prototype as a model, the present metal plate with a few modernizations was produced about the year 1460 and is probably the work of a very skillful goldsmith. If duplicates in paper had been produced in the customary manner, the raised parts such as nose, halos, folds of vestments, crown, rays and inscription, would have appeared in black on white in the imprint. But in the illustration shown, just these parts are deeply molded into the paper. In like manner the production of paste moldings was effected, in that the plate was pressed down into the paste which was applied on the paper. In the present case, however, no paste, but paper pulp was used, similarly as it is employed in performing stereotyping with paper pulp. However, it is in no wise claimed that the production of this matrix took place almost simultaneously with the production of the metal plate; still the many, and most probably genuine, worm holes indicate a venerable age.

Investigations concerning the age of the paste impressions bring the conviction that at least a part of them belong not to the 15th but to the first quarter of the 16th Century. About 1525 duplicate

---

* "The Oldest Stereotype Matrix" by N. L. Schreiber, in Gutenberg Jahrbuch, 1927.

plates of initials and border ornaments were probably brought to the market, placed in trade and thus it appears possible that in that period some artisan had already discovered a duplication process or method similar to stereotyping as that art is understood today. Based upon the arguments just enumerated and explained, it appears that the paper stereotyping process harks back to almost the era of Reformation (about 1529). Indeed, it has been previously claimed that even then Conrad Dinckmuth of Ulm in Swabia, Germany, used a method of stereotyping when he, in 1483, printed his religious work in folio entitled, "Der Seelen Wuerzgarten" containing 134 pictures from only 19 wooden plates. Dinckmuth was a citizen of Ulm and founded, in 1483, the third printing plant of that city. He continued to operate until 1486.

A number of other scholars confirm the findings expressed above, and excerpts from their publications,[1] dealing with the first experiments in the art of stereotyping are herewith recorded. Attempts to make metal casts of relief printing through the medium of matrices, may be as old as the first invention of printing with mobile types. It has been proven beyond doubt that already in the 15th Century cast duplicates of plates cut in metal were made, most probably with the aid of the sand-casting method. Since this method was thoroughly familiar to the brass founders and goldsmiths of that period, the idea must have been near at hand to use it to make duplicates of carved printing plates. The original plate was pressed into moist molding sand and from the thus obtained matrix a cast was made in brass or type metal. It is established that on casts of plates cut in metal in the 15th Century there can occasionally be found a sinking of the plate towards its center and this is a typical occurrence in cast metal plates.

Impressions of nail heads, which can also be observed on these plates cannot be accepted as a proof that the plate had been cast, since the carved original metal plates had to be nailed upon a base in order to be printed, together with the type matter.

Furthermore it is an established fact that in the 16th Century, duplicates of wood cuts were cast in metal and that a regular business was established in the sale of such casts. Around 1570 this trade must have been quite important, because it is established that in many instances the same book illustrations, borders and

---

[1] "What did Gutenberg Invent?" by Gustav Mori, Mainz, 1921.
"The Origins of Duplicate Plates" by Johannes Luther, Leipzig, 1903.

initials were in the possession of, and used by, different book printers in widely separated places throughout Europe.

A proof that metal duplicate casts were used is found in the nail marks occasioned by the mounting of these casts on blocks; these marks show on the printed page. Our illustration No. 18 shows an initial made in the year 1582 and here the four marks made by the nails used to attach the plate to a base, are distinctly noticeable.

In any case we find in these plate duplication processes the immediate precursor of later stereotyping, and that art of stereotyping cannot basically have differed from these century-old processes. Of course, it is agreed that the beginning of stereotyping in today's sense of the word occurred when the copies were cast, not from rigid plates, but from type matter.

We do not possess any factual knowledge of how the casting operation proper was performed; it must be taken for granted that a sand casting process was used, and our knowledge of sand casting methods was hazy until the first printing manuals were published in the 18th Century. In his celebrated text book, Gessner [1] explains the method of sand casting in the following terms:

(In his description Gessner always refers to a "flask". The definition of this term is "a shallow frame of wood or iron used in foundries to contain the sand and patterns employed in molding and casting". In the following the term "casting tray" is used in place of the word "flask".)

The ingredients of casting sand are fine sand, to which is added calcinated baking-oven glue, the redder this glue the better. This mixture is finely pulverized and passed through a fine meshed sieve. Thereupon the mixture is placed upon a level board. The center is hollowed out and good beer is poured into the cavity—much or little according to the amount of sand used. This is well stirred with a wooden spatula. When, through the pouring of this beer, the mixture begins to steam, the mass must be well mixed in order that every single particle of sand is moistened. Then the sand is formed into a heap. Gradually and very carefully a little of it is taken up with the wooden spatula, making sure to separate the wet globules which stick together. When it is too dry it breaks easily in the casting operation; if it is too wet, it does not cave in when casting but cakes and falls out of the casting tray. By moistening it with spirits of ammonia it produces a clean cast.

---

[1] Christian Friedrich Gessner, "So Noetig als Nuetzlich Buchdrucker Kunst," Leipzig, 1740.

The type is placed on the flat sand or form-board. When a letter cut in wood or type high is to be reproduced, then straight boards or furniture must be placed around the form-board and the letter placed so as to protrude so high as to give the thickness of the cast desired. Then the face of the type is cleaned with a brush and the casting tray is placed over it, held down firmly with the left hand, so that there is no shifting.

Thereupon the type is dusted by means of a dauber filled with coal dust; then the moist sand is loosely poured upon it until the casting tray is filled up. At first it is gently pressed down and afterward harder pressure is exerted until the casting tray is firmly packed full. Thereupon the casting tray is evenly and gently raised. Should the type adhere to the sand, a tap on the tray with a knife will cause it to separate. The overflow of the sand is pared off at both sides of the tray with a knife so that this excess sand does not drop from the cast in the tray on to the type. The sand is delicately cut out so that the type metal may flow easily. By permitting the form to dry somewhat it flows much easier.

The form or figure is blackened with a candle having a good flame and is then placed on a level and smooth board, which is not much larger than the casting tray itself in such a manner that the side of the figure is situated below. In order that the flow of the type metal may pass over the board and well over the figure, place another board over it, enclose it tightly in the tray between the two boards in a hand vise and then pour the type metal in. When the metal is melted, roll a piece of paper together and stick it into the metal. If the paper chars, the metal is satisfactory; if a flame appears, the metal is too hot.

A method akin to stereotyping was used in Bavaria around the year 1566 by the celebrated geographer Philip Apian, or as he called himself in the Latin manner of the Middle Ages "Apianus". This man was a geographer born on the 14th of September, 1531 in Ingolstadt, Bavaria, and followed his father in that city as a professor at the university. He was forced, however, being a Protestant, to flee in 1568. He then became a professor of mathematics in the university at Tuebingen, Germany, and died there on the 14th of November, 1598.

Apian became celebrated through his Bavaria land maps published in 1568. His real name was Bienewitz. "Biene" translated into English means "bee" and in Latin the word for bee is "apis". All of the great savants of the Middle Ages latinized their names; hence

9. Johannes Gutenberg

ANNALES TYPOGRAPHICI
AB ARTIS INVENTÆ
ORIGINE
AD ANNUM MD.
Opera
MICH. MAITTAIRE A. M.
Hagæ-Comitum
Sumptibus Isaaci Vaillant.

i Joannes Gutemberg.   iii Laurentius Costerus.   iv Aldus Manucius.
ii Joannes Faustus.   v Joannes Frobenius.

10.

instead of using his German name of Bienewitz he used the Latin appellation "Apianus".

In the Bavarian State archives, housed in the State Library in Munich, are preserved some of the plates used by Apian for his map of Bavaria, published in his "Bavaria Descriptio Geographica", in Munich in 1455. This was printed in a folio of 24 pages. Christopher von Aretin stated in 1801, in his treatise on the oldest examples of the printing art in Bavaria, that this map was still, in many respects, the best map of the Kingdom.

Vincenz von Pallhausen in 1804 described the process in his treatise, entitled "Stereotyping Invented in Bavaria in the 16th Century", as follows:

"In the local government's archives are to be found plates which were used by the celebrated Bavarian geographer, Philip Apian, for the printing of his map or geographic chart of Bavaria. These plates prove conclusively that Apian, since before and after him no stereotypes were known, was the first inventor of stereotyping, even if not the first successful applier of this art."

These plates are in effect just what stereotype plates are today, of a tinny composition, and each of them contains, as do today's plates, an entire printing page. Either Apian did not understand how to apply this invention in the way we do today, or perhaps he did not desire to do so, since it was not essential for the achievement of the goal he was striving to attain.

His map was cut entirely in wood. The names of the localities, however, he did not desire or could not cut in like manner; thus he hit upon the idea of imprinting them therein. In order to accomplish this he invented the above referred to stereotype plates upon which as many names of places as he had room for were combined. The parts with the names he then cut out of the plate and attached with mastic onto the wood cut.

It may be that Apian cannot be proclaimed the inventor of stereotyping in the present day sense of the word, but on the other hand it cannot be denied that his plates were made in a truly stereotyping manner and that it would have taken a minimum of inventiveness in Apian's time to carry this out to the degree of perfection it has attained in our time.

To present the method pursued by Apian, Pallhausen had made and attached to his article an imprint, both of such a stereotype plate as well as an imprint of one square of the map. The first shows the stereotyping combination and the second shows the application made of same. (See illustrations No. 20 and 21.)

In an article on this process, Douglas C. McMurtrie states that the method of making these stereotypes was probably sand casting; the impression of type being taken in molding sand and the molten lead being poured in. This method was known to have been used at an earlier date for the duplication of wood cut engravings, a fact that Mori, the historian, and other authorities have already mentioned.

Hitherto it has been accepted as an historical fact that the so-called wet matrix process of stereotyping was invented by Claude Genoux, of Paris, to whom was granted a French patent on the process in the year 1828. Research in stereotyping processes which the writer conducted for the past few years has resulted in obtaining unimpeachable proof that the wet mat or papier maché process of stereotyping was not first invented by Genoux in 1828, but that in the year 1690, over 130 years before Genoux published details of his invention, the practical knowledge of a method of stereotyping, closely akin to the wet mat process of stereotyping, was common property throughout Germany and probably in all European countries practicing printing.

The foundation for this statement is to be found in a detailed description of making wet mats with macerated paper pulp and of molding and casting them (i.e. stereotyping), contained in a publication consisting of two quarto volumes, comprising altogether over 3,000 pages, printed and published in a second edition in 1696 in Nuremberg. The contents of these books are comparable to those of modern universal recipe books. The writer is indebted to Professor Dr. J. Schnack, Curator of the Library of the University of Marburg, for photostats of the original text, this institution being the only one known to possess a copy of each of the two books. It is probable that the first edition of these books was published in 1675; however, no library could be found possessing such a first edition.

A free translation into English of the title page of the first section of the work (see illustration) has the following text:

"A Manual for Persons Interested in Arts and Handicrafts"

First Part

Containing information on all kinds of very useful and well tested

and concerning Metallic Gold and Silver Assaying—Pearling—Fluxes—Folding and Covering.
Furthermore, Instructions for Making all kinds of Images and Figures—for Casting Glass and Artificial Fluxes—for the Making of all Sorts of Glass for Painting Purposes—for making Porcelain and Ceramic Objects—for Casting Metal Mirrors—for Polishing of Iron and Steel—and how to

ETCH

also Including many other Secrets pertaining to the Natural Sciences and Arts—derived in part from Personal Experience—in part from many well known Sources; Reliable Libraries, and honestly compiled by An Odd Admirer of the Natural Arts and Sciences.

A translation of the original text of the *second* part of this volume reads as follows:

"A Manual for Persons Interested in Arts and Handicrafts"

NUERNBERG,

published by Johann Zeigers
1696

Second Part

Containing Instructions for the Making of Beautiful and Well Tested Lacquers—Turpentine and Oil Varnishes—for Rare Multicolored Woodenware—for all Kinds of Colors for the Staining of Wood—thoroughly tested Methods for Gilding and Silvering all kinds of Objects—for Form Casting of Wood and other Materials—for making Beautiful Works in Mother-of-Pearl, Bone and Horn—and for all kinds of Cements and Glues to be used in the making of a Great Variety of Articles.
Likewise, Information about Beautiful Works of Art in Corals—different methods of making Turkish Papers, including other Curious Methods of making paper and Illustrations—on the Art of Etching and Drawing—on the Art of making beautiful Objects out of Marble—the Casting of Gypsum and Isinglass—information on methods of Polishing Colored Linen, Taffeta Cloth and Leather—on making Colored Parchment Transparent, and finally of making Scented Sealing-wax in all Colors.

All of this Information compiled on the Basis of Experience of long Duration and from Reliable Sources, painstakingly, diligently and at great Expense, and kind-heartedly imparted by an Odd Admirer of Natural Arts and Sciences.

NUERNBERG

Johann Zeigers
1696

The text in these Nuremberg volumes is couched in German in use during the Thirty Years War (1618-1648). To render this text into English as written in that epoch might prove interesting; however, employing modern English in addition to comparing the old method to present day stereotype foundry terms will no doubt best serve our purpose.

This is what is contained in Volume One, Chapter XLIL, number 14. (For original of page, see illustration No. 24.)

Preparing the Form: "If you desire to execute printing, proceed as follows: You will need a form made up of newly cast types and a perfectly true base or galley with adjusted furniture or sticks, these being of brass or lead. Place a case thereon, and lay the type form thereon. The quads must be of such a height that the head of the type protrudes hardly more than the thickness of a knife blade. All of the type must be corrected in the composing stick, then the type is placed in the galley and locked. Then take a small frame (chase) which is placed in the galley in which the type has been composed (assembled). This frame (chase) must be placed against the galley and should be about two fingers higher than the type surface. The galley in which the type is locked should have no screws, but it should be, in some other propitious manner and according to necessity, securely locked.

Making of the Wet Matrix: "Thereupon take paper pulp or white paper, well moistened in water (i.e. disintegrated, beaten) and spread this upon the type in the frame (chase).

Molding: "Then beat it in well with a brush in order that it may attain the same thickness all over. Thereupon also place the stone pan into the frame and screw the pan securely under the press. Thus the water will flow off; then remove it from the press. This little pan must be wider at the top than at the bottom in order that the paper mass (wet matrix) may fall out when it is cooled off.

Drying Table Operation: "Then place the little iron pan in the

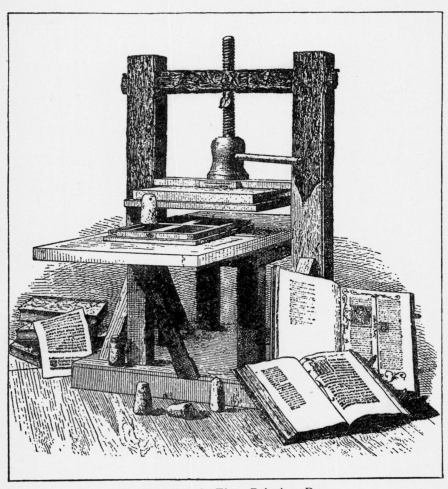

11. Gutenberg's First Printing Press

Et pluraliter doceamur docemini do-
ceantur. ffuturo docetor tu docetor il-
le. Et pluraliter doceamur doceminor
docentor. Optatiuo modo tempore
presenti et preterito imperfecto vtinã
docerer docereris vel docerere docere-
tur Et pluraliter vtinam. doceremur
doceremini docerentur. Preterito per-
fecto et plusquamperfecto vtinam doctus es-
sem vel fuissem esses vel fuisses esset vl
fuisset. Et pluraliter vtinam docti esse-
mus vel fuissemus essetis vel fuissetis
essent vel fuissent. ffuturo vtinam doce-
ar docearis vel doceare doceat. Et plr
vtinam doceamur doceamini doceant
Coniunctiuo modo tempore presenti

12. Facsimile Page of Block Printing

iron crucible, heat type metal in a casting pan and pour into the little pan upon the crucible. Thus the crucible becomes hot and quickly dries out the paper (wet matrix) on the type form, and the paper (wet matrix) does not shrink. When the metal has cooled off pour another batch in the pan and continue repeating this procedure until convinced that the paper pancake (flong) is well dried out.

Casting: "When you desire to cast, prepare two little wooden boards or tin plates, thicker all over than the flat paper flong, and lock the flong between them. Place smooth sheet of paper against the flong on the one board or tin plate, this paper having been rubbed over with red chalk; in this manner it will drop off easier. Then it must be securely screwed in a press. Place a tin funnel at the casting aperture, the funnel being as broad as your casting opening and the opening as wide as the flong. When casting pour in rapidly and forcefully upon the paper flong, paying attention to whether you are casting against the flong or away from it; against being the proper procedure. Bear in mind further advantageous manipulations and always see to it that the cast possesses good weight and firmness. When you form the flong on the type, rub well over the type and all the furniture with oil or some other fatty substance; by doing this the paper flong (wet matrix) will not stick.

"In case the application of a fatty substance should not be deemed advantageous, bend a wire around the outside, between the paper pancake (flong) and the counter board. When you screw it into the press, the wire tightens and does not slip during the casting operation. Fill out the overhanging portion of the type with wet paper."

A comparison of this wet paper pulp and the wet mat methods reveals that practically every step in this old process was imitated about two centuries later by Genoux.

The designation "pancake", i.e. flong, is also found in the above rendered translation. This term has hitherto been attributed to Genoux, who employed it in his original patent, and also to James Dellagana, a Swiss-born stereotyper of London. The term "stereotyping" was naturally not employed in the "Manual" of 1696; this term was coined a century later in 1795, by the celebrated French printer and typographer, Firmin Didot, of Paris.

Among the first experiments in stereotyping, in the sense of the definition at the beginning of this chapter, were those made in Europe in 1701. Johannes Mueller, clergyman of the Reformed

Church in Leyden, Holland, discovered a new way of utilizing the art of printing by employing movable types. After the pages had been composed, corrected and set up in a form, he turned this form over on its face and cemented it into one solid plate by means of a mastic (window putty) or, in a second experiment, with a metallic composition (lead). Later on Mueller immersed the bottoms of the types nearly up to the shoulder of the letter in the mastic or solder, thus rendering the entire page one solid mass.

The first trial of this process was made in 1701 with a book of prayers of Jean Havermans, printed by Mueller's son, William. Later on, Mueller and his son associated themselves with Van der Mey, the father of the celebrated Dutch painter, Jerome Van der May, and these three men, in 1711, prepared, in the above described manner, for Samuel Luchtmans, a bookseller of Leyden, the pages of a quarto and of a folio edition of the Bible. One hundred years later, Luchtmans' successors sent copies of this stereotyped Bible to Paris, accompanied them by a letter stating that "we have sent you a copy of our Stereotype-Bible. All the plates of it are now in our possession, and notwithstanding that many thousand copies have been printed from them, they are still in very good condition. They are formed by soldering the bottoms of common type together, with the same melted substance, to the thickness of about three quires of writing paper."

This invention of Mueller may be considered as an intermediate link between the operations of the common letterpress printing and those of stereotyping, as practiced at the present day. Mueller soldered his plates together, and therefore he required separate composition of the types for each form made. Stereotyping, however, in the modern sense of the word, means reproduction by casting and its advantage is multiplication without re-setting of type.

The great objection, however, to Mueller's method was its costliness, as the type used was no longer available for any other use. Johannes Mueller died in 1720, and his art of preparing solid blocks was, at the death of his associate Van der Mey, not employed any more.

France and Holland both claimed that to a citizen of their country was due the honor of having first discovered stereotyping.

Baron Willem Hendrik Jacob van Westreenen van Tiellandt, the Dutch historian and archaeologist, published in 1833 his "Report on the Researches relating to the First Invention and the Oldest practices of Stereotype Printing." In this latter book, written by command of the Dutch Government, Westreenen seeks to prove that Pastor Mueller was the first inventor of stereotyping, and was, although born and raised in Germany, a citizen of Holland by reason of his protracted residence in that country. He concludes his masterly exposition with the words: "We must proclaim our conviction that it is to the Netherlands that the honor is due not only of the initial, first invention, but at the same time the honor of the first improvement on the first use of stereotyping."

A process of so-called stereotyping, somewhat similar to the one practiced by Mueller and Van der Mey, is reported to have been used shortly afterwards by Athias, a printer in Amsterdam. Athias executed at a great expense, in what year is unknown, an English Bible, of which he preserved all the forms of the type, in such a manner that nothing could be added to, nor taken from them. Gessner, a Zurich printer, who first related this fact, adds that he had seen these solid forms carefully preserved. It is also generally recorded that Athias ruined himself by this speculation, such an edition of the entire Bible having tied up an immense amount of money.

A great advance in the new-born art of stereotyping was effected by William Ged (born 1690, died 1749). We owe the following data concerning Ged to his own book entitled: "Bibliographical Memoirs of William Ged, including a particular Account of his Progress in the art of Block-Printing. 1781. London."

By birth a Scotchman, Ged was successful as a goldsmith in Edinburgh, and was widely known for his inventions and improvements in his business. As a goldsmith, he became, to a certain degree, a banker and was brought into connection with the trade by furnishing money for the payment of the printers. In the year 1725, one of the printers complained to Ged that he was seriously embarrassed by being forced to send to London for type, there being then no type-founders in Scotland, and that much of the English type was imported to undertake the business of letter-founding. Ged was struck with the idea of making plates from the composed pages, believing that it could be successfully done. He borrowed a page of composed type, and made many experiments with a variety of materials, but did not complete his invention until two years afterwards.

The following was Ged's method of stereotyping: He set up his page with movable type, locked his form and then the page was laid upon gypsum or plaster of Paris, or some other semi-liquid

[41]

substance, just as it was drying; when it was dried completely he removed the form from the gypsum cast and, using this cast as a matrix, he formed solid plates of lead. From these he printed on the ordinary letter-press. The letters on the edges of the plates stood up rather higher than those in the center.

Although in possession of some capital, Ged offered one-fourth interest in his invention to an Edinburgh printer, on condition that he advance the sum necessary to establish a stereotype foundry. This partnership lasted two years, but the printer failed to fulfill his promises. A London stationer, named William Fenner, visiting Edinburgh, next offered to establish a foundry in London, in full working order, for one-half of the profits. Ged, now exceedingly anxious for the success of his invention, accepted these terms; disposed of his business in Edinburgh, and followed his new partner to London to find himself again deceived. With many plausible pretenses, the stationer induced the unfortunate inventor to add a type-founder to their partnership, who furnished refuse type, which Ged rejected as totally unsuited to his purpose. Still undiscouraged, Ged applied personally to the King's printers, with a proposal to stereotype some type which they had recently introduced. The printers naturally consulted the type-founder who had made the type, and he, as naturally, denied the utility of the invention. An interview, however, was arranged which led to the curious result of the type-founder laying a wager that he could make the stereotype himself. The foreman of the King's printing-house was made the umpire. Each of the disputants was furnished a page in type of the Bible, under the promise that he would furnish the stereotype in eight days. Upon receiving the type, Ged went immediately to work, and the same day finished three plates of the page, took impressions from them, and carried them to the umpire, who acknowledged his success with much astonishment.

The fame of the invention soon afterwards reached the Earl of Macclesfield, who offered Ged and his partners the vacant office of printer to the University of Cambridge and on the 23rd of April, 1731, Ged eagerly accepted the position. A lease was sealed to him and his associates for the privilege of printing Bibles and common prayer-books with his new process. Ged went to Cambridge but the letter-founder prevented his success by treacherously furnishing imperfect type, and even when Ged sent to Holland for new fonts he was again deceived. He encountered every possible form of opposition from the compositors who, when they corrected one fault,

13. Interior of a 16th Century Printing Shop

14. Type Casting as Practised in 1683. (From Moxon)

purposely made half a dozen others, and the pressmen, when the masters were absent, battered the letters in aid of the compositors. In consequence of these proceedings, the books were suppressed by authority, and the plates sent to the King's printing-house, and from there to a type-foundry, where almost all of them were melted and re-cast into single types. After all this ill usage Ged, who appears to have been a man of great honesty and simplicity, returned, financially ruined, to Edinburgh. His friends in that city were anxious that a specimen of his art should be published and therefore subscribed a sufficient sum for the stereotyping of a single volume. The unfortunate inventor apprenticed his son to a printer in order that he might no longer be subjected to the enmity of the trade. With the assistance of his son, Ged produced in 1736, after eleven years of endeavor, the first public proof of his success, an edition of the works of a Roman historian, Sallustius. On account of the inferiority of the type, this volume was not a fine specimen of the art, but was sufficient to prove that the invention was completed. Ged's son devoted himself to acquiring a knowledge of printing but just at the moment that he was fully prepared to effectually assist his father, the unfortunate inventor died. Although suffering so bitterly at home, Ged refused several offers, either to go to Holland, or to sell his invention to printers of that country, declaring that he only desired to serve his native land, and would not hurt it by giving the printers of another country such an advantage.

A few rare samples of his stereotype plates escaped the melting pot and came into the possession of Thomas Curson Hansard, who made a reprint of two such plates for his book entitled "Typographia".

These reprints demonstrate Ged's rather raw execution of his particular method of stereotyping. The secret of Ged's invention slumbered after his death, until it was re-discovered and greatly perfected by Lord Stanhope in London. After Ged's death in 1749, his son published a pamphlet wherein he explained the advantages of his father's invention and proposed a subscription, in order to finance new editions of Ged's books. It appears, however, that this subscription did not materialize.

The Clay Process

During the same period when Ged was working out his stereotyping process, a French printer, Gabriel Valleyre by name, invented in 1730 a method of casting plates in molds, which he used for making calendars which were placed at the opening page of church books. The method discovered by Valleyre was the so-called clay process. He pressed the set up form of movable type in clay or other earthy substance; removed the cast made in this manner from the form and then poured molten copper into it. His clay or his copper was faulty; the edges of the letters were not clearly and sharply defined; the surface of his plates became rounded and many letters were broken. One advantage of his process was that it took the mold from low spaces and quadrats without filling them up. (A long time afterwards Valleyre's method was revived, improved, and employed in the Government Printing Office in Washington.) The thus modified "clay stereotyping method" was used there as follows: The form was placed upon a movable bed of an iron molding-press. A flat iron plate was screwed upon the inside of the lid of the press, and upon this plate a thin layer of prepared clay was spread. Preliminary impressions were taken to obtain the outlines of type and to remove the dampness from the mold. The surface of the form of type was rubbed with benzine; the lid of the press closed and clamped by means of a lever, the movable bed of the press was raised and the mold thus obtained by pressure. Then the mold was taken out and placed in a slow-drying oven. This operation took a few minutes for drying, and then the molding-plate, separated by a thick wire, bent into shape to fit the bottom and sides of the plate, was clamped fast to a companion plate of equal size. Into the opening between the plate, formed by the wire, molten stereotype metal was poured, and the stereotype cast by this clay method was formed.

J. Michel Funckter, whose methods are described as having been practiced in Germany about 1740, merits being mentioned because his operation was akin to the one practiced by Ged and later on by the printers in France. Funckter, a printer of Erfurt, published in that city in 1740 a little pamphlet entitled: "Short but useful introduction to the cutting of wood and iron plates, to make types, ornaments and other drawings and also to the art of baking plaster, preparing sand molds for type-casting, vignettes, medals and forming of matrices therefrom." This pamphlet called the attention of many printers to the new art of making solid printing plates.

Alexander Tilloch, editor of the "Philosophical Magazine" and part proprietor of the "Star", a London daily newspaper, conceived the idea of stereotype printing in 1781, and in the following year he entered into partnership with the printer to the University of Glasgow, Andrew Foulis by name, in order to carry on the business of stereotype printing.

At the start of their venture, they advertised the following arguments regarding solid-plate printing to the book-printers and book-sellers: "If founding could be applied to single letters, why not to pages, to get rid of a sacrifice of capital submitted to at first because of the enormous expense of block-cutting. Founding of pages, on the first view of it promises many advantages in point of economy; and to science it holds out, what can never otherwise be obtained—the possibility of procuring, in a short time, Immaculate Editions. From books cast into solid pages, no more copies would be printed than might be wanted for immediate sale; the money thus saved from being sunk into paper to be piled up in warehouses for years, as at present, would serve as surplus capital to print other works; all errors as soon as discovered, could be rectified in the plates, to prevent them from appearing in later copies, instead of running through a large edition, as at present."

POLYTYPING AND LOGOGRAPHY

Conforming to the chronological order of this booklet, a report is now due on two methods known as Polytyping and Logography.

Polytyping is the art of producing by mechanical means, from engraved plates or otherwise, any number of plates capable of multiplication. The "sister arts", Stereotyping and Polytyping, are so connected and the processes, which have been used in one, have often so great an alliance with those of the other, that it is not easy to separate them. The process of Polytyping differs from Stereotyping in the fact that while a stereotype is taken by pouring molten metal on the mold, the polytype is made by a method akin to die-sinking.

Polytyping was used only for the reproduction of small woodcuts or typographical ornaments. For that purpose it was considered by some founders to be superior; duplicates could be produced more rapidly than by stereotyping and at a cheaper rate, and the blanks or whites of the polytype were much deeper than those of the stereotype.

Logography is a method of composition consisting in the art of arranging and composing for printing with entire words, their roots and terminations, instead of single letters.

The first experiments with Logography were made by Henry

Johnson, a compositor of London, in the printing establishment of his employer, Mr. Walter, owner of the "Times". A patent for Logography was granted him in 1783. Johnson's aim was to simplify the basic technique of type-setting, which had remained stationary for centuries. He cast certain of the most used words and syllables and used these casts together with the ordinary type, hoping thereby to speed composing to a degree. Although this method was never universally adopted, it found imitators and perfectors even up to our times. Johnson also intended to save labor for the compositor, for instead of lifting the word "and" in three letters, if cast as a logotype, he picks it up as one. The combined letters stated to have been found of greatest value were:

be	com	con	ent	ion	in
for	ge	ing	ld	me	the
and	th	ve	al	re	os

"The London Times", when it was first published, used logotypes for a while but then abandoned them, on account of their proving practically useless, the compositors being able to set up more type in a given time by the old method than by using logotypes. Other weighty objections urged against logotypes are the additional space of case-room they require (about 480 cases), if they are sufficiently numerous to be of material service; and the waste of type which results from the necessity of destroying a whole word whenever a single letter is battered. After some years, the experience of the "Times" and a few other unsuccessful experiments, led to the total abandonment of the logotypes, but recently they have attracted the attention of inventors.

The names given in the course of years to the different inventions of this nature were many, for instance, Logography, Logotypography, Polyamatiamie, Typocheographie, Hamapoligrammatiamme (!).

As far as the art of Polytyping is concerned, the first invention therein was made in 1784 by Franz Ignaz Joseph Hoffmann, a native of Alsace, who had drifted to France and settled in Paris. Hoffmann was inspired, through Ged's work and through a remark concerning several metallic combinations made by Darcet in 1773. The method Hoffmann discovered was: With a page composed of types in the usual manner, he made an impression on a mass of soft fatty earth mixed with plaster of Paris or gypsum, and prepared with a glutinous paste of syrup of gum and potato starch. This impression

TYPOGRAPHIA HARLEMI PRIMVM INVENTA
Circà Annum. 1440.

15. Printing Office in Haarlem. A. D. 1440

16. Interior of a Dutch Printing Office from a Book Printed at Haarlem in 1628

became a matrix, into which a composition of lead, bismuth, and tin being pressed at the moment of casting, gave plates which exhibited in relief, facsimiles of the types which had been used to form the matrix. The impossibility of sinking each single letter absolutely in the same horizontal direction and in the same depth into the matrix composition, in connection with other relatively less important drawbacks, convinced contemporaries that this method was entirely impracticable and unserviceable. The apparatus used for Polytyping somewhat resembled a pile-driver.

A further practice of Hoffmann was that he formed two sorts of types or puncheons; one for detached letters, and the other for letters collected into the syllables most frequently occurring in the French language. This was simply following up Johnson's independent discovery of logography. Hoffmann was granted a patent and a franchise in 1785, and his three volume work, printed with logotypes, created quite a sensation, notably in France, but notwithstanding this success, his establishment was closed in 1787 through a Government decree. It appears that the reason for this act was that Hoffmann had been engaged in printing prohibited writings.

In 1785, Joseph Carez, a printer at Toul in France, happened to obtain some numbers of Hoffmann's "Journal Polotype". He was struck with the advantage which the new process seemed to offer, and carried on a series of experiments in editions which he called "omotyped", meaning the junction of many types in one. Carez executed several liturgical and devotional works, and among others the Vulgate Bible in nonpareil, which possesses great neatness. Carez carried out his process in the following manner: The page being locked up, was placed downwards on a block of wood suspended from one arm of an iron lever. On the top of a wooden pillar there was a cardboard tray smeared over with oil. A quantity of molten type-metal was taken from a furnace, and poured into the cardboard tray. The moment the metal began to be clouded by cooling he let fall upon it the block of wood and the page attached. In this way an impression of the page was formed. This plate, after being trimmed, was fixed to the under side of the block, and let fall upon some fused metal placed as before on the bed of the machine, and thus was obtained a plate in relief fit for printing. The most serious drawback of the Carez method was the difficulty encountered in getting his type-form off the chilled metal.

In 1786, Pingeron, a skillful mechanic, varied the Hoffmann

process. For the purpose of stereotyping, he proposed making a composition, formed of talc, gypsum, clay, Venice tripoli, and formers sand, capable of receiving a clear impression; to press into this mass the face of a page composed of types and then to pour melted type-metal into the matrix thus formed. He also used a sand pit for molding, and a composition of German spar, salam-moniac, etc., which would bear several castings before being de-stroyed.

All experiments of this nature were doomed to failure, as they were in direct opposition to the basic principle of the art of printing —the division of written matter into small movable parts, namely into single letter types.

The art of stereotyping received a great deal of attention during that period of money inflation when the French government ordered the printing of the colossal quantities of paper money, so-called assignats. This work had to be done as fast as possible, and it was necessary to guard against forgery of those bills. Recourse was taken to stereotyping and not only were the hitherto known methods practiced, but a number of new ones were discovered. The first issue of assignats was printed in 1790; they were, however, scarcely out of the hands of the printer before they were counterfeited and great difficulty was experienced in recognizing the genuine assignats of the government. It became evident that every plate would have to be identical. A modification of Hoffmann's polytype process was resorted to; casts were taken of the separate parts of the bills and these became matrices, these again were united and a single matrix formed, which was struck into molten metal. This operation was called clicher, the word being used by the die-makers to express the striking of melted lead, in order to obtain a proof. It signifies to let a writing fall perpendicularly and forcibly upon molten metal. Since this time up to the present day the word "cliche" has been generally applied to stereotype plates by the French.

In 1795, when the Revolutionary Convention had begun to issue lottery tickets, a printer named Gatteaux was charged by the National Assembly to print these tickets. The process he developed was to sink the face of the type into a plate of cold metal by means of a screw press. Gatteaux's brother-in-law, Anfry, invented a harder metal than that heretofore used for types, which prevented their being damaged when being violently impressed into a plate of lead. This hard metal of Anfry was largely composed of silver, therefore very costly.

During this same period, the printing establishment of Firmin Didot (born 1764, died 1836) operated an extensive stereotyping plant. Didot is the name of a family of eminent printers in France, who have pursued the calling with remarkable success from the year 1713 to the present day. Firmin Didot deserves special mention for his elegant and correct cheap stereotyped editions. He published as his first, Gaillet's "Logarithms" which he announced as a "stereo-typed" work, thus being the coiner of the now so familiar word. This book was set up in types and the pages afterwards incorporated in one solid mass, the plate soldered at the base. This shows that at the start, Didot followed the process invented almost a century ago by Mueller and Van der Mey.

First Commercial Stereotype Shop

Louis Etienne Herhan, a workman in the employ of Didot, was born in Paris on the 3rd of August, 1768. He was a well-known typographer, and collaborated with the celebrated French printers and publishers, Hoffmann and the Didots, in the manufacture of the French paper money, the assignats. He died in 1854.

Herhan devised a new process of stereotyping upon which he obtained patents in 1798 and 1800. Herhan worked in conjunction with his employees, Errand and Renouard, under the supervision of Count Schlabrendorf. He had copper type made, in which the letters were sunken, but in such a manner that the letter-face did not appear reversed on it. With these copper types he set up his form, and from this copper form he made a cast in lead. The printing plate therefore was made DIRECTLY from the copper composition of the form. This very costly experiment had the great disadvantage that the sunken letters did not permit of correction, and without possibility of correcting, the process was impracticable. Thus every type needed in a printing shop, using Herhan's method of stereo-typing, had to go through the separate manual operations of filling, dressing, arranging, striking with special punch, lining and properly adjusting for the nicety of printing. A labor for which no adequate remuneration ever could be expected.

After Herhan's first patent was granted, Pierre Didot, Firmin Didot and Herhan entered into a partnership to exploit it. They issued a pamphlet called "Prospectus of stereotyped editions". This is the first prospectus of its kind. They announced therein the formation of a partnership for the purpose of quickly and accurately employing the new stereotyping methods for which they enjoyed a patent. They specifically stated that in their stereotyped editions, correctness would be a special merit, which would be carried to the highest degree of perfection, based upon the fact that even if in the first impression a few mistakes would creep in, it would be an easy task to correct these on the plate, which is always at their disposal, before making new impressions. They further stated that they would sell these stereotype plates in two sizes, 18mo and 12mo sized pages, the latter at francs 3.75 or 75 cents a page. In case of loss or deterioration they offered to furnish another copy of the same plate at the price of francs 12.50 or $2.50. Independent of the advantages of most perfect correction and of being able to furnish these books or plates at a very modest price, since copies were printed only when needed, there would be no storing of paper, no warehouse charges, etc.

The new editors also called attention to the fact that should a customer lose a volume, forming part of a set, they would replace same at the original price, the plates for reprinting always being at their disposal. This prospectus aroused a deluge of derisive remarks and criticisms. The consensus was "that this so-called new art of stereotyping, which embodies all the inconveniences of an old process long abandoned because of its imperfections (meaning the process of Hoffmann), tends to retrograde the art of printing; that by stereotyping one can never reproduce an impression as beautifully as made by movable types; that without showing any visible advantage for the announcers, it would be ruinous for all others who would make use of such plates." [1] The prices were objected to as prohibitive, etc. All this clamor did not keep the three associates from going ahead with their stereotyping business. In 1810 about 2,000 plates were made in Paris every month.

Another important stereotype job shop was the establishment of Mame Bros. in Paris. They claimed that in their time their process was the best and the simplest one. It required one operation less than that of Mr. Didot, who after having composed his page in movable types in relief was obliged to immerse it in a cooling material in order to obtain a matrix from which he obtained his stereotype plate. Mame Bros. warned the users of their process that great skill and care would have to be exercised in carrying it out and further that the Mame method necessitated considerable capital, but the plates would last for an indefinite period and that thousands

---

[1] M. Stoupe: Memoire sur le retablissement de la communauté.

17. First Stereotype Matrix Made from a Metal Cut Depicting The
Coronation of The Virgin. (15th Century)

18. Initial from a Work Printed by David Sartorius in 1582.
The Four Black Points in the Corners are the Heads of Nails
Showing in the Impression

of volumes could be printed without fear of deterioration of the plates. The Mame Bros. also claimed that from the day they took over Herhan's plate they had in their establishment manufactured 2,000 pages or plates regularly per month and that over 200 works in all sizes had been stereotyped by their improved method.

Later on quite a number of stereotype plants were established in France, using the Herhan and Mame methods, and also utilizing the many improvements that were made as time passed.

Jean Pierre Joseph Darcet, the celebrated French chemist, born in Paris, in 1777, experimented with stereotyping. Darcet's principal works were in the main confined to the manufacture of artificial soda, bicarbonate of soda, alum, sulphuric acid, hydrate of baryte, and the composition of alloys, and he produced a new alloy suitable for clichage and for stereotyping methods. All results of his research work were published in the Annals of Chemistry and Physics. At the time of his death, which occurred in Paris the 2nd of August, 1844, Darcet was Director of Tests at the Royal Mint, and a member of the Academy of Science, as well as of the Academy of Medicine.

Another pioneer in the art was Jean Philippe Guy le Gentil, Count de Paroy, born in Paris in 1750, as the son of a noted statesman, the Marquis Guy Le Gentil de Paroy. In 1765 Paroy entered into military service as second lieutenant, and in 1793 he was made commander of the garrison-battalion of the Lyonnais Regiment with the rank of lieutenant-colonel. He cultivated the arts and notably engraving, and was received as an honorary amateur member in the Academy of Painting in 1785. He invented a new process of stereotyping called "Pankototypie", about which he, in 1822, published an account entitled "Precis sur la Stereotypie". Marquis de Paroy died in Paris in 1824. The contents of Paroy's "Abstract" are very interesting; however, he brings little that differs from what Camus had already explained of French stereotyping methods.

It would lead too far to recount all the different adaptations of the existing processes; worthy of mention are Rochon, Thouvenin, Gengembre, Bulliard and Lheritier. Boudier produced in 1798 some specimens of stereotype printing by a process entirely different from Herhan's, proceeding as follows: Boudier's mold was taken from a page of type by sinking its face into a mass of soft clay. Into this clay matrix melted copper was afterwards poured, in much greater quantity than was required to form a plate, as it was upon the weight of the metal that Boudier depended for its entering completely into all the cavities and angles of the mold. When cold, the plate was reduced in a lathe to such thickness as was required. This process, however, had no special outstanding merits to commend its use and therefore did not become a practical success. Boudier obtained a patent on his process in 1801 and published stereotyped school books and music.

In the year 1803 a printer named Pierre de Joyeuze proposed a new method of stereotyping, which consisted of making a relief mold with clay from a page composed of movable types. His process had the advantage of cheapness, but it also had all the old defects of plates cast in clay.

PLASTER OF PARIS PROCESS

Each and every one of the inventions and processes thus far described was an important step forward in the building up of the art of stereotyping, but none of these methods was practiced to any great extent by others than by the men who invented them. The adoption of stereotyping throughout the entire printing world was due to the efforts and the labors of an Englishman, Charles Mahon, Earl of Stanhope. Stanhope did not invent any entirely new method of stereotyping. He did, however, improve and supplement the existing methods to such a degree as to make them practicable for shop work and to insure the universal use of his perfected method.

Charles Mahon, Third Earl of Stanhope, an eccentric and ingenious nobleman, was born in London on the 3rd of August, 1753. In his ninth year he was sent to Eton School, and at this early age began to give strong proofs of his mechanical and mathematical taste. In his nineteenth year he was sent to Geneva, and placed under the tutelage of the celebrated French jurist and writer, Alain Rene Le Sage. A few months later he was awarded a prize, offered by the National Academy of Stockholm for the best paper written in French on the construction of the pendulum.

The Earl was the originator of a great many inventions and improvements in the arts and philosophy. Among those which attracted most attention were his electrical experiments; his scheme for safeguarding buildings from fire; a machine for solving problems in arithmetic; a method of roofing houses; a kiln for burning lime, and a steamboat. He also evolved a plan for preventing forgeries in coins and bank notes. In the realm of the printing art he invented the printing press which bears his name. The Stanhope press was first tried out at the plant of "The Shakespeare Press", in London, and was immediately received as a remarkable advance in the art of printing. Stanhope also devised a system of logotypes, but his efforts to introduce it into general use were unsuccessful.

The Earl of Stanhope died on the 15th of December, 1816, in Chevening, Kent, his ancestral seat, deeply lamented by all, but more especially by the humbler class of citizens, whose esteem and friendship he had won by his interest and exertions in their welfare.

In the year 1800 Lord Stanhope became desirous of establishing stereotype printing in England where, although it had been twice invented and practiced, it had for many years fallen into disuse, and was practically abandoned and forgotten. His experiments and inventions in the art of stereotyping, which form a good deal of the subject matter of this book, were of fundamental and lasting value to the art. The Stanhope processes of stereotyping were of great importance to the development of stereotyping, and for many years they dominated the entire art not only in England but throughout the entire world. Stanhope saved stereotyping from disuse and oblivion, after practically every attempt to stereotype on a practical, businesslike scale had been put into discard, and forgotten not only by the authors of such previous attempts, but also by all printing craftsmen. Many authors of works on printing mention Lord Stanhope, giving wide publicity to his press. However, as to the important role he played in stereotyping, references are not missing, but with few exceptions they are, compared to his other work, short and none present a complete recital of Stanhope's great contribution to the art of stereotyping.

Stanhope conducted a thorough investigation of experiments and inventions made before 1800 and found that Alexander Tilloch, the editor of the Philosophical Magazine in London, had conducted a series of experiments in making plates for the purpose of printing by plates instead of using the movable types.

Alexander Tilloch, Doctor of Jurisprudence, was born in Glasgow on the 28th of February, 1759, where his father was a tobacconist and had, for many years, filled the office of magistrate. In 1781, whilst editing the Philosophical Magazine, Tilloch invented a method of stereotyping without having at that time any knowledge of William Ged's invention of stereotyping. In perfecting his invention Tilloch had the assistance and joint labor of Andrew Foulis, printer to the University of Glasgow. After great labor and many

[59]

experiments Tilloch and Foulis overcame every difficulty and were able to produce plates, from which the printing could not be distinguished from the printing from the very types from which these plates were cast. In their public announcements to the printing world of London, the inventors stated that although they had reason to fear, from what they found William Ged had met with,[1] that their efforts would experience a similar opposition from ignorance and prejudice, they persevered in their objective for a considerable time, and at last had resolved to take out patents for England and Scotland, to secure for themselves, for the usual term, the benefits of their invention.

A patent was granted to Tilloch and Foulis on the 8th day of June, 1784, under His Majesty's Patent Office Number 1431. The text of this document is interesting: forty-five lines are devoted to phraseology setting forth the nature of the privileges accorded by the patent, and only fifteen lines cover the claims of the invention.

The exploitation of the invention protected by this patent was initiated, but owing to some circumstances of a private nature, not connected with the stereotyping art, the business was discontinued for a time, and Tilloch, having moved from Glasgow to London, the concern was dropped altogether; however, not until several volumes had been stereotyped and printed under the direction of Messrs. Tilloch & Foulis. Tilloch also invented the high spaces and quadrats used later on.

In 1789 he, in connection with others, purchased the "Star," a London daily newspaper, and became its editor until his death on the 26th of January, 1825.

Mr. Tilloch's co-inventor and business partner, Andrew Foulis, was born in Glasgow on the 23rd of November, 1712. There were two brothers Foulis: Robert Foulis, celebrated as printer and letter-founder of Glasgow, produced in conjunction with his brother, Andrew, some works in the art of typography that will cause their names to be recorded in the temple of fame.

They were both natives of Glasgow. The elder brother was born April 20th, 1707. Robert was originally a barber, and practiced that art on his own account for some time. While thus humbly employed, he came under the notice of the celebrated Dr. Francis Hutcheson, then Professor of Moral Philosophy at Glasgow University. This acute observer discovered his talents, inflamed his

[1] See Kubler, "Historical Treatises, Abstracts and Papers on Stereotyping", New York, 1936, pp. 131-158.

19. Philipp Apianus (1531-1589)

20. A Map Block by Apian

desire for knowledge, and suggested to him the idea of becoming a bookseller and printer.

Andrew, the collaborator of Tilloch, seems to have been designed for the church, entered the University in 1727 and probably went through a regular course of study. For some years after they had determined to follow a literary life, the brothers were engaged in teaching languages during winter and in making short tours into England and to the Continent in the summer. These excursions were of great advantage to them; they brought them into contact with eminent men, enabled them to form connections in their business, and extend their knowledge of books. Thus prepared, the elder brother began business in Glasgow about the end of 1739, and in the following year published several works and shortly afterwards he took his brother Andrew into partnership. Three years later his connection with the University of Glasgow began. In 1743 he was appointed their printer under condition "that he shall not use the designation of university printer without allowance from the University Board in any books excepting· those of ancient authors." The first productions of his press, which were issued in 1742, were almost exclusively of a religious nature. In this year he also published the first Greek work printed in Glasgow.

Lord Stanhope invited Dr. Tilloch to live for a time at his mansion in Chevening. He also assured himself of the collaboration of Andrew Foulis, to whom he paid the fee of eight hundred pounds for his work. In 1802 the result of all these labors and of innumerable experiments was the perfection of the Stanhope Plaster of Paris Process of Stereotyping. Lord Stanhope then established and financed a stereotyping plant in London and placed it under the management of Andrew Wilson, a well-known London printer; the latter issued a prospectus announcing the new invention in glowing terms and also edited a manual explaining the Stanhope Process. It contained a list of stereotype imposing furniture necessary for one page (an iron frame, an iron side-stick and foot-stick, an iron head, and two to four iron quoins, with four bevelled brasses, to give a slope to the edges of the stereotype plate); instructions for the burning of the gypsum; instructions for molding, pouring of the gypsum, etc.; instructions for the dressing of mold, making it fit for being put in the oven to be dried; explaining the nature and the making of oven used for baking the molds; instructions for process of casting.

The process practiced in the stereotype shop of Stanhope and

Wilson is described as follows: The face of the types set up in the form was first rubbed with fine olive or sperm oil, in order to prevent the adhesion of the plaster of Paris mold to the form. The types having been set with high quadrates and spaces, they were plastered over with the liquid gypsum (nine parts of plaster, finely ground in a semi-liquid state with seven parts of water) to the thickness of about one-half of one inch, so that a level cake was formed on the surface of the types. As soon as the plaster hardened, which it did almost immediately, the case was separated from the types, and on being turned up, showed a complete hollow or mold-like representation of the faces of the types and everything else on the page. Then the set up types were of no further use, and were re-distributed. The cake was put into an oven and baked like a piece of pottery. Next, it was laid on a square iron pan, having a lid of the same metal, with holes at the corners. The pan was then immersed in a pot of molten metal and, being allowed to fill up by means of the holes, it was at length taken out and put aside to cool. On opening the pan, the metal had run into the mold side of the cake, and formed a thin plate all over, exhibiting the perfect appearance of the faces of the types on which the gypsum was plastered. These plates were about one-sixth of an inch thick, and were printed from in the same manner as in the case of printing from types.

In 1804 the Stanhope-Wilson plant changed its policy and undertook the publishing of stereotyped books, which were to be sold through bookshops. The first publication was "Frelynhausen on the Christian Religion", a work which had long been a favorite of the late Queen, and was translated from the German by her command. Mr. Wilson continued his labors for some time, but not receiving the encouragement from London booksellers which he had expected, he endeavored to establish himself as a stereotype bookseller. He published editions of several standard school books; however, again his venture was not accompanied by success. Hodgson, recognized as one of the outstanding experts on printing of the period, wrote that "Wilson, as a stereotype printer, must ever rank among the most eminent; the plates which were cast by him, having never been excelled if ever equalled. His best performance, and which at the same time is a most favorable specimen of this mode of stereotyping, on account of the fidelity with which such a mass of minute letters is rendered, is probably the octavo edition of 'Walker's Pronouncing Dictionary', published in 1809."

In 1804, with the approbation of Lord Stanhope, the joint invention was offered to the University of Cambridge; however, differences between the contracting parties arose, and the project was abandoned. Wilson was at first dejected, then aroused, and gave vent to his feelings in a stereotyped pamphlet carrying the title, "Arbitration Between the University of Cambridge and Andrew Wilson".

The stereotyping business of Stanhope and Wilson was carried on for a number of years, but never was it a commercial success, owing in part to the lack of interest shown by printers and publishers, and in part to direct antagonism displayed by many members of the printing craft. As an example of such antagonistic articles as were published in trade journals, we cite one which appeared in the Monthly Magazine of London in April, 1807:

"Stereotype printing has not been adopted by the booksellers of London because it does not appear that more than 20 or 30 works would warrant the expense of being cast in solid pages; consequently the cost of the preliminary arrangements would greatly exceed the advantages to be obtained. On a calculation, it has appeared to be less expensive to keep certain works standing in movable types, in which successive editions can be improved to any degree, than to provide the means for casting the same works in solid pages, which afterwards admit of little or no revision. As the extra expense of stereotyping is in all works equal to the expense of paper for 750 copies, it is obvious that this art is not applicable to new books, the sale of which cannot be ascertained. Although these considerations have induced the publishers of London not to prefer this art in their respective businesses, yet it has been adopted by the Universities of Cambridge and Oxford; and from the former some very beautiful editions of Common Prayer Books have issued to the public; probably the art of stereotyping applies with greater advantage to staple works of such great and constant sale, as prayer books and titles, than to any other."

This very disparaging statement was hotly contested by Mr. Wilson, Lord Stanhope's partner, in a lengthy article addressed to the London booksellers and printers.

Even after plaster of Paris stereotyping had been practiced on a relatively modest scale for almost twenty years, the opposition against the art had not yet abated.

Hansard, the celebrated London printer and writer on printing subjects, wrote in the year 1825: "No printer should stereotype who wishes his type to be a credit to his house. The wear of material in casting is miserable, the gypsum is at best a fine powder, and grinds away the edge and face of the letter when rubbed in with a brush, in a frightful manner. The letter can never be entirely freed from the plaster and will present a very dirty appearance ever after."

Equally bitter in his condemnation of stereotyping was Johnson, printer and author of a celebrated book entitled "Typographic" (1824). In this two volume work, Johnson devotes but a few meager lines to the subject of stereotyping. He writes: "We conceive that the inventor of stereotyping is not worth the pains of our tracing; and more particularly when we reflect that so many of our brethren who well deserve (from their ability) a comfortable subsistence, and who ought to be enabled (from their profession) to move in a respectable sphere of life, are now through this process, reduced to a very humble pittance; thereby bringing the first art in the world down to the level of the lowest; and, at one season of the year, nearly one-half of the valuable body of men alluded to may be considered as destitute of employ on account of the standard works, which was the summer's stock work."

The plates made by the Stanhope plaster of Paris process were of wonderful depth, sharply cut and gave the very best impressions. There were, however, in the practical use of the plaster process, many inconveniencing manipulations. The method was a slow one, causing great loss of time. The type became dirty, small specks of plaster adhered to them and necessitated cleaning before re-distribution of types. The sheet was smudged through the high spaces that were necessary with plaster casting. The most important drawback was that from the plaster matrix only one cast could be made.

About the same time when Stanhope was engaged in his experiments, Poteral, of Paris, created a stir in the printing world by announcing that he had invented a more simple method of stereotyping than any yet in use. A commission of the National Institute of France was appointed to examine his claims. From its report it appears that Poteral had executed nothing according to his projected plan, which was in fact merely a modification of part of Herhan's method. Poteral proposed to form matrices for casting hollow faced types, instead of type in relief; to compose the pages with these types, and then to cast from them a stereotype plate, formed of compound metal. The commission's report was entirely unfavorable and the process was never put into practice.

Kellberg   Eschenau   Sulzbach   Vechslts   Wassermünchs

Oeting   Reichnhall   Berchtesgadn   Scherding   Lecchaus

Adelzhausn   Diser gradus in der Obern   München   Abach
Gmündt   unnd Untern Leisten/thün   Sechs ain Teütsche meil.   Newkirchen

Feurbach   Deren gradus so auff der   Viechtach
Veldolfing   Seitten hieneben Ver= zaichnet/thün Vier ain teütsche Meil wegs.   Schmihen

Pfarkirchn   Pfreimbt   Pfaffenheyen   Peisserhof   Schwaben

Peiskin   Passaw   Peiserhof   Pechtal   perg fl.   Pierpasin

Nürmberg   Lauff   Rot   Hiltpoltstain   Weissenburg   Lam

Herschpruck   Uttlhouen   Ortnburg   Neumarckt   Dachau

Möringen   Roinsburg   Regen   Aldorff   Wert   Eutzburg

Biburg   Freistat   alta sandew   Joh.   Fricting   Ilm flus

Schwindeck   Waltenreit   Minslaz   Zetnpach fl.   Zeisnach

Kurthausen   Schwalnperg   Kier   Euch.   Nab   Zueffaypach

Oberndorff   Am hart   Reicherstorf   Alling   Wampas

21. A Stereotype Plate by Apian

22. Frontispiece of The Kunst and Werck Schul. 1696

In 1809, Charles Brightly, Printer of Suffolk, published a small pamphlet giving a detailed account of a method pursued by him in founding stereotype plates. He was convinced that the whole art of stereotyping depended on the equal temperature between the metal and the molds. Otherwise Brightly's process resembled the Stanhope method considerably; however, it possessed greater simplicity in its arrangement. Brightly was perhaps the first to demonstrate the economy of the Stanhope process when applied to a certain class of printing.

Moses Poole obtained an English patent on a wet mat on the 20th of July, 1839, the number of the English patent being 8159. His method was as follows: Take one sheet, cover with glue, on this put a thin coating of a composition of equal parts of paste and well ground potters earth mixed with water to the consistency of paste; another sheet of tissue is placed, and so forth, until the whole assumes the required thickness of about one-eighth inch. The last sheet of paper should have applied to it a coating of sweet oil. In his patent Poole always refers to flat and curved plates.

A process, thought out and practiced by the Frenchman, M. Daule, is of a much simpler nature than Stanhope's method. The difference between the two is that Daule recommends that the matrix composition should contain a little more plaster of Paris and a little less water. The matrix, when it has the necessary consistency, should remain in the pan and be dried therein. Finally the cast is not made by sinking but by placing it between two iron plates in a casting box and metal is poured in with a ladle.

The general rules laid down for the use of the Stanhope process also find application when stereotyping according to the Daule Method.

Daule stated in his prospectus that his method in comparison with the Stanhope process had the advantage that the utensils used for the former were not as expensive as with the Stanhope method; there is less heating material necessary because it is not necessary to maintain such a large pot with metal in flux; that as far as the alloy is concerned much less is lost by burning and waste and especially much time is saved since a plate made by the Daule process is cast in a few moments. In using the Stanhope method, however, a lot of time is lost throughout the sinking operation, the automatic casting of the plates, the cooling and striking of the pans. If a plant is equipped with two Daule casting boxes, the first can be opened when the matrix is cast in the second box, thus work can be finished faster. The Daule process of stereotyping met with far reaching success and was adopted by many plants that heretofore had been using the Stanhope method.

Augustus Applegath, in conjunction with his brother-in-law and business associate, Edward Cowper, was the inventor of several of the most important improvements in presses and printing machinery made in his time. He also devoted himself to improving the art of stereotyping. His invention was primarily for printing bank and bankers notes, or other printed impressions, when difficulty of imitation was desired. The patent privilege accorded to him was dated the 22nd day of June, 1818.[1]

Sir Marc Isambard Brunel was a British inventor and engineer, born in Normandy on the 25th of April, 1769. He entered the navy where he served six years. Then he took up his residence in France, but being a Loyalist he was forced to flee on account of the Revolution. He journeyed to New York in 1793 and practiced there as an architect and civil engineer. He submitted a plan for the dome of the Capitol in Washington; also designed and constructed the old Bowery Theatre, which was burnt down in 1821. Brunel died in 1849. He was accorded an English patent in 1820 on a stereotyping process, which contained modification of the Stanhope method.

A patent was granted in 1821 protecting the stereotyping method of James Ferguson of London; it presented an innovation insofar as it suggests the use of cork for the remedying of the inequalities of the thickness of stereotype plates.

A great improvement in the stereotype art was introduced about 1820 by Mr. Thomas Allan, printer in Edinburgh, into his own plant. It consisted in casting a number of plates at one time, and at the same time considerably lessening the risk of broken casts. This was effected by means of a pot sufficiently deep to contain molds placed in a perpendicular position. The plates of the Encyclopaedia Britannica, which is the most extensive work ever stereotyped, were almost entirely produced by Allan's process, in pots containing each five molds; and it was especially advantageous for large plates, the risk of breakage by the old method increasing in a greater ratio than the increase in the size of the page.

Sir William Congreve was a British artillerist and inventor, born on the 20th of May, 1772, educated in Singlewell School in

---

[1] In 1815 Cowper made "curved stereotyping plates", and obtained a patent on his invention in 1818, but the use of such plates did not become practical until 1855.

Kent and in Cambridge University. He first studied law, then turned to journalism as editor of a political paper. He died in Toulouse the 16th of May, 1828.

Congreve was an ingenious and versatile man of science. He was the author of many inventions such as one for four-color printing, in which several color plates were printed simultaneously, a process which was widely used in Germany. He took out patents for colored watermarking of paper, and for making unforgeable bank note paper. The first friction matches made in England (1827) were named after Congreve by their inventor, John Walker. A patent was granted Congreve in 1822 on improvements in the manufacture of stereotype plates, and pertained to improvement of the Stanhope process.

All of the above cited inconveniences, drawbacks and criticisms of the plaster of Paris method of stereotyping led members of the trade to further experiments and advance in the art, the ultimate aim being to devise a stereotyping process which would eliminate these drawbacks and to make stereotyping simpler, cheaper and more practicable. The first important and far reaching step in that direction was the invention of the papier mache or wet mat process.

Der Curieusen

Kunst-
und

Werck-Schul

Erster Theil/

Lehrend

allerhand sehr nützliche und bewährte

Feuer-Künste/

Metallische Gold- und Silber-Proben/Perlen/Flüsse/Doubleten und Folien,

der Natur ähnlich; imgleichen auch allerley Bilder
und Figuren abzuformen / in Glaß und künstlichen
Flüssen abzugiesen / auch allerley Glaß zur Mahle-
rey/ Porcellan- und Töpffer-Arbeit zu machen/ me-
tallene Spiegel zu giesen / zu poliren / Eisen
und Stahl zu härten und zu
etzen;

Sampt vielen andern Natur- und
Kunst-Geheimnussen/

Theils aus eigener langwieriger Erfah-
rung/ theils aus vielen bewährten Authoribus ge-
treulich/ mühsam und aufrichtig zusammen
getragen
Von
Einem sonderbaren Liebhaber der Natürlichen
Künste und Wissenschafften.

Nürnberg/
In Verlegung Johann Ziegers / 1696.

23. Facsimile of Table of Contents of the Werck Schul

14 So du die Schrifft abformen wilst.

So handel also: Du must haben eine neu- gegossene Schrifft / und ein gantz just Fundament / oder Schiffilein mit justen Stegen / das von Messing oder von Bley gemachet seye / darauf lege eine Rahme / und setze die Schrifft darein / und die Quadraten sollen so hoch seyn / daß die Caracter der Schrifft kaum ein Messer-Rück darüber gehen / und die Schrifft muß alle im Winckelhacken corriciret werden / und wann die Schrifft in das Schiff gesetzet / und geschlossen ist / so must du ein Rähmlein haben / das an das Schifflein darein die Schrifft gesetzt ist / geschifft seye / und dieser Zarg solle an das Schifft geschoben werden / und solle ungefehr zwey Finger hoch über die Schrifft erhöhet seyn / das Schiff darein die Schrifft geschlossen ist / solle keine Schrauben haben / sondern sie solle sonsten wohl nach Gelegenheit geschlossen werden / darnach so nimm Papier-Zeug / oder weiß Papier / gar wohl in Wasser gestossen / und zettele das in dem Zarg herum / auf die Schrifft / und stosse es fein mit einer Bürsten nieder / daß an einem Ort so dick seye als an dem andern / darnach so setze den steinern Tiegel auch in den Zarg hinein / und schraube den Tiegel unter einer Preß wohl nieder / so rinnet das Wasser darvon / dann drücke es auß der Preß herfur / und das Pfännlein solle oben weiter seyn als unten / daß der Zeug herauß könne fallen / so er kalt wird / setze dein eisern Pfännlein so in den steinern Tiegel eingelassen ist / auf den Tiegel / und mache eine Gießpfannen mit Zeug heiß / und gieß in das Pfännlein auf den Tiegel / so wird der Tiegel heiß / und trucknet das Papier auf der Schrifft bald auß / und schwindet nicht / und wann der Zeug kalt wird / so gieß einen andern in das Pfännlein / das thue so lang / biß du vermeynst / daß der Fladen wohl außgetrocknet seye / und so du nun giessen wilst / so mache 2 Prettlein oder Blech die breiter seyn als der Fladen / auf alle Ort / darzwischen schließ den Fladen / und gegen dem Fladen auf dem einen Brett / oder Blech / solle ein glatt Papier seyn / mit Röthelstein überfahren / so gefällt es desto lieber / und solle fein in ein Preßlein eingeschraubet werden / und auf das Gießlech / setze einen blechernen Trichter / der muß so bereit seyn / als das Geßloch / und das Gießloch so breit / als der Faden / und so du giest / so schütte den Zeug mit Gemalt gar geschwind hinein / und habe eine Aufmerckung / ob du gegen dem Fladen giessen solst / oder darvon / und mercke auf vorigen / und andere Vortheil mehr / und schaue allweg daß der Guß einen guten Nachdruck habe / 2c. und wann du das Papier auf die Schrifft abformen wilst / so überfahre die Schrifft und alle Dinge wohl mit Oel oder einer andern Fettigkeit / so leget sich das Papier nicht an / die Fettigkeit oder Schmier solle nicht gut seyn / aussen herum beuge einen Drath zwischen dem Fladen / und dem Gießen-Brett / so du es in die Preß schraubest / so beist der Drath ein / und laufft im Giessen nicht auß / und die Uberheng der Schrifft fülle auß mit nassem Papier / du magst oben vergebene Schrifft zusetzen.

15. Ein

24. Facsimile of Instructions for Wet Paper Pulp Stereotyping

CHAPTER THREE

THE PAPIER-MACHE OR WET MAT PROCESS

It was between 1828 and 1829 that the papier-mache or wet mat process of stereotyping was invented. This invention represented a tremendous advance in the art of stereotyping and up to this present day paper mats have dominated the art.

Claude Genoux, a French printer, is the developer of the so-called "papier-mache" (mashed paper) or "wet mat" method of stereotyping.

Some contemporaries claimed that an Italian, named Vanoni, by trade a maker of plaster casts of statuary, invented a system of forming molds for papier-mache in London in 1846, and thus, indirectly, gave the idea for the invention of matrices from that material. Others claim that in 1840, six years prior to Vanoni's arrival in England, a patent was granted to Poole, printer in London, for "Improvement in casting for printing purposes," and that the subject patented was the papier-mache stereotyping matrix.

Genoux's patent upon papier-mache matrices, however, was granted eleven years before Poole received his patent, and seventeen years before Vanoni was heard of. While Genoux was working as compositor in the printing establishment of Rusaud in Lyons, France, he conducted his experiments, made his invention and was granted a patent upon same on the 24th of July, 1829.

The text of the wet mat patent granted to Genoux by the French Government read as follows: "Patent Number 3965, granted for a period of ten years to Genoux (Jean-Baptiste) of Lyons, for a perfected process of stereotyping."

"The Matrix which I have the honor of submitting to you is composed of seven layers of paper; the last, or uppermost layer is oiled and reddened (sanguine). Between these layers I lightly apply by means of a brush a mastic composed of clay, hide-glue and a little oil. Any sort of mastic may be employed; I have adopted this special one on account of it being more economical.

"I place this combination of layers upon the type form and I make an impress with the aid of a roller, proceeding as in taking off a simple proof. I place the whole in the press and cause same to dry. After it is dried I paste a cardboard frame all around the back of the matrix in order to give more depth to the face of the type; thereupon I place it between two iron plates, upon which I have pasted several sheets of paper, there where the cardboard frame of the thickness which I desire to impart to the mold, has been applied.

"I pour the fused metal through a large aperture made in one of these plates, and thereupon the mold is perfect.

"My invention is entirely in the paper, being that without its help I cannot obtain anything perfect."

On the 30th day of August, 1836, a "Patent for improvement containing additions" was granted to Rusaud of Lyons, purchaser of the first Genoux patent. The preamble of this document reads as follows:

"When Mr. Genoux ceded his process of stereotyping to Mr. Rusaud, his first tests were far from the hopes he had given birth to; a large number of plates could not be used, because they were badly executed, and very often the matrix broke at the first cast. Also, Mr. Genoux having sold his process in several localities, the purchasers did not succeed in deriving any benefit from their acquisition. Genoux personally came to Lyons two years after he had sold his process to Rusaud, well aware of the fact that the latter's foundry was the only place where Genoux's process had been put in practice and demanded to be admitted in Rusaud's shop in order that he might be initiated in the new discoveries and improvements made since the sale of the original process.

"It was due solely to his work, expenditure and perseverance that Mr. Rusaud has conquered over all difficulties and obtained satisfactory results."

On the 26th of November, 1836, a second patent of improvements and additions to the original Genoux patent was granted to Mr. Landrin of Paris, another of the many purchasers of the original wet mat process. This amendment contains a number of improvements in the handling of wet mats.

Genoux sold his patent to his employer Rusaud, who in turn transferred it to another printer, J. A. Pelagaud by name. Genoux thereupon journeyed to Germany with the intention of finding there a purchaser for his patent rights. An article appeared in 1834 in Dingler's Printing Trade Journal reading as follows: "Monsieur Genoux, French book printer, gave a demonstration in Vienna a short time ago of his new method of printing with solid fixed types

('Stereotyping'), of which he is the inventor. In accordance with his invention, Genoux first prepared a material which he called 'flan.' This material was in form and thickness about that of a paper book cover. Into this material he made an impression of the form he had composed, thereby making a matrix. Into this seemingly very weak mold, he poured lead, thereby casting a metal plate of about the thickness of 40 to 45 one-thousandths of an inch. This plate was a reproduction in relief of the form impressed on the 'flan,' and was of greatest cleanliness and precision."

In 1834, the same year this article appeared, Genoux sold his patent rights to George Jacquet, owner of the royal-printing-establishment in Munich. Jacquet then advertised to the trade that he stood ready to sell, against payment of an honorarium, the necessary information regarding the manufacture of these "wet mats" to printers.

Although compared to the old plaster process this paper method of stereotyping did wonders as far as rapidity, cheapness and beauty of the plates were concerned, still it took a very long time before this process was universally acknowledged.

In fact, it was not until over seventeen years had passed since the granting of Genoux's basic patent that a master printer, Tetin by name, founded a stereotyping shop in Paris in 1846 using Genoux's invention, which, by the way, Tetin in due time greatly improved.

Genoux's method of stereotyping was to paste four or five sheets of dampened tissue paper lightly together on a sheet of plate-paper, lay same on the surface of the type, strike the laminated sheet with a heavy brush until the soft papier-mache had taken an exact impression of the type. On this "flan" or matrix, as it was then called, a sheet of plate paper was spread and beaten in by another application of the brush. This completed the matrix, which was then dried and hardened. Casts were taken from the mold thus obtained by simply placing it in a flask (flat caster) and pouring stereotype metal upon it by means of a ladle.

The advantages of Genoux's papier-mache (wet mat) process presented over the plaster of Paris method were: The comparatively short time it took to accomplish; a series of plates could be made from one and the same flan. (In the plaster process the mold is destroyed in releasing the "shell" or cast, therefore only one plate can be produced without remolding.) That the molds could be preserved indefinitely for later use, that molds could be packed and sent any distance without damage, and finally that the paper molds could be bent without damaging them.

The papier-mache process of Genoux's is the basis of all paper stereotyping as it is practiced to this very day. It is unchanged in principle, although the materials used have been improved, certain drawbacks overcome, and the machines used for the different manipulations augmented and modernized.

The word "flan" is used above as a designation for a "papiermache" matrix. The term is attributed to Genoux, who employed same in his original patent, and also to James Dellagana, a Swiss stereotyper in London. The English phonetic form for this French word "flan" is "flong." The explanation for the word "flan" is that in Paris there exists a kind of pastry called "flan" made in layers, and which has the appearance of piled up, somewhat flabby buckwheat cakes. The resemblance between a layer of such flabby cakes of "flan" and the pasted layers of the wet papier-mache mats suggested the name for paper stereotype matrices. This name has, however, never been universally adopted, and is practically in disuse everywhere except in France and England. The generally employed term for a papier-mache mat is "wet mat."

Genoux, after demonstrating the great value of his invention by printing the entire dictionary of the French Academy with stereotype plates, made with his wet mats, sold the use of his patent rights on a license basis to the following firms: Chirin & Mana in Torrino, Russaud in Lyons, Seguir, Sr., in Avignon, Douladont in Loulouse, Levrault in Strasbourg, Geo. Jaquet in Munich, and others.

In the year 1839 Moses Poole applied for and was granted an English patent on a papier-mache stereotype matrix. In the preamble of the patent, 8159, Poole states: "This invention of improvement in casting for printing purposes was communicated to me by a certain foreigner residing abroad." In other words, Poole learned of the Genoux process in France, and on his return to England he patented that process in his mother country. However, it appears that he was the first to claim in a patent that he could obtain flat plates, or curved surfaces or forms, to be employed in printing with flat or cylindrical printing presses.

In 1840, eleven years after Genoux was granted his patent on the wet mat, a contemporary claimed that although Genoux had discovered a radically new method of stereotyping and had sold the secret of his process to a number of plants in different localities, his method had not proven to be a success, since it had not been

i. b. Mos. c. 49. Herr ich warte auf dein heil.

M. Johann Jacob Müller Pfarr
herr bey den Barfüssern und
Senior. ætat. ão. 40. AOR. 1679.

25. Johann Jacob Mueller (1679)

6 Et beatus is, qui non fuerit offensus in me.

7 Quum autem abiissent, cœpit Jesus dicere turbis de Johanne; Quid exiistis in desertum ad videndum? arundinem quæ à vento agitatur?

8 Alioqui, quid exiistis ad videndum? hominem qui vestibus mollibus vestitur? Ecce qui mollibus vestiuntur, in domo regum sunt.

9 Alioqui, quid exiistis ad videndum? Prophetam? Etiam dico vobis, & excellentiorem quàm Prophetam.

10 Ipse enim est de quo scriptum est, Ecce, ego mitto nuncium meum ante faciem tuam, qui diriget viam ante te.

11 Amen dico vobis, quòd non surrexit inter natos hominum, qui major sit Johanne Baptista; minor autem in regno cœlorum, major est eo.

12 A diebus autem Johannis Baptistæ, & usque nunc, regnum cœlorum cum violentia accipitur, & violenti rapiunt illud.

13 Omnes enim Prophetæ & Lex usque ad Johannem prophetaverunt.

14 Et, si vultis vos, recipite quòd is est Elias, qui venturus erat.

15 Cui sunt aures ut audiat, audiat.

16 Cui autem assimilabo generationem hanc? Similis est pueris, qui sedent in foro, & acclamant sodalibus suis.

17 Ac dicunt; Cecinimus vobis, & non saltastis: ululavimus vobis, & non planxistis.

18 Venit enim Johannes, qui non comedit neque bibit, & dicunt; Dæmonium est illi:

19 Venit filius hominis comedens & bibens, & dicunt; Ecce, homo edax & potor vini, & amicus publicanorum & peccatorum. Et justificata est sapientia à cultoribus suis.

20 Tunc cœpit Jesus exprobrare civitatibus illis in quibus editæ fuerant virtutes ejus plurimæ, neque conversæ fuerant.

21 Et dicebat; Væ tibi Corazin, Væ tibi Bethsaida: quoniam, si Tyri & Sidonis editæ

D

26. Facsimile Page of First Stereotyped Book (1701)

adopted even on a small scale. It was stressed that the Stanhope process of plaster stereotyping was the only one that had proven its merit and thus universally used throughout Europe.

In September, 1829 Count Pravana reported on this invention before the Academy of Torrino, and on the 10th of August, 1831 M. Francoeur explained its nature in the Societe d'Encouragement in Paris.

Thomas Bolas, a member of the Society of Arts in London, claimed that a similar process to the Genoux one was employed by several persons previous to 1829; he evidently referred to the old German wet paper pulp process of 1690.

In 1853 George Todd wrote about "Stereotyping: its purport and its varieties," in the following manner:

"That cheap literature owes much to stereotyping, is beyond question; as the process is one of those which economise the outlay in printing. For works of small circulation it is useless, or worse than useless; but when there is a very large demand for a book, or the demand spreads over a considerable space of time, then does stereotyping lessen the expenses of the publisher. It does so for the following reasons. If the publisher over-estimates the demand for a new book, he prints too many copies, some of which remain a dead loss to him on his shelves; if he under-estimates the demand he prints too few, and has all the expense of composing the type to incur over again. But if he bestows the time and labour of making stereotype casts from his type, he can then print from these plates just as many copies as are wanted, and do this from time to time during an indefinite period. He need not keep the type standing; he can distribute and use the type for other works, knowing that he has a source of power in his stereotype plates. And, moreover, he can make two or a dozen or any number of stereotype casts from each page; so that he could print two, or a dozen, or any number of copies at once, with the requisite press or machine arrangements, and all with one original 'setting up,' or composing. There is this consideration, too; that a woodcut becomes somewhat worn when a large number of impressions have been taken from it; but by a series of stereotype casts from it, the power of printing from it becomes practically illimitable. The reader will then bear in mind that, so far as any one copy is concerned, stereotype printing is not better than type-printing; on the contrary, the highest class of work is generally type-printed; but when a large quantity of one kind is required, the advantages of the stereotype method, both in time and money, are quite irresistible.

"It is certainly extraordinary that, after two castings, a stereotype plate, even from a woodcut, should be fine and sharp enough for printing; it shows how great is the skill now attained in the art. That there are two castings, many readers are apt at times to forget; but a moment's consideration will show that such must necessarily be the case; for the first cast will give hollows instead of protuberances, and vice versa; and hence another is required to restore the original aspect of the surface—just as in all other processes of casting, founding, or moulding; where a model is employed to yield a mould, and the mould is employed to yield casts. In stereotyping, the page of type, or mingled type and woodcuts, is the model; a plaster impression from this is the mould; and the stereotype plate is the cast. The method was first practised at Edinburgh a century and a quarter ago; but it was not brought much into requisition until towards the close of the last century; and did not become a really important commercial element in printing until 1832, when the vast sale of the Penny Magazine produced a revolution in cheap literature."

Then Todd goes on to explain in detail the plaster process of stereotyping, and then continues as follows:

"This is the ordinary stereotype process, but many recent novelties have been introduced in aid of it. The application of gutta percha to printing was noticed in a former number of this series; but we may here describe one or two of these applications more fully. Mr. Muir, of Glasgow, has invented a mode of stereotyping, managed in the following way. A page of common type is first set up, and well fixed; a warm cake of gutta percha is applied to it, screwed down tightly, and allowed so to remain a quarter of an hour; when this gutta percha mould is removed, it is brushed over with fine black-lead, and an electro-copper cast taken from it; the printing is then effected from this cast. It is found that gutta percha constitutes a very convenient and efficient substance for the mould, owing to the readiness with which it can be softened, and its toughness when cold; while the electro-copper cast is said to bear the action of the printing press throughout a much greater number of copies than an ordinary stereotype plate.

"The same inventor also practises a plan in which the gutta percha performs not only its own work but that of the electro-copper also. A mould is taken from an engraved wood-block, in gutta percha; and this mould, when brushed over with black-lead, is made to yield a cast also in gutta percha, in an exactly similar way; and from this cast the impressions are printed. It seems difficult to conceive that, after this double process, all the delicate lines of a wood-engraving should be preserved on the surface of such a material as gutta percha; and yet, without this preservation, the method would be practically valueless.

"Bitumen is another substance which is competing with gutta percha for an honourable place among stereotyping materials. Messrs. Manchin and Morel have introduced a method which, though not yet much adopted in this country, is said to have found considerable favour in France. The cast, either from a woodcut or from type, through the intermedium of a mould, is formed of a bituminous substance, which is harder than type metal, and gives the markings with great clearness. It is said to be somewhat more expensive than common stereotype; we learn, however, that it is now being tested, and if found practically advantageous, will be brought at once into use.

"It is really almost difficult to follow the novelties in this department of the printing art. There is a method of making stereotypes from paper, or rather papier-mache. From the description given in another part of this series, it will easily be understood that the pulpy nature of papier-mache would enable it to be used as a stereotyping material; but this application seems to be abandoned for others, especially that of stereotyping by electro-deposition.

"So far as scientific completeness goes, no other stereotyping can bear comparison with the beautiful process last named: it is a very triumph of science applied to the arts; and as we find that our artistic manufacturers and fancy printers are every day availing themselves more and more of the process, we may safely conclude that it superadds practical usefulness to scientific precision."

Up to approximately the year 1852 stereotyping as practiced by the various methods described so far in this booklet was employed solely in the printing of books. In the above year Genoux's papier-mache or wet mat stereotyping was adopted by the French daily newspaper "La Presse" in Paris. This step opened an immense and fertile field to the art of stereotyping. (For an abbreviated history of the newspaper see Chapter 4.)

In 1856 James Hogg and John Napier took out a patent for improvement in stereotyping. A sheet of stout printing paper, or a cloth, was coated with a paste of red ochre and fine whiting, thin glue, fine starch and wheat flour with a little alum. This was laid upon the form to be reproduced, which had been previously oiled. A pull was taken on the press or with a mallet and planer. A mold also could be made in plaster of Paris. It was left on the form to dry.

An improvement on the wet mat stereotyping process embodying an idea of using dry material was made in 1863 by Alfred Vincent Newton, an English mechanical draughtsman. He was granted a patent for "An improved mode of and apparatus for producing stereotype plates." His application first describes the prevailing process as consisting of several sheets of glued paper, beaten in with a brush while moist, then heated to dry; in his improved process the molding material used is soft paper or dry pulp of such thickness that under pressure a sufficient depth will be ensured to hollows or counters to produce a good casting. To obtain the mold a sheet of dry paper or paper pulp of soft or spongy character is laid on the form of type to be copied and upon the layer of paper a sheet of steel or brass or India rubber is placed, and the whole is passed between pressing rollers which may be covered with rubber. A matrix is thus produced and from it a stereotype plate is obtained in much less time than by the old wet mat process.

Alfred Leighton, a color printer in London, took out a patent in 1864 for improvements in the construction, manufacture of printing surfaces in relief. The novelty of his invention consisted in the fact that these surfaces were elastic, being made of an India rubber compound and vulcanized in the molds.

Celluloid: The advantages of celluloid are manifold, but one great deterrent to its use was found in its inflammability. However, at the time of the chief use of celluloid in the stereotyping industry the product was of such a nature that it would burn only by subjecting it to an open flame.

The predecessor of celluloid was a discovery by the well known inventor Parks of Birmingham, England. He named it "Parkazene," and it was made of dehydrated wood naphtha and nitrocellulose. Later on, in 1869, Hyatt Bros. of Newark, N. J., owners of a printing establishment, while engaged in experimenting to find a press blanket substance which would withstand atmospheric influences, invented celluloid. The name was derived from the fact that cellulose was used to make the product. Newark became the most important center for making celluloid in the world, and in 1877 as many as fifteen American factories were producing celluloid, the

DE PROPHEET
HOSEA.

Inhoudt deses Boecks.

DE Propheet *Hosea* (gelijck oock *Amos*, ende meer andere) is bysonderlick van Godt gesonden tot het Koningrijck Israëls ofte der tien Stammen, (hoewel ondertusschen Juda oock meer-maels van hem bestraft wort) onder dewelcke hy tot een Bewijs van Godts grote Lanckmoedigheyt ende Getrouwigheyt, eenen langen Tijt, (als Cap. 1. Vers 1. te sien is) gepropheteert heeft: waer van de Heylige Geest gewilt heeft, dat het Sommier der Kercke Godes in dit Boeck schriftelick soude worden na-gelaten, begrijpende, *voor eerst*, Prophetische Af-beeldingen, ende seer scherpe Bestraffingen van den sondigen ende vervallisen Staet des gantschen Koningrijcks, bysonderlick der snoode Af-goderije met de goudene Kalveren, die ten Tijde van *Rehabeam*, *Salomons* Sone, van haren eersten opgeworpen Koning, *Jerobeam* den Sone *Nebats*, waren op-gericht, als Israël sich eerst van Juda ende den waren Godts-dienst af-sonderde (1 *Reg.* 12. 27, 28, &c.) waer op voorts eene afgrijselicke Heydensche Ongebondenheyt, ende als een over-stroomende Vloet van allerley Sonden gevolgt is, soo tegen de eerste als tegen de tweede Tafel van Godts Wet, ende dat onder alle Stants-persoonen, die daer over van Godt door desen Propheet heftiglick worden gescholden: met veelvoudige ende seer beweeglicke Vermaningen ende Nodigingen tot oprechte ende tijdelicke Bekeeringe. Doch alsoo de Godtloosheyt ende Hart-neckigheyt van de Koningen af, tot den minsten des Volcks toe, daglicks wies ende d'Overhant nam, wort haer ten tweeden gepropheteert de geheele Verwoestinge ende Ondergang haers Rijcks ende Staets, gevangelicke Wech-voeringe na Assyrien, mitsgaders eenen langduerigen desolaten Toestant onder de Heydensche Natien. *Ten derden*, worden de Boetveerdige ende Gelovige getroost met schoone Beloften van Godts Genade in haren hemelschen Koning, JESU CHRISTO, tot welcken sich alle Uytverkorene, niet alleen uyt Israël, maer oock uyt de Heyden, souden bekeeren, ende in hem eeuwiglick gezegent ende salig zijn.

Het eerste Capittel.

[Dense two-column blackletter Bible text, largely illegible; Hosea chapter 1, verses 1–10, with marginal notes.]

---

27. Facsimile Page of First Stereotyped Bible (1701)

MARS	AVRIL.
MArs a 31. jours ꝗ la Lune 30	**A**Vril a 30. jours ꝗ la Lune 29.
1 d s. Aubin , Evêque	1 g s. Hugues , Ev.
2 e s. Ceadde Evêque	2 A s. François de P.
3 f ste Cunegonde	3 b s. Richard , Ev.
4 g s. Casimir Prin. P.	4 c s. Ambroise Ev.
5 A s. raulin, Evêq.	5 d s. Vincent Ferr.
6 b s. Godegrane Ev.	6 e s. Pierre , Martyr.
7 c s. Thomas d'Aq.	7 f s. Egesipe , Hist.
8 d s. jean de Dieu	8 g s. Denis, Evêque.
9 e ste Françoise, veu.	9 A ste Marie Egyp.
10 f s. Droctovée Ab.	10 b s. Terence , M.
11 g Les 40. Martyrs	11 c s. Leon , Pape.
12 A s. Gregooire Pa.	12 d s. jule , Pape.
13 b ste Euphrasie, V.	13 e ste Ide , Veuve.
14 c s. Lubin, Evêque	14 f s. Tiburce & f. C.
15 d s. Tranquille. Ab.	15 g s. Ortaire, Conf.
16 e s. Cyriaque, Mar.	16 A s. Paterne , Ev.
17 f ste Gertrude, Vier	17 b s. Anicet, P. & M.
18 g s. Cyrile de jeruf.	18 c s. Parfait, Pr. M.
19 A s. Joseph.	19 d s. Timon, Diacr.
20 b s. Joachim	20 e s. Marien d'Aux.
21 c s. Benoist Ab. M.	21 f s. Anselme, Arch.
22 d s. Camel en, Ev.	22 g L'Invent. S. D.
23 e s. Procule Evêq.	23 A s. Georges , M.
24 f ste Caterine de S.	24 b ste Beuve, Vierg.
25 g L'Annonciation	25 c s. Marc , Evang.
26 A s. Jean d'Egypte	26 d s. Clet, Pape M.
27 b s. Rupert, Evêq.	27 e s. Anthime , Ev.
28 c s. Protere, Evêq.	28 f s. Vital , Mart.
29 d s. Eustase, Abbé	29 g ste Catherine
30 e s. Rieul. Evêque	30 A s. Eutrope , Ev.
31 f ste Balbine , v.	

28. Page from the "Book of Hours" by Valleyre

new product. When heated to 120° C. celluloid becomes plastic so that any desired form can be given it.

Emil Janin of Paris, in 1880, was the first to conduct successful experiments for making printing plates of celluloid. He hit upon the idea whilst experimenting with the plastic properties of celluloid. He also invented the putty which was necessary for the making of the matrices. This compound he found in the so-called Janin's cement or putty. He tested his cellulose printing plates successfully in Paris and then came to Vienna and London to demonstrate that his plates stood 100,000 impressions and more as against ordinary plates which began to deteriorate after the first 30,000 impressions.

The advantages of his celluloid plates were:

(1) Flexibility in heat which permitted of easy and quick change even on rotary presses.

(2) Durability under all possible conditions and making of a great number of good impressions.

(3) Repairs could be made as easily as with ordinary plates.

(4) Speed of production which occupied about one-half hour for any plate size.

For color printing celluloid plates were better than ordinary plates as none of the colors used had any chemical influence on the plate. A further advantage was that the transportation of celluloid plates was cheaper than ordinary plates, their weight being less, and thus resulting in postal savings.

The Janin celluloid process of stereotyping, as a substitute for metal in the casting of plates, consisted in the following features:

The composition had the same consistency as putty. The mixture was spread upon a thin iron plate to a thickness of $\frac{3}{8}''$ and a piece of blotting paper was pressed over the whole to absorb the superfluous glycerine. This was then placed on the type face downwards, subjecting same to gentle pressure in a press and applying a slight heat on the iron plate. After about four minutes the composition hardened and was lifted from the form. Now a hot press (steam table) was necessary. The matrix, now ready to take casts from, was laid upon the table of a hot press (steam table) and a piece of celluloid of the same size on top. The head of the press was heated by steam, screwed down on the celluloid, which was thus softened. Great pressure was applied whereby the celluloid was forced into every part of the matrix, whereupon cold water was admitted into the press, hardening the celluloid. Then the cast was easily removed from the matrix and trimmed and was immediately ready for use.

The operation of this process took a little less time than the papier-mache method but it was in actual practice for only a short time. Then it was discarded and forgotten.

Xylonite: This product was introduced into stereotype plates by J. E. Heidegger in Vienna in 1884. Xylonite was a product that had all the advantages of celluloid and none of its faults or disadvantages. It was produced from a cheap plant fibre, was not as porous as wood or metal, was especially adapted for illustration work and was exceedingly elastic. The plates made of Xylonite were from 60% to 70% cheaper than ordinary printing plates, and the material, after having been used, could be easily reclaimed and used over again. The method of applying the process was the same as practiced by Mr. Janin in the making of his celluloid stereotype plates.

Mame Bros. of Paris purchased Herhan's hollow copper matrix stereotyping process. They sent to the printing trade circulars with the following text:

"In 1801 the celebrated printing expert and artist, Herhan, exhibited at the Louvre the result of his research work in stereotyping, namely an edition of the 'Conjuration of Catalina Sallustius.' We attach to this circular a sample of this printing, a page of this work printed by his original process, and are confident that it will convey proof to an enlightened public that Herhan plates are capable of meeting the Elzevir competition."

The hollow types or movable matrices which Mame Bros. invented are made of copper instead of lead and regulus as hitherto employed in making ordinary types. They go thru the regular procedure, being stamped instead of cast. With the aid of exceedingly ingenious machines it was possible to impart to these new types the same height, the same strength of body and in proportion the same thickness as cast movable types possessed. The composition of a page was performed in identically the same way as in any ordinary printing plate.

A. Isermann, the well known printer and stereotyper and pioneer user of the plaster of Paris method in Hamburg, claimed that he had invented the wet mat process independently of Genoux, but had not deemed it worth while to take out a patent on the invention. One of the best known stereotypers in Europe, M. Archimowitz of Karlsruhe, endorsed the wet mat method and thru his widely distributed book, "Stereotyping Processes," he converted a great number of plaster of Paris stereotyping plants into wet mat enthusiasts.

The wet mat process met with considerable resistance on the part of many stereotypers at the time of its introduction. For instance, an important typographic plant in Leipzig received an order and made the matrices for the job on wet mats using the Genoux procedure. When the head of the pressroom examined the plates he threw them out as totally unfit and ordered all plates to be remade with the plaster of Paris method.

Butter Bros. of Komotau in Bohemia published a booklet, entitled "The Value of Stereotyping in Book Printing in 1873." This pamphlet, widely circulated, was intended to interest the small town printer in stereotyping. Butter Bros. called attention to the fact that printers in small towns lacked prompt deliveries of type material, were forced to have their type lying idle, were hindered by lack of capital to put in an adequate supply of type. Butter offered stereotyping as a remedy for all these ills, and due to his untiring efforts stereotyping was soon widely practiced in small plants throughout Central Europe.

A system called "cold" stereotyping (not to be confused with the dry mat cold method) was practiced in many shops. It did away with the drying of mats on a steam table. The drawbacks of this hot drying were that the type material expanded under the influence of the heat, and the materials contained in the paste, used to combine the layers of the wet mat, melted and stuck. The "cold" drying method was first employed by Ryles & Son in their plant in Bradford, England. The mat, while still moist, was removed from the type matter, put into a specially constructed frame which held it tight and then was left to dry out without heat.

In 1901 Robert Krafft of Berlin invented a matrix comprising an inner and outer layer and an intermediate layer of pulp, composed of a mixture of freely ground turf (peat), glycerine, starch, paper pulp and a small percentage of an antiseptic such as carbolic acid.

In 1902 Leopold Elias patented a stereotype matrix composed of asbestos covered with a thin covering of plant glue.

In 1911 Niels Bendixen of Copenhagen invented a method of producing a special rapid drying mat for stereotyping of halftones. Bendixen made an etching from a photograph, coated it with a fatty paste containing paraffine, fish glue and pipe clay. A wet mat made with another special soapy paste was placed on top of the coated etching, covered with blotting paper and placed in a heated drying press. The coating on the etching loosened itself from the etching and adhered to the paper mat, transferring to the paper all the details of the etching. In this manner a paper mat was procured, which was flexible and adapted to be sent by mail, and wherein immediately after its production one or several castings could be made using stereotype metal.

The distinguishing feature of Bendixen's matrix was that it possessed the quality of drying very rapidly. The ordinary dry mat is much cheaper, simpler and better adapted for syndicate work.

ARM^d GASTON CAMUS de l'Acad. des Inscriptions & Belles Lettres
Député de la Ville de Paris
Né le 4 Avril 1740
Président de l'Assemblée Nationale le 28 8bre 1789.

29. Armand Gaston Camus

30. Charles Earl Stanhope (1753-1816)

CHAPTER FOUR

A SHORT HISTORY OF THE NEWSPAPER

BEFORE CONTINUING our compilation of the different steps undertaken in the art of stereotyping, remarks pertaining to the history of the newspaper in Europe and America will be of interest.

A newspaper in its modern acceptance can only be properly dated from the time when in Western Europe the invention of printing made a multiplication of copies a commercial possibility.

We find news in a form similar to what we call a newspaper in the times of the Assyrians and Egyptians, and later on in the Roman Empire. Julius Caesar ordered a regulated publication of short hand-written records, called "Acta Senatus," of the courts of law and of public assemblies. Another publication, called "Acta Diurna" (daily acts), recorded descriptions of public works, buildings in progress; lists of deaths, births and marriages; trials for divorces, which were of frequent occurrence among the Romans. These hand-written publications were made accessible to the people through posting of same on public buildings.

Soon after the Chinese had invented their method of block-printing, they established an official gazette and printed it in Pekin. This publication is still in existence and is called "The Court Transcript."

There is, however, no uninterrupted connection between these different hand-written or printed publications and the real beginning of newspaper makings; these date from the beginning of the 16th century.

The ancestors of the modern newspaper are four-fold: Troubadours or wandering minstrels, the leaflet, the letter and the so-called market-relations or statements of an isolated piece of news.

The troubadours have been called the wandering journalists of the Middle Ages. They roamed through many countries, visiting the courts and castles of the mighty, and in song and speech they brought to the world of those days what we moderns glean from our daily newspapers. They gave the best and the newest in the sphere of music and poetry, and being widely traveled personages, they disseminated knowledge of all events, big and small, that happened in the cities and countries they had roved in. This news was delivered by the minstrels in epigrammatic, vigorous songs, which were often memorized by the hearers and carried further.

After the art of printing from engraved wooden-blocks was invented, the next step was to disseminate news through hand-bills or leaflets. The contents of such leaflets were made up from the momentous events, for example, the dangers of the Turkish invasion of the Occident, the acts and utterances of emperors, rulers and great men, great ceremonies, finances, battles. Also short, vivid accounts of occurrences of Nature, pestilence, crimes, executions, etc. During the period of the Reformation, the ninety theses of Luther were printed as leaflets and distributed all over the country.

A very important member in the chain leading to the newspaper was the written letter. In the Roman Empire the high officials in the provinces had slaves or liberated slaves in Rome send to them regularly reports by letter covering all political and social events of the empire. In the Middle Ages, princes, monasteries, city administrations, learned men, etc., had writers of occupation report to them on various topics. Then scribes appeared who reported only on commercial matters of importance; these men had as seat of their activities great commercial centres, Venice, Ulm, Rome, Antwerp, Augsburg.

In due time these letter-writers dropped the form of addressed letters and issued written circulars, becoming thus less personal in their reports. In the 16th century scribes began the practice of selling accumulated news in copies. The men who conducted these flourishing news agencies were called scrittori d' avisi (writers of news) and formed the first reporters' guild.

The next step was a certain regularity of making and delivering such news information. The first printed news-sheets, which through the combination of giving news and giving same regularly resembled the present day newspaper closely, were the so-called market-reports or "relations." These publications were issued semi-annually for distribution at fairs held at the commercial centers and contained all important news, covering the past six months. The inventor of this system was Michael von Aitzing, who in March, 1583 issued the first relatio historia (historical report).

In July, 1588 an English newspaper appeared intermittently, called "The English Mercurie, for the prevention of false reports, imprinted and sold by the Queen's printers, Field and Barker, London."

Within a few years London had no lack of such Mercuries, Corantos, Gazettes. Many imitators followed on the Continent and as the next step there appeared the weekly news-sheet, of which one, issued in Strasbourg in 1609, carried the following title: "Account of all capital and memorable histories which on and off have occurred in Upper-and-Lower-Germany, also in France, Italy, Scotland, England, Spain, etc., etc., in this year 1609. All newes shall, as I may obtain and collect same, be set up in print."

The first English newspaper in the present day sense of the word was established in London by Nathaniel Butter, in 1622. It was a small quarto of eighteen pages, called the "Certain Newes of the Present Weeke." The editor solicited subscribers by the following advertisement:

"If any gentleman, or other accustomed to the weekly relations of newes, be desirous to continue the same, let them know that the writer, or transcriber rather of this newes, hathe published two former newes, the one dated the second, the other the thirteenth of August, all of which do carry a like title, with the arms of the King of Bohemia on the other side of the title page, and have dependence one upon another: which manner of writing and printing he doth purpose to continue weekly, by God's assistance from the best and most certain intelligence. Farewell, this twenty-third of August, 1622." This was the first English newspaper because it was the first publication of news which the editor publicly proposed to continue regularly.

Very shortly afterwards a number of "Weekly News Books" put in their appearance, such as "News from Flanders," "News from Italy," etc. On March 7th, 1649, in Number 7 of "The Impartial Intelligencer" there is to be found the first regular advertisement. It is from a gentleman in Candish in Suffolk, from whom two horses had been stolen.

France printed its first weekly newspaper in 1632. It was established in Paris by Dr. Theophrastus Renaudot, a physician, famous for his skill in collecting gossip and news to amuse his patients. Encouraged by the reception his news received from not only clients but also from others, he realized it would be advantageous to print periodically and sell his accumulations of news. He obtained a sole privilege from Cardinal Richelieu for publishing "The Paris Gazette" and the first number appeared in April, 1632. King Louis

XIII was a frequent contributor to the Gazette, taking his little paragraphs to the printing office himself and seeing them set up in type. Renaudot asked six centimes for each issue. His children and grandchildren kept up the publication; in 1765 the paper was the first to bring stock exchange quotations, and in 1792 also the first newspaper to publish theatrical advertisements.

The first daily newspaper appeared in Leipzig, Germany in 1660, the same still being published. In 1695 the censure fell in England and in 1709 the first daily newspaper was published in London, called "The Daily Courant." In 1777 the first daily in France was issued, the "Journal de Paris," and in 1778 the first Sunday newspaper, Johnson's "Sunday Monitor," in London.

The following pages are devoted to an abbreviated historical record of newspaper development in the United States of America. It would be entirely beyond the scope of this book to follow through this development with even meager details from the beginning to our day.

However, due to the many demands for a brief outline of this phase of printing history it is offered herewith, but closes with the day when wet mat stereotyping entered the newspaper plants, i.e. about 1865.

In the first paragraphs general information is given, then first newspaper ventures in the thirteen colonial states are recorded, thereupon a list of the first newspapers printed in the remaining thirty-five states of the Union, and finally notes concerning printing plant conditions in the colonial, Revolutionary War and Civil War periods.

As was the case in Europe, the first American mediums of disseminating news were the written and the spoken newspaper. The latter was read to the inhabitants after church service on the steps of the church or on the public square by the Town Crier; also at times in the public tavern. Written copies of what had been spoken were posted in places near the church. The appellation "newspaper" was first used in 1670, and appeared in a letter addressed to Charles Perrot, the second editor of "The Oxford Gazette;" a reader stated: "I wanted your newes paper Monday last past."

Further precursors of newspapers were the printed sheets. There was no regular publication; they were issued only once and were called "broadsides." One of the earliest, 1689, was a sheet 8" x 4½", printed only on one side; its publisher and printer was Samuel Green. Other broadsides, or handbills, were circulated rather

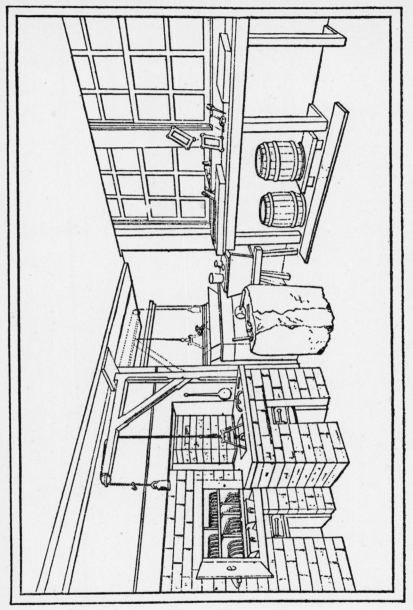

31. Interior of a Stereotyping Foundry in 1830

32. Correcting Stereotype Plates

extensively about this time, for towards 1689 the Massachusetts authorities passed a resolution: "Whereas many papers have been lately printed and dispersed, tending to the disturbance of the peace, any person guilty of printing or even concealing such like papers, should be accounted enemies of the Government, and be proceeded against as such with the uttermost severity." Thus no freedom of the press existed at that time.

In 1690 a sort of a newspaper was printed and published by Benjamin Harris, who was an exiled English newspaper publisher who had settled in Boston as a bookseller and proprietor of the London Coffee House. It was issued under the name "Publick Occurrences." It was a small 4-page sheet 7½" x 11½", two columns to each page, except the fourth, which was free from any printing. The sheet was suppressed by the Governor of Massachusetts, and after its suppression no other paper was founded until 1704.

At Bridgeton a written newspaper called "The Plain Dealer" was publicly posted at Matthew Potter's bar. A notice informed the public that those interested might read the paper by calling at the tavern every Tuesday morning.

The clergy of New England frequently related or referred to items of news. The bellman as he made his rounds sometimes told other things besides giving the hour and informing the public that all was well. News was circulated thru pulpit announcements and semi-public letters. Foremost among writers of news-letters was John Campbell, the postmaster of Boston. He made it a practice to send rather regularly letters to the governors of the New England Colonies. These letters, after being read, were passed along to others. Sometimes they were publicly posted so that their contents might be read after the manner in which news was communicated in ancient Rome. These Campbell letters might be termed written newspapers.

So numerous were the requests on John Campbell for extra news advices that neither he nor his brother, Duncan, was able to make the supply equal to the demand simply by the pen. He was forced to employ the printing press. His first printed news-letter appeared on Monday, April 24th, 1704, and was called "The Boston News-Letter." It was printed on both sides of a half sheet folio, 7" x 11½", by Bartholomew Green (who later became its owner) in a small wooden building on Newberry Street, and for over forty years it was printed at that address. The old home had burned down, and Green's son-in-law, Richard Draper, built a new home

[99]

for the paper. In 1776 the publication of the paper was suspended. Then William Brooker started the second newspaper in America, "The Boston Gazette," on December 21st, 1719. Other Massachusetts papers to follow the Gazette were: The Courant (1721), The Weekly Journal (1727), The Rehearsal (1731), The Post-Boy (1734) and The Evening Post (1735).

The first Pennsylvania newspaper, "The American Weekly Mercury," which appeared on the 22nd of December, 1719, was the first newspaper in the Middle Colonies, and was published in Philadelphia from the press of Andrew Bradford, the local postmaster, and his son William Bradford, who was to be the publisher of the first newspaper in New York. At first the paper was sold by "Andrew Bradford at The Bible in the Second Street and John Copson in the High Street." Upon Bradford's death in 1742 the next issue was put in mourning with the inverted column rules. His widow, Cornelia Bradford, suspended the paper for one week because of the death of her husband, and then continued the black borders for the next six weeks. The paper bore her name on its imprint until its suspension early in 1747.

Benjamin Franklin worked at his trade as printer in the office of Samuel Keimer. The latter started a paper, the second in Pennsylvania, the title of which was "The Universal Instructor in all Arts and Sciences; and Pennsylvania Gazette." The first number appeared on September 24th, 1728. After nine months the paper had less than one hundred subscribers, and Keimer was glad to sell at any price to Franklin and his fellow printer, Meredith, who assumed control in October, 1729. The new firm shortened the title to "The Pennsylvania Gazette." After the fourth issue Franklin announced a "Half Sheet twice a Week," and gave America its first semi-weekly; after a few issues he returned to weekly publication. The profits of the paper from 1748 to 1766, or 18 years, were about $60,000 for subscriptions and over $20,000 for advertising.

The first daily newspaper in America appeared in Philadelphia on September 21st, 1784; it was entitled, "The Pennsylvania Packet and Daily Advertiser," and was published by John Dunlop and David Claypoole. It was a 4-page sheet of four columns to the page and was sold at four pence a copy. The first page and the last were entirely filled with advertisements. The third page consisted half of advertisements and half of text. The only page which did not contain any advertisement was the second; it was filled with news and essays.

William Bradford was the founder of the first paper in New York. After he had learned the printing trade in England he accompanied William Penn to America in 1682. Upon his return to England in 1685 he procured a press and type and again set sail for Philadelphia, where he opened a book shop and did a general printing business.

Bradford became Royal Printer in New York in 1693. On the 8th of November, 1725 he published the first issue of the "New York Gazette." From 1725 to 1730 the "New York Gazette" consisted of a single sheet of four pages.

The paper was invariably poorly printed—doubtlessly due to the fact that Bradford had used the type for a long time before he began to print his newspaper. Bradford retired from the newspaper world on November 19th, 1744, the date of the last issue of the "New York Gazette." The name was changed to "The New York Evening Post" in 1744.

The second newspaper in the city was "The New York Weekly Journal," first issued on November 5th, 1733 by John Peter Zenger, a German who had come to New York in 1710 with a group of palatines sent over by Queen Ann. He set up his own printing shop in 1726, first on Smith Street and later on Broad Street. A contemporary correspondent wrote that "Zenger rides too fast and speaks in the spur when he ought to make use of the reins." In his second number Zenger published an article on "The Liberty of the Press," and followed up with other articles radical in tone. On the 17th of November, 1734 he was arrested and imprisoned.

Because of his attack on the arbitrary and corrupt administration of the British Colonial Governor Crosby, Zenger had been arrested on the charge of seditious libel. In the trial which followed Zenger was fortunate in having to defend him Andrew Hamilton, probably the ablest lawyer of Philadelphia.

"The laws of our country have given us a right—the liberty of both exposing and opposing arbitrary power in these parts of the world at least by speaking and writing truth."

In his impassioned address to the jury in the famous trial of John Peter Zenger in August, 1735, eighty year old Hamilton used these words in closing his plea for the liberation of his client who was held in jail for nine months by the King's Governor for printing an attack on the arbitrary and corrupt administration of Colonial Governor Crosby.

A jury of twelve courageous and upright men acquitted Zenger of seditious libels against the Crown and the fight for the freedom of the press was won. From that time the press was to become an unhampered medium of education, a purveyor of news and a guardian of public welfare. From that day in 1735 newspapers were destined to play a leading part in Revolutionary development by educating the Colonists on their rights as free men. Here was the genesis of the Bill of Rights—our present guarantee of liberty.

The following is a record of the first newspaper printed in the remaining original thirteen states.

CONNECTICUT

"The Connecticut Gazette," the first paper in Connecticut, made its appearance on April 12th, 1755 at New Haven. The first number bore the imprint: "Printed by James Parker at the Post Office Near the Sign of the White Horse."

Benjamin Franklin had been induced by President Clap to purchase a printing plant with a view of establishing the former's nephew, Benjamin Mecom, in business at New Haven. The material arrived in the fall of 1754, but Mecom changed his plans and Parker was secured to take up the work. In 1764 the "Gazette" was suspended for a short time but was afterward revived by Benjamin Mecom on July 5th, 1765. In an editorial announcement Mecom added the following statement about subscribers: "All kinds of Provisions, Fire Wood and other suitable country Produce, will be taken as pay of those who cannot spare money, if delivered at the Printer's Dwelling House or any other place which may accidently suit him."

DELAWARE

James Adams, a native of Ireland, was the publisher of "The Wilmington Chronicle," the first newspaper in Delaware. After working for about seven years in the office of Franklin in Philadelphia, he set up a press in that city, but a year later moved to Wilmington, where he first printed books and almanacs. In 1762 he started the "Chronicle" but failed to get enough subscribers to make the venture profitable, and after six months discontinued the sheet.

GEORGIA

For 30 years after Georgia was founded the Colony depended for its news upon the papers of South Carolina, and its merchants were forced to advertise their goods in Charleston papers. On April 7th,

33. Stereotype Foundry

34. Moulding in Plaster

1763, however, the first number of "The Georgia Gazette" was issued at Savannah by James Johnson at his printing office on Broughton Street. On November 21st, 1765 it suspended publication on account of the Stamp Act, but was revived again in May, 1766 and lasted as late as February, 1776.

MARYLAND

William Parks, who had learned his trade in England, brought out the first paper in Maryland. In setting up his press in 1726 he had been made "Public Printer to Maryland." One year later he began publishing "The Maryland Gazette" at Annapolis. As the colony was but sparsely settled at the time, Parks had great difficulty not only in getting subscribers, but also in securing advertisements. The paper was discontinued in 1733.

NEW HAMPSHIRE

The first newspaper in New Hampshire was published by Daniel Fowle of Boston under the name of "The New Hampshire Gazette," on October 7th, 1756.

On November 1st, 1765 the "Gazette" came out with the usual black border like so many other papers of the same time, and announced that it would cease publication because its printers were unwilling to pay the obnoxious stamp tax.

In 1776 it issued a publication urging the Provincial Congress not to establish an independent government because such a proceeding might be taken as a desire to throw off British rule. The editor was at once called before the Provincial Congress, severely censured, and admonished in the future never to publish articles reflecting upon the Continental Congress or the cause of American independence.

NEW JERSEY

The first printed newspaper did not appear in New Jersey until the War of the Revolution had started, but it was not hard to understand this tardy beginning. New York and Philadelphia papers circulated then as they do today through New Jersey. The suspension of some of these newspapers, the increase in subscription price, the poor delivery by post riders, many of whom were in active military service—all of these things, coupled with the exciting events of the war, created an independent demand for news on the part of the patriots of New Jersey.

A paper printed weekly in 4-folio page, and entitled "The New Jersey Gazette," to be sold at the price of 26 shillings per year, the New Jersey Legislature to guarantee 700 subscribers within six months and the printer and four workmen to be exempted from service in the militia, was printed by Isaac Collins who already had a plant in Burlington. The first number came off his press on December 5th, 1777.

NORTH CAROLINA

In 1755 Benjamin Franklin, then Postmaster General for the Colonies, appointed James Davis, who had migrated from Virginia to North Carolina, Postmaster of Newburn. The latter established in the same year "The North Carolina Gazette." It bore the following imprint: "Newburn: Printed by James Davis at the Printing Office in Front Street; where all persons may be supplied with this paper at Six Shillings per annum; and when Advertisements of a moderate length are inserted, for Three Shillings the First Week and Two Shillings for every week thereafter. And where also Book Binding is done reasonably." Published on Thursdays it usually appeared in a cheese pot size folio.

RHODE ISLAND

After James Franklin, the founder of "The New England Weekly Courant," left Boston, he went to Newport, Rhode Island, where on September 27th, 1832 he established "The Rhode Island Gazette." It was the first newspaper in that state, and while it made an heroic struggle for existence, it only lasted eight months. After Franklin's death his wife, Ann Franklin, made several unsuccessful attempts to revive the paper. The second newspaper, "The Newport Mercury," was founded in Newport in 1758 by James Franklin, Jr. When the son died in 1762 his mother, Ann Franklin, ran the paper in partnership with Samuel Hale. Upon her death in 1763 Hale ran the paper most successfully, as he was one of the first editors and publishers to realize that advertising depends upon circulation for its value.

SOUTH CAROLINA

Eleazer Phillips, a New England printer, went to South Carolina in 1730 where he established a book and stationery shop in "Charles Town." Associated with him was his son, Eleazer, Jr. The latter established a paper on March 4th, 1730 called "The South

Carolina Weekly Journal." The paper, however, failed to get enough subscribers to warrant continued publication and suspended in about six months.

VIRGINIA

One reason why Virginia did not have a newspaper earlier than 1736 will be found in an assertion of Sir William Berkeley, who was Governor of the Colony for 38 years. In his report to the Lords of the Committee for the Colonies in 1671 he said: "I thank God we have not free schools nor printing, and I hope we shall not have these one hundred years. For learning has brought disobedience and heresy and sex into the world, and printing has divulged them and libels against the Government. God keep us from both."

On August 16th, 1736, however, William Parks brought out at Williamsburg "The Virginia Gazette." This first paper in Virginia has been described as "A small dingy sheet containing a few items of foreign news; the ads of Williamsburg shopkeepers; notices of the arrival and departure of ships; a few chance particulars relating to persons or affairs in the Colony; and imbecile effusions celebrating the charms of Myrtilla Florella or other belles of the period." Parks was made Printer of the Colony at a salary of 200 pounds—payable in tobacco, the currency of the time. If he was unsuccessful in establishing his paper on a permanent basis it was through no fault of his, but due to the opposition to a free press in the Colony. In his announcement Parks stated a subscription price of 15 shillings per annum.

In the following a short resume is given of the first newspapers printed in the remaining States of the Union.

ALABAMA

The first paper in what is now Alabama was "The Mobile Sentinel," first published on May 23rd, 1811 by Samuel Miller and John B. Hood at Fort Stoddard. These men were so determined to be the first in Mobile journalism that they started south before the city was annexed, but were compelled to stop for the printing outside Mobile in the neighborhood of St. Stephens, where they began to print the "Mobile Sentinel" while under the protection of Fort Stoddard. Sixteen issues of this paper were brought out, but whether a single one of them was actually printed in Mobile is not known.

ARIZONA

The first paper in Arizona, "The Weekly Arizonian," was started at Tubac by Sylvester Moury on or about March 3rd, 1859. The press on which the paper was printed came around the Horn in 1858, and was brought from Guaymas Tubac by wagon. In 1860 the paper was removed to Tucson. It ceased publication in 1861. In advertising the sale of its plant it included among the office equipment two Derringer pistols. This mention showed "shooting irons" to be a necessary adjunct in the offices of many of the western papers. As a matter of fact, one reason for the suspension of this newspaper was the fact that its publishers were charged with a stage robbery, and in resisting arrest one of them was killed. In the fall of 1879 the old press was taken to Tombstone, where it was used to print "The Nugget," the first paper in that camp.

ARKANSAS

Journalism began in Arkansas when Wm. E. Woodruff printed at the Post of Arkansas the first number of "The Arkansas Gazette" in 1819. A native of Long Island, he had arrived at the Post in October 1819 from Franklin, Tenn., bringing with him by canoes and dugouts a press and some type. Being the Printer of the Territory, he ceased to bring out the "Gazette" at the Post in 1821, and went to Little Rock which had been made the capital. Here he revived his paper and continued it as the official organ of the state until 1833.

CALIFORNIA

At Monterey Robert Semple and the Rev. Walter Colton brought out the first paper in California on August 15th, 1846. It was called "The Californian." Semple was described as follows: "He is in buckskin dress and foxskin cap; he is true with his rifle, ready with his pen and quick at the type case." Colton once asserted that the materials in his office had been used by a Roman Catholic Monk in printing a few historical tracts; that the press was old enough to preserve as a curiosity, and that the types were all in pi and were so rusty that it was only by hard scouring that the letters would be made to show their faces. There were no rules or leads, and in their absence two or three sheets of tin were cut with the help of a jack knife for substitutes. Fortunately there was enough ink for the press, but unfortunately no paper. A supply of paper,

35. Stereotype Foundry in 1829

36. Wet Mat Stereotyping Plant

sent to California to be used to wrap cigars, was purchased from a coasting vessel, and on these sheets, not much larger than the common sized foolscap, was printed the first issue of the "Californian." One-half of the paper was in English, the other half in Spanish. Single copies sold for 12½ cents and considered cheap at that. "The Californian," after six months, boasted that it had been able to meet expenses, but in spite of this assertion it was forced to move from Monterey to Yerba Buena—now San Francisco—with Robert Semple as its sole publisher.

Colorado

In Denver "The Rocky Mountain News" is the oldest paper in Colorado. Its first issue appeared on April 23rd, 1859 in a struggling home-seekers' settlement which had not yet a definite name. The discovery of placer gold some months earlier had made a settlement at the junction of the Platte River and Cherry Creek. On each bank of the river there was a rival townsite, so that William M. Myers dated his paper as published at Cherry Creek, Denver Territory. The first issue of the "Rocky Mountain News" was printed on brown wrapping paper. At the start it was published weekly but later it became a daily. It has been published uninterruptedly since its establishment with a single exception, in the early '60's when a flood in Cherry Creek washed the plant out of existence.

The day the "Rocky Mountain News" started was one of the most exciting in frontier journalism. When the news of the discovery of gold in Pike's Peak region had reached as far east as the Missouri, it promptly started two small newspaper plants. One left Omaha and was owned by William M. Byers. The other set out from St. Joseph, Missouri, and was owned by John L. Merrick. Merrick was the first to arrive, but not knowing that competitors were on the way, he leisurely commenced work on the first issue of "The Cherry Creek Pioneer." Ten days later the Omaha plant arrived, and the competition for the first paper in Colorado began. The settlement offered a suitable prize to the winner and appointed a committee of citizens to referee the contest. Both the "Rocky Mountain News" and the "Cherry Creek Pioneer" announced their date of first publication April 23rd, 1859. At 10:30 o'clock in the evening of April 23rd the first copy of the "News" a 4-page sheet, was pulled from the old Washington hand press. A little later the "Pioneer" also appeared on the streets. The decision of the committee, however, was that the "News" had won by twenty minutes.

[111]

Worn out by his efforts and depressed by defeat, Merrick the next morning offered to sell his plant to his rival. His terms were accepted and Merrick then set off for the mountains, not to hunt for news, but for gold.

DISTRICT OF COLUMBIA

Before the site of government was permanently located in the District of Columbia, a number of newspapers had been published in Georgetown. The first of these was "The Times and Potowmack Packet" established by Charles Fierer in February, 1789. Others were "The Weekly Ledger," 1790; "The Columbia Chronicle," 1793; and "The Sentinel of Liberty," 1796.

The first paper actually printed in Washington City was "The Government Observer and Washington Advertiser," the initial number of which Thomas Wilson issued on May 22nd, 1795. The paper was suspended about a year later on account of its owner's death.

FLORIDA

The first newspaper, called "The East Florida Gazette," was published at St. Augustine by William Charles Wells about 1783. This paper has been mentioned in later southern newspapers; however, no copy has been preserved. John Wells, brother of the publisher, left Charleston, S. C., where he printed "The Royal Gazette," for St. Augustine where he helped his brother to print books and possibly the "Gazette." Florida, being sparsely settled, did not have another paper until "The Weekly Meridian" was established in 1825 at Tallahassee.

IDAHO

The first paper to be published in Idaho after the territory was created on March 3rd, 1863, was "The Boise News," started on September 30th, 1863 at Bannock City—now called Idaho City. It was published by T. J. and J. S. Butler; J. S. Butler had left Auburn, Ore. in the fall of 1862 to look after a herd of cattle in the Powder River Valley. Later on he organized the pack train to take goods to Walla Walla, Wash. At Walla Walla he met Major Reese of "The Walla Walla Watchman," who had just bought out a rival newspaper. Butler purchased the extra outfit from Major Reese, sold his packing business and sent for his brother, T. J. Butler, who became the editor of the new paper.

The outfit sold to Butler was far from being complete. He found it necessary to make composing-sticks from the tin of an old tobacco box; he improvised an imposing-stone by using a large slab split from a pine log, which he dressed off on one side, mounted on a frame and covered with sheet iron; he chiseled a chase out of old horseshoe iron.

In spite of such handicaps, however, the "Boise News" was a fairly creditable production. It was continued by the Butler brothers for about thirteen months and often sold for $2.50 a copy.

INDIANA

Journalism in Indiana began at Vincennes when Elisha Stout, a printer from Lexington, Ky., brought out the first number of "The Indiana Gazette" on July 31st, 1804. The newspaper was produced under great difficulties. The paper was brought to Vincennes on pack horse which traveled over the old buffalo trail. The plant itself had been brought from Frankfort, Ky. down the Ohio River and up the Wabash, which was then called the Piroques. The printing office burned out in about two years, and the paper was revived on July 11th, 1807 by Stout under the title "The Western Sun."

IOWA

The first paper in Iowa was the "Dubuque Visitor," brought out at the Dubuque lead mines, which at that time were in Wisconsin territory, by John King on May 11th, 1836. He had founded the Dubuque Lead Mine in 1834, and having purchased in Cincinnati a hand press, some type and materials sufficient to issue a small weekly paper, he returned to Dubuque. William Carey Jones, a young printer from Chillicothe, accompanied King to take charge of the mechanical side of the paper.

In 1837 a new owner changed the title to "The Iowa News," and the name of the paper was again changed in 1841 to "The Miners Express." When in 1851 a new publication, "The Dubuque Herald," appeared, the Miners Express made preparations to bring out a daily paper, and on August 19th of that year it published the first daily paper north of St. Louis or west of the Mississippi.

KANSAS

The first paper to appear in Kansas was published at the Baptist Mission and called "The Shawnee Sun." Published exclusively in the Indian language it was a small quarter-sheet edited by the Reverend Johnston Likins and printed on the Mission press by

Jotham Meeker. The old fashioned press of the Mission was later taken to Prairie City and used to print "The Freeman's Champion," first issued in 1857 in a home-made tent, a gift of the women of that place.

The earliest English newspaper in Kansas was "The Kansas Weekly Herald" published in Leavenworth in 1854 by Osborne Adams. It was started before there was a single permanent building in Leavenworth; only four temporary tents had been raised before a typesetter was at work under an old elm tree on the first number. An editorial remark in the first issue said: "Our editorials have been written and our proof corrected while sitting on the ground with a big shingle for a table."

KENTUCKY

Kentucky was first organized as part of Virginia, and to promote its admission as a state, Lexington, at that time a most important town, voted in 1786 a free land to John Bradford, the Virginia planter, who had come to Kentucky after the Revolution. On the site given him by the town of Lexington Bradford put up a print-shop, and on April 11th, 1787 brought out the first number of "The Kentucke Gazette." The equipment for the shop had to come by wagon over the road to Pittsburgh, and then down the Ohio to Maysville, and then by "nag" over the trail recently blazed to Lexington. The initial number of the "Kentucke Gazette" was a single sheet of two pages, 10" x 19½", three columns to a page. The spelling of "Kentucke" was changed to the modern form "Kentucky" in 1789. Some time in 1848 the "Kentucky Gazette" ceased publication.

LOUISIANA

Among the refugees from San Domingo who settled at New Orleans, was L. Puclot. After much difficulty he succeeded in getting the consent of the Governor to print in French "The Moniteur de la Louisiana," which first appeared in 1794. In 1797 the "Moniteur" became the official state paper and in its pages are to be found most of the facts we know about the early history of Louisiana.

"The Louisiana Gazette," the first paper in New Orleans to be printed in English, was established in 1804. It was published twice a week by John Mowry. He started with only nineteen subscribers who paid an annual subscription of $10.00. Several attempts were made to turn the "Gazette" into a daily newspaper but they were

37. Metal House

I. JOHNSON & CO

[115]

Ain Warnung des Sündtfluss ober

erschrockenlichen wassers Des xxiiij. iars auß natürlicher art des hymels zū besorgen mit sampt außlegung der grossen wunder zaychñ zū Wien in Osterreych am hymel erschinen im XX iar.

38. A Leaflet of 1520 Depicting the Flood

not successful, principally owing to the large number of residents who could not read English.

MAINE

The first newspaper published in Maine (1785) was called "The Falmouth Gazette," and was published by Benjamin Titcomb who had learned his trade in a shop at Newburyport, Mass., and Thomas B. Wait, who had been connected with the "Boston Chronicle." The title was changed to "The Cumberland" in 1786, and when part of Falmouth was incorporated as part of Portland the masthead carried the name of Portland. Six years later the title was again changed, to avoid confusion with another Portland paper of similar name, to "The Eastern Herald." It continued to be published until 1804.

MICHIGAN

Journalism in Michigan began with a spoken newspaper conducted by Father Gabriel Richard, a priest of the Order of Sulpice in Detroit. He appointed the Town Crier, whose duty it was on Sunday to stand on the church steps and tell the public in general such news as was fit to speak. Advertising had its place in this spoken newspaper, which told of things for sale, etc., and for the benefit of those that were absent at the spoken edition a written one was publicly posted near the church. The Sacristan of St. Ann's Church assisted Father Richard and later became a printer and newspaper publisher.

Out of this spoken newspaper grew the first printed sheet in Michigan, entitled "The Michigan Essay," or "Impartial Observer." It first appeared in Detroit in 1809. The first section, about a column and a half, was written by the Father himself. James M. Miller functioned as editor and publisher. An editorial announcement informed the public that the paper would be published every Thursday and handed to city subscribers at $5.00 per annum, payable half yearly in advance.

MINNESOTA

The first newspaper in Minnesota was announced in its prospectus as "The Epistle of St. Paul." When the paper appeared, however, it bore the name of "The Minnesota Pioneer," and was published in St. Paul in 1849. It was a 4-page, 6-column sheet for the first few months, but later it was enlarged to seven columns. Its editor and owner was James M. Goodhue, a native of New Hampshire. The early issues were printed under difficulties. The only available printing office was the basement of the only public house in St. Paul. The editor, in describing his early experiences, said it was as open as a corn crib and that the pigs in seeking shelter under the floor frequently jostled the loose boards on which rested the editorial tray of the "Minnesota Pioneer". Many of the editorials written by Goodhue got him into serious difficulties—difficulties out of which he escaped only with the help of his fists and a pistol.

MISSISSIPPI

The first paper in Mississippi was "The Gazette." It appeared in 1800 at Natchez and was called "The Mississippi Gazette." Its editor and printer was Benjamin Stokes. The paper continued publication until about 1802.

MISSOURI

James Charless, a printer who had worked on the "Kentucky Gazette" at Lexington, was the founder of journalism in Missouri. Securing an old Ramage press and a few fonts of type, he put his plant aboard a keel boat on the Ohio and floated down that river to find a permanent location at what is now St. Louis, but what was then only a little settlement of about a thousand inhabitants. Here, in 1808, he pulled the first number of "The Missouri Gazette." In this period of American history Congress had divided its recently acquired provinces into the Territories of Orleans and Louisiana. St. Louis was in Louisiana Territory, so in 1809 Charless called his paper "The Louisiana Gazette." When Congress, however, again set up Missouri and Louisiana each as a separate territory, Charless in 1812 returned to the original name of "The Missouri Gazette." (This paper is now published as the "St. Louis Article.")

MONTANA

Journalism in Montana began in the cellar of a log cabin at Virginia City in 1864, when John Buchanan brought out "The Montana Post." He had brought a press and material from St. Louis. After two issues of the "Post" he sold the paper to D. W. Tilton and Benjamin R. Ditters. Ditters gained complete control of the paper, took it to Helena, and resumed publication there in 1868. The reason for the change was that Virginia City was a placer camp, and after its mineral beds were exhausted the miners left the city and there was no longer need for a newspaper. On April 23rd,

1869 Helena was swept by fire, and from that time until June 11th of the same year the "Post" continued to operate, but was unable to make any collections either for subscriptions or advertisements on account of the paralysis of business. On June 11th, 1869 the "Post" was compelled to suspend publication.

Nebraska

The first five papers in Nebraska were printed in Iowa. The first of these, and incidentally the first printed in Nebraska, was "The Nebraska Palladium." Number one was dated July 15th, 1854 and was printed at St. Marys, a hamlet just below Bellevue on the Iowa shore of the Missouri River. The first number to be printed in Nebraska was that of November 15th, 1854. For the privilege of turning out the first number E. N. Upjohn gave one dollar. Thomas Morton was its publisher and Daniel Reed & Company editors and proprietors.

Nevada

Among the prospectors who hastened to Nevada after the discovery of gold and silver in that region was Joseph Webb. He was not successful prospecting and settled for a while at the Carson River crossing where Dayton now stands. Gold had been found there in some quantities, and then it became a station for immigrants along the trail on their way to California.

Webb gathered up the gossip of the trail, supplemented by what news was told him by passersby, and then with pen and ink made a written newspaper which he sold to travelers, who paid for it with gold dust taken from Carson River with milk pans and wash basins.

He called his written newspaper "The Golden Switch." It started some time in 1854 and lasted about four years

At about the same time that Webb was getting out his sheet, Stephen A. Kensey was issuing a written newspaper called "The Scorpion," in the little village of Genoa.

The first printed newspaper, however, in Nevada was "The Territorial Enterprise" issued on November 18th, 1858 at Genoa by Alfred Jones and W. L. Jernegan. Later it changed proprietors and became "The Enterprise," and is best remembered as the paper on which Mark Twain worked.

New Mexico

The first newspaper printed in New Mexico was "El Crepusculo,"

(The Dawn) and was first published by Antonio Jose Martinez in Taos on November 29th, 1835. Only four numbers of El Crepusculo were issued, and these were on paper the size of foolscap. The paper failed to pay expenses and was suspended after the fourth issue.

The first newspaper to be printed in English, however, was "The Sante Fe Republican." This paper was a 4-page weekly in two parts —two pages in Spanish and two in English, and made its appearance in Sante Fe on April 4th, 1847. Its publishers were Hovey and Davis and its editor G. R. Gibson.

NORTH DAKOTA

Col. Clement A. Loundsberry was the founder of journalism in North Dakota, the last of the states and territories to have a newspaper.

On July 6th, 1873 he published "The Bismarck Tribune." His first issue was remarkable in that it contained an advertisement of every business establishment in Bismarck. In the fall of that year it was forced for a short time to print on wall paper on account of a snow blockade. For the same reason the following winter the size was reduced from a seven to a four column sheet.

"The Bismarck Tribune" had the usual experiences of frontier journalism in that numerous gun and revolver shots were frequently heard in the establishment; once its local editor narrowly escaped a lynching.

OHIO

The distinction of being the first paper in Ohio belongs to "The Sentinel" of the Northwestern Territory, brought out in the village of Cincinnati on November 9th, 1793 by William Maxwell, who had come to Ohio from New Jersey by way of Pittsburgh. He brought with him a Ramage press and a few fonts of type, which he set up in a log cabin print shop at the corner of Front and Sycamore Streets.

The paper, published on Saturdays, was a 4-page sheet and had three columns to the page.

Having mislaid the subscription list, Maxwell published a notice in the first issue that subscribers should call at the office for their paper.

OKLAHOMA

The first newspaper in Oklahoma was the national organ of the Cherokee Nation; on September 26th, 1844 there appeared at Tahle-

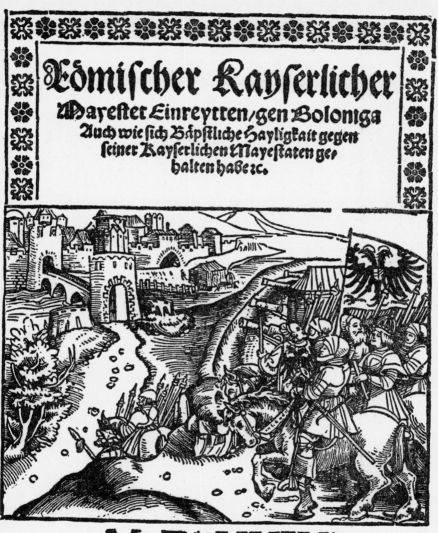

Römischer Kayserlicher

Mayestet Einreytten/gen Boloniga
Auch wie sich Bäpstliche Hayligkait gegen
seiner Kayserlichen Mayestaten ge=
halten habe ꝛc.

M. D. XXIX.

39. A Leaflet of 1529 Depicting the Capture of Bologna

[121]

Relation:

Aller Fürnem-
men/vnd gedenckwürdigen
Historien / so sich hin vnnd wider
in Hoch vnnd Nieder Teutschland/ auch
in Franckreich/ Italien/ Schott vnd Engelland/
Hisspanien/ Hungern / Polen / Siebenbürgen/
Wallachey / Moldaw / Türckey/ rc Inn
diesem 1 6 0 9. Jahr verlauffen
vnd zutragen möchte.

Alles auff das trewlichst wie
ich solche bekommen vnd zu wegen
bringen mag/ in Truck ver-
fertigen will.

40. Facsimile of Title Page of the First Newspaper (1609)

qual the first number of "The Cherokee Advocate." The paper was printed both in the English and Cherokee languages, and the Cherokee Nation fixed the subscription price at $3.00 per year "except to those persons who could read only the Cherokee language, and they shall pay $2.00."

"The Territorial Advocate," started at Beaver by E. E. Eldridge in May 1887, was the first real English newspaper in Oklahoma, and had the distinction of being probably the only newspaper ever published in the United States outside the pale of established law of any character. The Panhandle portion of the State of Oklahoma in which Beaver is located was, prior to 1889, known as "No-Man's Land."

OREGON

A press was secured from New York, a company was formed known as the Oregon Printing Association, and it brought out the first newspaper in Oregon on February 5th, 1846. It was called "The Oregon Spectator," and had for its motto: "Westward the Star of Empire Takes its Way."

Col. Wm. G. T. Vault was its first editor, and a few months later Henry A. G. Lee, a descendant of Richard Lee of Virginia, became editor. He demanded a salary of $600 which was considered too exorbitant, and he therefore severed his relations with the newspaper in 1846.

The third editor, George L. Curry, resigned in 1848 and decided to start a rival newspaper, and accordingly bought about eighty pounds of type from the Catholic missionaries. Having no press, and being unwilling to wait until one could be secured from the East, he constructed one of a rude sort chiefly out of wood and scrap iron. The type which he purchased had been used to print religious tracts in French and had but few letters "W". This obstacle was overcome by whittling a number out of hard wood.

Curry's paper was called "The Free Press" and lasted until October, 1848, when it ceased publication, largely on account of the wild rush of subscribers to the mines in the Territory.

SOUTH DAKOTA

The first newspaper published within the present boundaries of South Dakota was "The Dakota Democrat," founded at Sioux Falls City (now Sioux Falls) on September 20th, 1858. Its publisher and owner was Samuel Albright. He published the paper, which was a 4-page sheet with five columns to the page, rather irregularly until July 2nd, 1859. After that date he rarely skipped an issue until 1860 when he turned the paper over to Mr. Stewart, who changed its name to "The Northwestern Democrat."

The reason for this change was that Albright took with him the original heading of the paper—the "Democrat"—and the new owner was forced to use one which had previously been employed in printing a paper at Sergeant Bluff, Iowa. With the Indian War in 1862 the settlement of Sioux Falls was abandoned. In sacking the town the Indians destroyed the printing plant and carried away most of the type. After peace was declared the type came back again to the whites in the shape of ornaments used to decorate the pipes which the Indians fashioned out of the red pipe stone and sold to the settlers.

TENNESSEE

George Roulstone first brought out at Rogersville on November 5th, 1791 "The Knoxville Gazette." After issuing a few numbers he moved his plant to Knoxville, where he continued to bring out the paper until his death in 1804.

He remained authorized Public Printer to the Territorial or State Legislature all of this time, and his wife was later elected for two successive terms to fill the place.

TEXAS

The first newspaper of the Lone Star State was "The Texas Gazette," which made its appearance on September 29th, 1829, and was published by Godwin Brown Cotton in San Felipe, Austin County.

"The Texas Gazette" survived until 1832 when it was purchased by D. W. Anthony and united with "The Texas Gazette and Brazoria Commercial Advertiser," a paper started in 1830 by Mr. Anthony at Brazoria. The union was called "The Constitutional Advocate and the Texas Public Advertiser," and its first issue appeared on August 30th, 1832.

UTAH

When the Mormons were driven from Nauvoo, Ill., in 1846, they gathered on the banks of the Missouri River near the point where Council Bluffs now stands.

From here various bands were dispatched to the Rocky Mountains; one of the earliest of these to leave had a wagon loaded with an old Ramage press, a supply of paper and a few fonts of type. This outfit was hauled across the plains from the Missouri River to the Salt Lake Valley, a distance of over one thousand miles by team.

Upon its arrival at Salt Lake City preparations were made for printing "The Desert News," which was to be the official organ of the Mormon Church. Brigham Young appointed William Richards as editor, H. K. Whitney as typesetter, and his nephew Brigham H. Young as pressman. The first number appeared on June 15th, 1850. Its motto was "Truth and Liberty," and its price 15 cents per copy; travelers and immigrants were charged 25 cents per copy.

Currency was scarce, but the "News" accepted "flour, wheat, cornmeal, powder, tea, tallow and pork" in exchange for subscriptions.

For years it made its own supply of paper from rags gathered in the early settlements of Utah.

VERMONT

In the rooms of the Vermont Historical Society at Montpelier is still preserved the press on which was printed the first newspaper in that state. The claim has been made that this press was the first to be used in the English speaking colonies in North America, and that it did the best work in a mechanical way when set up in the house of Henry Dunster, the first president of Harvard College.

It printed at Westminster, Vermont, on February 12th, 1781, the first number of "The Vermont Gazette or The Green Mountain Post-Boy." From that date dates the beginning of journalism in what is now the State of Vermont. The paper, 17" x 12½", had for its motto: "Pliant as Waves where Streams of Freedom Glide; Firm as the Hills to stem Oppression's Tide."

Printed by Juda Paddock Spooner and Timothy Green it lasted until the beginning of the year 1783.

WASHINGTON

The old fashioned Ramage press which had been used to print the first number of "The Oregonian" in Oregon and several other papers of the Pacific Coast, was the press on which was pulled the first newspaper in Washington, "The Columbian." This paper appeared on September 11th, 1852, at Olympia, and was edited and owned by J. W. Wiley and Thornton F. McElroy. From the start

Wiley advocated a separation from Oregon. Thru the columns of his paper he arranged a meeting of some prominent settlers to arrange for the organization of Washington as a territory. "The Columbian" later became "The Washington Pioneer," and with this change was made over into a radical democratic journal. Because of its new political affiliation it became, in February, 1854, "The Pioneer and Democrat." It suspended in 1861.

WEST VIRGINIA

Dr. Robert Henry, a physician who had come to Berkeley County in 1792, started the first newspaper in West Virginia at Martinsburg in 1789. It was called "The Potomac Guardian and the Berkeley Advertiser," and had for its motto: "Where Liberty Dwells There's My Stand."

The earliest known issue is that of April 3rd, 1792, Volume 2, No. 73. It was a 9" x 15" sheet, and a copy is preserved in the Capitol at Richmond, Va.

WISCONSIN

The frontier printer occasionally started his paper before the arrival of other settlers. With intuitive foresight he seemed to know the probable locations of settlers along rivers and at the junctions of small streams.

Typical of papers thus established was "The Mirror" of Newport, one of the pioneer papers of Wisconsin, but by no means the first. Its editor, Alanson Holly, stated that he was printing "The Wisconsin Mirror" in the woods, and claimed that this had never been done in the United States before. However, Mr. Holly was in error when he thought his paper was the first to be printed "in the woods." Other papers had been started under conditions even more primitive, with the type set under the oaks themselves.

The first paper printed in the City of Milwaukee was "The Milwaukee Advertiser," founded in July, 1836. Later on the name was changed to "The Courier," and the latter was succeeded by "The Wisconsin."

WYOMING

Wyoming Territory, organized in May, 1869, was composed of land from three other territories, namely Idaho, Utah and Dakota. The first newspaper published within the boundaries of Wyoming was "The Cheyenne Leader." It first appeared on September 19th,

41. Theophraste Renaudot

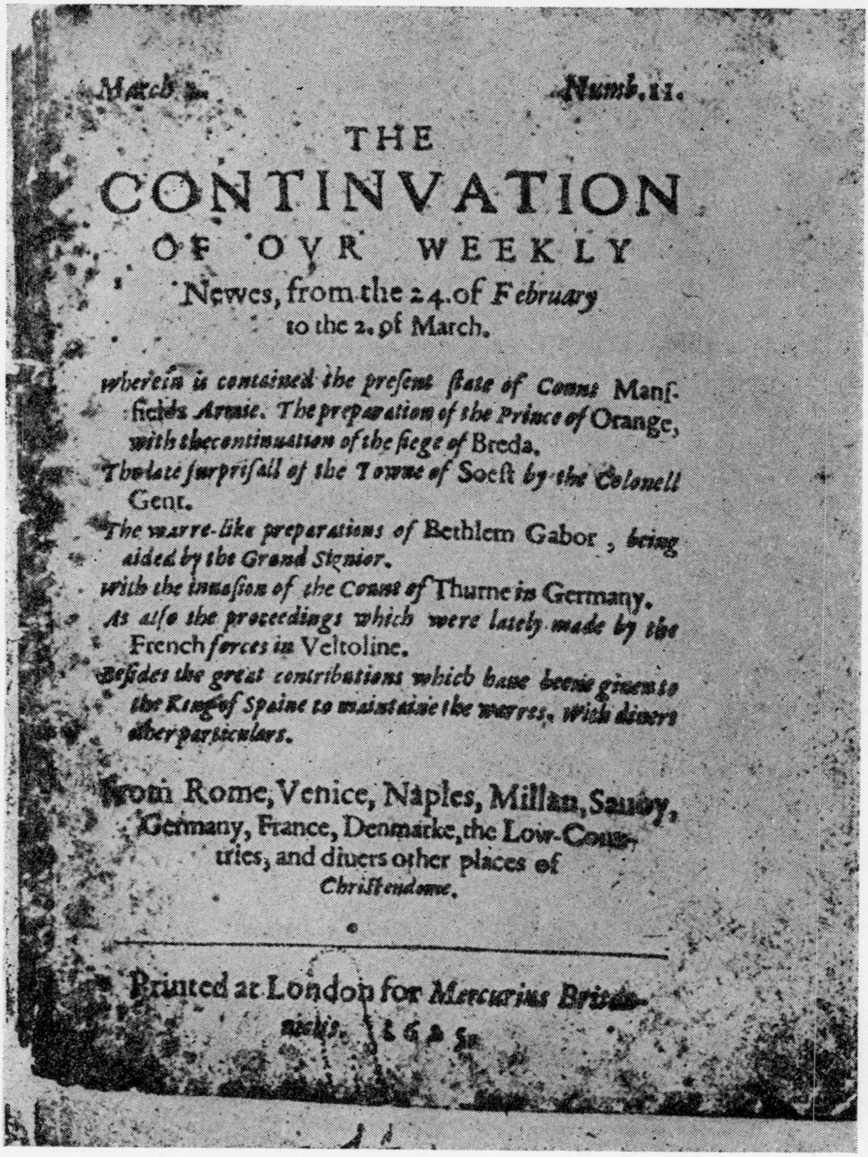

March 2. *Numb.* 11.

THE CONTINVATION OF OVR WEEKLY Newes, from the 24. of *February* to the 2. of March.

wherein is contained the present state of Count Mans*fields Armie. The preparation of the Prince of* Orange, *with the continuation of the siege of* Breda.

The late surprisall of the Towne of Soest *by the Colonell* Gent.

The warre-like preparations of Bethlem Gabor, *being aided by the Grand Signior.*

with the inuasion of the Count of Thurne in Germany.

As also the proceedings which were lately made by the French *forces in* Veltoline.

Besides the great contributions which haue beene giuen to the King of Spaine to maintaine the warres, with diuers other particulars.

From Rome, Venice, Naples, Millan, Sauoy, Germany, France, Denmarke, the Low-Countries, and diuers other places of *Christendome.*

Printed at London for *Mercurius Britannicus.* 1625.

42. "The English Mercurie"

1867, with N. A. Baker as editor and proprietor, from a primitive printing office on the east side of Eddy Street in Cheyenne. Published tri-weekly, the Leader sold for $12.00 a year, or 15 cents a copy.

Before closing this chapter, it will be of interest to stereotypers and others connected with the printing vocation to gather some information concerning the production end of newspapers from the colonial era to the period of the Civil War, when paper mats were first used in the production of a newspaper.

Newspapers in colonial times were generally printed on half sheets. Shapes and sizes varied greatly not only because of the scarcity of news of the various towns, but more frequently because of the scarcity of paper. In 1690 the first paper mill in the colonies was established in Germantown, Pa. Presses and types had to be imported from England. The first one was brought to America by the widow of the Reverend Glover in 1638. The first printing press manufactured in America was constructed by Christian Sauer, Jr., at Germantown, Pa. All of these old time presses were built of wood and only one page could be printed at a time. This handicap made four pulls necessary on the part of the printer before he could produce a printed newspaper of the whole sheet. Even in the case of the larger presses two impressions were necessary for every copy of the paper. Reliable printing ink also came from abroad. Substitutes were frequently attempted by the early printers and were manufactured from wild berries. The fading of the impressions in some of the early colonial papers may be traced directly to the use of such substitutes. The inking was done with half of a deerskin ball filled with wool and nailed to a stick of hickory.

Much of the poor printing of that period was due to the fact that the type had become badly worn out from frequent use; in one and the same paper more than one variety of type was used. To get new type it was frequently necessary for the printer to make a special trip to England. The first attempt to cast type in America was made in Boston about 1768 by a Scotchman by the name Michelson.

Concerning subscribers: Those living at a distance from the place of publication had to pay not only the subscription price of the paper, but also the cost of distribution by the mail carrier. A pine knot, a tallow candle or a bit of bear oil burning in a saucer afforded poor light for reading a newspaper by a farmer already tired from the day's toil clearing forest land.

The colonial editor experienced much difficulty in raising the necessary funds in cash to meet his expenses, and he also experienced much the same difficulty in getting his subscribers to part with provisions in exchange for newspapers. He was willing to take almost anything in exchange for subscriptions. Firewood, homespun cloth, butter, eggs, poultry—almost anything was acceptable to the printer.

The cost of producing a newspaper was about $30 a week.

Advertisements: When John Campbell brought out "The Boston News-Letter" in 1704 he announced that "Persons who have any Houses, Lots, Tenements, Farms, Ships, Vessels, Goods, Wares or Merchandise, etc., to be Sold or Let; or Servants at a Reasonable Rate from 12 pence to 5 shillings and not to exceed; Who may agree with John Campbell, Postmaster of Boston." This is fairly typical of advertisements inserted in colonial newspapers. Save for their headlines advertisements were frequently set up like regular reading matter, and in many localities advertisements for colonial papers could be left at the local Post Office.

During and after the War of the Revolution newspapers continued to be printed on the ordinary flatbed hand presses. The size of the editions of some papers had become so large that the men who pulled the levers complained of backaches. To overcome this difficulty inventors had already started to find some way out of it. Benjamin Dearborn, publisher of "The New Hampshire Gazette," had invented a wheel press which would print the whole side of a sheet at one pull of the lever.

The Revolutionary War automatically ended the importation of white paper from abroad. Paper mills had increased until there were over forty in the country. Several of these were laid waste by British soldiers and others made idle because employees had enlisted in the army. The remaining mills were unequal to supply the demand, so that during the latter part of the Revolutionary period and for some time later, the newspapers experienced great difficulty in securing the paper on which to print the news. One publisher reported that on account of the scarcity of paper he had printed but few sheets for the past three months, but that a parcel was now on its way to him and that in two weeks he would begin to print again.

At times when epidemics were appearing in the larger cities the publishers of newspapers disinfected their sheets before delivering them to newsboys and post-riders. Frequently, in order that the sheets might not be carriers of disease, they were put into stoves and thoroughly smoked before being wrapped for delivery.

The first paper to print two editions, a morning and an evening one of the same paper, was in the year 1796. In reality the paper had only one edition, for the sheet was printed all at the same time and was then divided; one-half went to the customer in the morning and the second to him in the afternoon.

The scarcity of ink caused the publishers of newspapers in the South to employ substitutes. Home-made inks, though often so poorly mixed that they did not spread evenly over the rollers, nevertheless gave a far better impression than did some of the substitutes. Many newspaper publishers were compelled to print their sheets with ordinary shoe blackening.

The Daily Courant.

Wednefday, March 11. 1702.

From the Harlem Courant, Dated March 18. N. S.

Naples, Feb. 22.

ON Wednefday laft, our New Viceroy, the Duke of Efcalona, arriv'd here with a Squadron of the Galleys of Sicily. He made his Entrance dreft in a French habit ; and to give us the greater Hopes of the King's coming hither, went to Lodge in one of the little Palaces, leaving the Royal one for his Majefty. The Marquis of Grigni is alfo arriv'd here with a Regiment of French.

Rome, Feb.25. In a Military Congregation of State that was held here, it was Refolv'd to draw a Line from Afcoli to the Borders of the Ecclefiaftical State, whereby to hinder the Incurfions of the Tranfalpine Troops. Orders are fent to Civita Vecchia to fit out the Galleys, and to ftrengthen the Garrifon of that Place. Signior Cafali is made Governor of Perugia. The Marquis del Vafto, and the Prince de Caferta continue ftill in the Imperial Embaffador's Palace ; where his Excellency has a Guard of 50 Men every Night in Arms. The King of Portugal has defir'd the Arch-Bifhoprick of Lisbon, vacant by the Death of Cardinal Soufa, for the Infante his fecond Son, who is about 11 Years old.

Vienna, Mar. 4. Orders are fent to the 4 Regiments of Foot, the 2 of Cuiraffiers, and to that of Dragoons, which are broke up from Hungary, and are on their way to Italy, and which confift of about 14 or 15000 Men, to haften their March thither with all Expedition. The 6 new Regiments of Huffars that are now raifing, are in fo great a forwardnefs, that they will be compleat, and in a Condition to march by the middle of May. Prince Lewis of Baden has written to Court, to excufe himfelf from coming thither, his Prefence being fo very neceffary, and fo much defir'd on the Upper-Rhine.

Francfort, Mar. 12. That the Marquifs d'Uxelles is come to Strasburg, and is to draw together a Body of fome Regiments of Horfe and Foot from the Garrifons of Alface ; but will not leffen thofe of Strasburg and Landau, which are already very weak. On the other hand, the Troops of His Imperial Majefty, and his Allies, are going to form a Body near Germefheim in the Palatinate, of which Place, as well as of the Lines at Spires, Prince Lewis of Baden is expected to take a View, in three or four days. The Englifh and Dutch Minifters, the Count of Frife, and the Baron Vander Meer ; and likewife the Imperial Envoy Count Lowenfteip, are gone to Nordlingen, and it is hop'd that in a fhort time we fhall hear from thence of fome favourable Refolutions for the Security of the Empire.

Liege, Mar. 14. The French have taken the Canon de Longie, who was Secretary to the Dean de Mean, out of our Caftle, where he has been for fome time a Prifoner, and have deliver'd him to the Provoft of Maubeuge, who has carry'd him from hence, but we do not know whither.

Peru, Mar. 13. Our Letters from Italy fay, That moft of our Reinforcements were Landed there ; that the Imperial and Ecclefiaftical Troops feem to live very peaceably with one another in the Country of Parma, and that the Duke of Vendome, as he was vifiting feveral Pofts, was within 100 Paces of falling into the Hands of the Germans. The Duke of Chartres, the Prince of Conti, and feveral other Princes of the Blood, are to make the Campaign in Flanders under the Duke of Burgundy ; and the Duke of Maine is to Command upon the Rhine.

From the Amfterdam Courant, Dated Mar. 18.

Rome, Feb. 25. We are taking here all poffible Precautions for the Security of the Ecclefiaftical State in this prefent Conjuncture, and have defir'd to raife 3000 Men in the Cantons of Switzerland. The Pope has appointed the Duke of Berwick to be his Lieutenant-General, and he is to Command 6000 Men on the Frontiers of Naples : He has alfo fettled upon him a Penfion of 6000 Crowns a year during Life.

From the Paris Gazette, Dated Mar. 18. 1702.

Naples, Febr. 17. 600 French Soldiers are arrived here, and are expected to be follow'd by 3400 more. A Courier that came hither on the 14th. has brought Letters by which we are affur'd that the King of Spain defigns to be here towards the end of March ; and accordingly Orders are given to make the neceffary Preparations againft his Arrival. The two Troops of Horfe that were Commanded to the Abruzzo are pofted at Pefcara with a Body of Spanifh Foot, and others in the Fort of Montorio.

Peru, March. 18. We have Advice from Toulon of the 5th inftant, that the Wind having long ftood favourable, 22000 Men were already fail'd for Italy, that 2500 more were Embarking, and that by the 15th it was hoped they might all get thither. The Count d'Eftrees arriv'd there on the Third inftant, and fet all hands at work to fit out the Squadron of 9 Men of War and fome Fregats, that are appointed to carry the King of Spain to Naples. His Catholick Majefty will go on Board the Thunderer, of 110 Guns.

We have Advice by an Exprefs from Rome of the 18th of February, that notwithstanding the preffing Inftances of the Imperial Embaffadour, the Pope had Condemn'd the Marquis del Vafto to lofe his Head and his Eftate to be confifcated, for not appearing to Anfwer the Charge against him of Publickly Scandalizing Cardinal Janfon.

ADVERTISEMENT.

IT will be found from the Foreign Prints, which from time to time, as Occafion offers, will be mention'd in this Paper, that the Author has taken Care to be duly furnifh'd with all that comes from Abroad in any Language. And for an Affurance that he will not, under Pretence of having Private Intelligence, impofe any Additions of feign'd Circumftances to an Action, but give his Extracts fairly and Impartially ; at the beginning of each Article he will quote the Foreign Paper from whence 'tis taken, that the Publick, feeing from what Country a piece of News comes with the Allowance of that Government, may be better able to Judge of the Credibility and Fairnefs of the Relation : Nor will he take upon him to give any Comments or Conjectures of his own, but will relate only Matter of Fact ; fuppofing other People to have Senfe enough to make Reflections for themfelves.

This Courant (as the Title fhews) will be Publifh'd Daily : being defign'd to give all the Material News as foon as every Poft arrives : and is confin'd to half the Compafs, to fave the Publick at leaft half the Impertinences, of ordinary News-Papers.

LONDON. Sold by E. Mallet, next Door to the King's-Arms Tavern at Fleet-Bridge.

43. The Whole of the First Number of the "Daily Courant," the First Daily Paper in England, London 1702. The size of Page 6¼ in. by 11½ in.

PUBLICK
OCCURRENCES

Both *FORREIGN* and *DOMESTICK*.

Boston, Thurfday Sept. 25th. 1690.

IT is defigned, that the Country fhall be fur-nifhed once a moneth (or if any Glut of Oc-currences happen, oftener,) with an Ac-count of fuch confiderable things as have ar-rived unto our Notice.

In order hereunto, the Publifher will take what pains he can to obtain a Faithful Relation of all fuch things; and will particularly make himfelf beholden to fuch Perfons in Bofton whom he knows to have been for their own ufe the diligent Obfer-vers of fuch matters.

..That which is herein propofed, is, Firft, That Memorable Occurrents of Divine Providence may not be neglected or forgotten, as they too often are. Secondly, That people every where may bet-ter underftand the Circumftances of Publique Af-fairs, both abroad and at home; which may not only direct their Thoughts at all times, but at fome times alfo to affift their Bufineffes and Ne-gotiations.

Thirdly, That fome thing may be done towards the Curing, or at leaft the Charming of that Spi-rit of Lying, which prevails amongft us, whe t-fore nothing fhall be entered, but what we have reafon to believe is true, repairing to the beft foun-tains for our Information. And when there ap-pears, any material miftake in any thing that is collected, it fhall be corrected in the next.

Moreover, the Publifher of thefe Occurrences is willing to engage, that whereas, there are ma-ny Falfe-Reports, malicioufly made, and fpread among us, if any well-minded perfon will be at the pains to trace any fuch falfe Report fo far as to find out and Convict the Firft Raifer of it, he will in this Paper (unlefs juft Advice be given to the contrary) expofe the Name of fuch perfon, as A malicious Raifer of a falfe Report. It is Suppofed that none will diflike this Propofal, but fuch as intend to be guilty of fo villanous a Crime.

THE Chriftianifed *Indians* in fome parts of *Plimouth,* have newly ap-pointed a day of Thanksgiving to God for his Mercy in fupplying their extream and pinching Neceffities under their late want of Corn, & for His giving them now a prof-pect of a very *Comfortable Harveft.* Their Example may be worth Mentioning.

.Tis obferved by the Husbandmen, that altho' the With-draw of fo great a ftrength from them, as what is in the Forces late-ly gone for *Canada,* made them think it almoft impoffible for them to get well through the Affairs of their Husbandry at this time of the year, yet the Seafon has been fo unufually favourable that they fcarce find any want of the many hundreds of hands, that are gone from them; which is looked upon as a Merci-ful Providence.

While the barbarous *Indians* were lurking about *Chelmsford,* there were miffing about the beginning of this month a couple of Chil-dren belonging to a man of that Town, one of them aged about eleven, the other aged a-bout nine years, both of them fuppofed to be fallen into the hands of the *Indians.*

A very Tragical Accident happened at *Wa-ter-town,* the beginning of this Month, an Old man, that was of fomewhat a Silent and Morofe Temper, but one that had long En-joyed the reputation of a Sober and a pious Man, having newly buried his Wife, The Devil took advantage of the Melancholy which he thereupon fell into, his Wives dif-cretion and induftry had long been the fup-port of his Family, and he feemed hurried with an impertinent fear that he fhould now come to want before he dyed, though he had very careful friends to look after him who kept a ftrict eye upon him, leaft he fhould do himfelf any harm. But one evening efcaping from them into the Cow-houfe, they there quickly followed him found him hanging by a Rope, which they had ufed to tye their Calves withall, he was dead with his feet near touch-ing the Ground.

Epidemical Feavers and Agues grow very common, in fome parts of the Country, whereof, tho' many dye not, yet they are forely unfited for their imployments; but in fome parts a more malignant Fever feems to prevail in fuch fort that it ufually goes thro' a Family where it comes, and proves Mortal unto many.

The Small-pox which has been raging in *Bofton,* after a manner very Extraordinary is now very much abated. It is thought that far more have been fick of it then were vi-fited with it, when it raged fo much twelve years ago, neverthelefs it has not been fo Mortal, The number of them that have

44. First Attempt at an American Newspaper

CHAPTER FIVE

THE DRY MAT, OR COLD STEREOTYPING PROCESS

JUST AS the deficiencies and shortcomings of the plaster of Paris process led to the invention of the papier-mache process of stereotyping, thus in due time the drawbacks of the latter made the invention of a better method a necessity. The quality of the work done by means of the wet mat method could hardly be improved upon, therefore the activities of practical stereotypers and inventors were directed towards obtaining equally excellent printing results, doing away, however, with the many drawbacks encountered in the use of the wet mat process.

The shortcomings of the papier-mache or wet mat method were few but far reaching. This steam table, or hot process of stereotyping employs "wet mats" which are generally hand-made in each plant from day to day; a series of special matrix papers and high grade tissues are pasted together with a mixture of flour paste and gum arabic to make these wet mats.

In almost every newspaper plant the preparation of wet mats and especially of such paste came under the duties of the foundry superintendent, and these experts usually had their own special and jealously guarded "secret" paste formula. (Ged and Stanhope exercised the same secretiveness.) There were, however, a number of printing supply concerns who made and sold secret pastes to the trade under various names such as pulchre paste, ivorite, nickello, electroline paste, etc., etc. It was to a certain extent due to this secretiveness practiced in practically every plant possessing a stereotype foundry that stereotyping was about the only phase of newspaper production which had not kept pace with 20th century progress.

Owing to the fact that all pastes used for the purpose of uniting the different paper layers of the wet mat have a tendency to sour and to mould, it is not practicable to prepare wet mats very far in advance.

Then again, uneven pasting as well as fermentation in the paste often causes wet mats to blister and blow up when they are molded and cast.

Deficiencies of the Wet Mat: To dry out the paste and the paper, the form of type with the wet mat has to be subjected to a high temperature, generally done on a steam table. It is obvious that the mat and the type cannot be separated until this mat has been thus hardened by heating, and in this operation the type is necessarily heated also. It is in this particular that the main objection to the wet mat process exists, the heating of the type being a positive source of destruction to the type. When needed for "make overs" for later editions the superheated forms must be rapidly cooled, subjecting them to uneven expansion and then contraction, soon ruining even the most expensive foundry type.

The stickiness and bother of the "paste pot" work and above all the inhuman necessity of the stereotypers working in an atmosphere of intense heat, thereby endangering their health, are foremost arguments against the use of wet mats. The comparative slowness of the wet mat process is also objectionable in newspaper work, where the gain of time after the copy is received in preparing the matter for the press is of greatest importance. Four to seven minutes of valuable time is consumed in baking the wet mats on the forms.

In spite of the fact that with the wet mat steam table process of stereotyping such bodily inconvenience is suffered by the workmen, much invaluable time is lost and great expense incurred, newspaper publishers felt that as long as there was nothing thoroughly proven to be better, more rapid, and still giving the same quality of printing obtained with the old wet mat process, they were justified in sticking to the old method and in not discarding their steamtables.

But in the meantime fertile minds were at work on the problem of making a matrix, eliminating the paste pot, the steam tables and their attendant vices, and saving invaluable time in getting out the daily newspaper. The end result of all this labor and experimenting is the DRY MAT, enabling cold stereotyping. Up to the advent of the present day dry mats, so-called dry mats were made on a paper machine in one piece and not pasted together as is the case with the wet mat. They were beaten in with a brush in a cold state and no steam was used. Owing to inherent deficiencies of these dry mats themselves, the dry mat idea did not make converts very rapidly. Although very few foundries bothered to "pet" these dry mats enough to be able to use them, the idea was conceded to be a good one. The time saved was also looked upon as a very favorable factor, but the ever varying thickness of the dry mat, the proclivity to blistering, buckling, chipping and pulling, the uncertainty of the proper humidifying, were not overcome until many years afterwards and after innumerable experiments and setbacks.

Dry Pulp for Mats: In 1863 the idea of using dry pulp appeared for the first time. This method of manufacture was not practicable, too difficult, and these mats could not be made on a commercial scale.

The first attempt to use a dry cold process and to mold by rolling a mat only once was made by George Eastwood of Kingston-upon-Hull, County of York, England, in 1887. It retained certain features of the wet mat but introduced the idea of a dry mat process and should be designated as a semi-dry mat. The text of the specifications of the patent granted to Eastwood explains his process in the following manner:

"According to my invention I follow what is practically a dry process in the manufacture of the matrices, so that the heating of the type can be dispensed with, and I back up the blanks with sand during the ordinary process of warming and drying the matrices, and I thereby obviate the liability of the blanks to become flattened by the pressure of the molten metal used in taking the castings.

"For the purpose of my invention I make a mold of two parts—namely, a facing and a backing. The facing is composed of two or more sheets of tissue paper or other like material pasted together with a composition containing glycerine and a suitable starchy material, which composition keeps them in a flexible and elastic state, prevents the paper from becoming too hard before use, renders it sensitive to moisture, greatly reduces the contraction on application of heat, and hardens the matrix or mold when heated. The backing consists of a dry thick sheet of soft paper, blotting paper, felt, or other like suitable substance capable of receiving and retaining an impression, and one side of which when used, is covered with a thin sheet of soft paper which is thinly coated on both sides with an adhesive material.

"In taking the matrix the facing is placed upon the type and the back of the facing is then covered first with a piece of muslin or other suitable thin textile material and next with a woolen or India-rubber blanketing, which (except when of India rubber) is preferably used warm. The whole is then rolled or pressed. This having been done, the blanketing and the muslin are removed and then the backing is placed upon the back of the tissue paper that forms the facing. That face of the backing which bears the composition being put in contact with the tissue paper, the composition on the

[137]

backing should be nearly dry. The blanketing is placed upon the backing and the whole is again rolled or pressed. The matrix is at once formed and when removed from the type has simply to be warmed through to harden the composition.

"Instead of the two rollings or pressings above described one rolling or pressing will suffice if the backing be placed upon the facing, in the first instance, with the blanketing over them, the use of the muslin in this case being dispensed with; but a good result is not so certain."

This was the basic idea of a dry mat. It was not until after six further years of experimenting that Eastwood invented a dry mat which was the first dry mat in the present day definition.

There has been some controversy as to whether the Englishman Eastwood or the German Schimansky was the original inventor of the dry mat cold process of stereotyping. A careful examination of the English and German patents of these men shows that Eastwood applied for his original patent on the 27th of November, 1893 (English Patent No. 22732), and Schimansky for his first patent on the 28th of December, 1894 (German Patent No. 86865).

The honor of inventing the first entirely dry mat and making a new product which constitutes the basis of all later dry mats, belongs, therefore, to George Eastwood.

The former experiments of Eastwood on the subject of cold stereotyping, which led to the entirely dry mat have been described above. The text of Eastwood's patent is worthy of being recorded in full, since his new matrix opened a new era in the art, the era of cold stereotyping. (Eastwood employs the Franco-English term "flong" in place of the general appellation "matrix" or "mat.") Eastwood describes his invention as follows, the parentheses containing annotations of the author of this book. "It consists in the manufacture of a flong from one thick sheet of blotting paper or other bibulous paper faced on one or both sides when dry with composition or paste. The invention also comprises a special composition or paste for the purpose, the said composition or paste being one that will dry, consolidate and harden upon the surface of the paper.

"In carrying out the invention the composition or paste (coating) is preferably applied to the bibulous paper by means of a brush and in a warm state. It is then allowed to dry, and when it is dry the flong is complete and can be kept in stock in the dry state for practically any length of time.

"In practice I find it desirable to face both sides of the paper

The Boston News-Letter:

Published by Authority.

From **Monday** May 8. to **Monday** May 15. 1704.

Westminster, November 11. 1703.

The Humble Address of the House of Commons, Presented to Her Majesty in the following Expressions.

Most Gracious Sovereign,

WE Your Majesties most Dutiful and Loyal Subjects, the Commons in Parliament Assembled, do humbly return Your Majesty our most hearty Thanks for Your Majesties most Gracious Speech from the Throne.

We are truly Sensible of Your Majesties earnest Endeavours to bring the War to a glorious and speedy Conclusion, of which Your Majesty has given us so fair a prospect by Your Great Wisdom and Conduct in engaging the King of *Portugal* and Duke of *Savoy* in Your Alliance, for recovering the Monarchy of *Spain* from the House of *Bourbon*, and restoring it to the House of *Austria*.

We do most gratefully acknowledge Your Majesties singular care in the good management and application of the Publick Money, whereby Your Majesties Exchequer hath greater Credit, in this so expensive a War, than was ever known in the most flourishing times of Peace, and Your most signal and unparallel'd Grace and Goodness to Your People, in contributing out of Your own Revenue, towards the Publick Service, particularly Your Majesties most seasonable assistance to the Circle of *Suabia*. The many Blessings we enjoy under Your Majesties most auspicious Reign, and Your tender regard to the general Welfare & Happiness of Your Subjects, justly require our utmost returns of duty and gratitude. And Your Majesty may be assured, that Your faithful Commons will support Your Majesty in Your Alliance, and effectually enable Your Majesty to carry on the War with rigour: to which nothing can more contribute, than a firm Union among our selves. We therefore crave leave fu ther to assure Your Majesty, that we will, according to Your Majesties desire, carefully avoid any heats or divisions that may give encouragement to the common Enemies of the Church & State.

To which Her Majesty return'd Her most Gracious Answer, in the following words.

I Am very well pleased with your Assurances of Supporting Me in the present War, and your kind acknowledgments of My endeavours to bring it to a happy Conclusion.

You may assure your selves, I shall always pursue the true Interest of the Kingdom and Omit nothing that may promote the general Welfare of My People.

Her Majesty of *England*'s Congratulatory Letter to the King of *Spain*, & the King of *Spain*'s Answer.

My Lord and Brother,

I Have heard with great Satisfaction, of Your being declar'd King of *Spain*, and do heartily

Congratulate You upon this Account, and with that the *Spanish* Crown, which is Your Right, may prove as Prosperous to You as it has been to Your Ancestors; and to give proof of My Friendship to the House of *Austria*, My esteem for Your Person and Merits, and My concern for Your Honour and Interest, I am resolved to employ all the strength of My Arms in Your favour. I have Ordered the Duke of *Marlborough*, Captain General of My Forces, to Assure Your Majesty, that I shall neglect no Opportunities, of giving You real proofs of the Sincerity with which I am,

My Lord and Brother, Your most Affectionate Sister,

ANNA REGINA.

The King of *Spain*'s Answer to Her Majesty.

My Lady and Sister,

I Am the most affected with the Assurances of Your Friendship, signified in the Letter deliver'd to Me by the Duke of Marlborough, Your Embassador and Captain General of Your Forces; since thereby You have so generously renew'd the Affection and Promises made to the House of Austria, in the beginning of Your Reign. If Our Arms be blest with Success according to Your Wishes, I do Assure Your Majesty, that they shall be only employ'd against Our Common Enemies, and for the advantage of Your Kingdoms, and the Preservation of the Liberties of Europe. I desire Your Majesty to Honour Me with Your Wise Counsels, which are a terror to Your Enemies, but the Support of Your Allies, and the happiness of Your Subjects. And I shall always follow them with respect and deference, as having manifestations of Your good and sincere aims. I look upon it as a Sign of Your most particular Esteem, that Your Majesty has made choice of the Duke of Marlborough, to be Witness of the regard I have for Your concerns, and of My admiration of the Merits of Your Person. And that I will do nothing more earnestly, than to have Opportunities to shew with what Sincerity and Gratitude I am,

Lady and Sister, Your most Affectionate Brother,

CHARLES.

Advice from *Rome* and *Italy*.

The Pope's partiality in the Affair of the *Spanish* Succession discovers it self more and more. His dissimulation can no longer hold out against the force of his inclination: and considering his deportment within this little while, there is great reason to believe, that a very small thing would perswade him to declare openly for *France*. His Holiness call'd a Congregation of State, on purpose to consider, whether or no he should recal his Nuncio from *Vienna*, because the Arch-Duke had assum'd the Royal Title, and for that the Emperor refused to give him audience. However the question being put, by some carry'd in the Negative by several voices, some sort of proof that the Disciples have more wit than their master.

Yet in the midst of all his troubles and ...

45. First Newspaper to be Established in the English Colonies in America

Numb. 18.

 THE
New-York Gazette.

From *February* 28. to Monday *March* 7. 1725-6.

Continuation of the Treaty of Commerce between the Emperor of Germany and the King of Spain.

Article 27.

THe Subjects on both Sides shall be allowed to chuse, at their own Pleasure, Councils, Agents, Attornies, Solicitors and Brokers.

28. In all the Ports and trading Cities which both their Majesties shall agree upon, National Consuls shall be established to protect the Merchants on both Sides, and they are to enjoy all the Rights, Authorities, Liberties and Immunities the most befriended Nations do enjoy.

29. Those Consuls shall be empowered to take Cognizance of the Differences and Disputes between the Merchants and the Masters of the Ships, and between the latter and their Crews, to decide them; so that there shall be no Appeal from their Sentence to the Judge of the Place of their Residence.

30. As to the Judges Conservators, who in the former Reigns were a considerable Magistracy in Spain, which the most favoured Nations were allowed to chose for themselves, with a Power to judge peremptorily in Civil and Criminal Cases, among those of their own Nation, it has been agreed, That in case his Royal Catholick Majesty grants for the future this Privilege to any Nation, the same shall be likewise granted to his Imperial Majesty's Subjects: Mean while, impartial & speedy Justice shall be done by the ordinary Magistrates and Judges, from whose Sentences no Appeal shall be made but only to the Council of Commerce at Madrid.

31. The Escheat, or any Right of the like Nature, shall not be made use of with Respect to each other's Subjects, but the Heirs of the Deceased shall succeed them, either by Will or *ab Intestato*, without any Lett or Hindrance; and in Case of Dispute among two or more Heirs, the Judges of the Place are to decide the Matter peremptorily.

32. If a Merchant or other Subject of either of the contracting Parties should chance to die within the other's Dominions, the Consul or some other of their publick Ministers, if there be any, shall repair to the House of the deceased, and take an Inventory of all his Merchandizes and Effects, as likewise of his Books and Papers, in Order to secure them for the Heirs of the Deceased.

33. In case any Ship belonging to the contracting Parties or their Subjects should be wrecked upon each other's Coasts, the Fiscal Officers shall claim no Right to it, and all plundring shall be severely forbidden; moreover, Assistance is to be given to those who suffer Shipwreck, for saving and securing all they can.

34. His Catholick Majesty shall, under no Pretext whatsoever, set a limited Price to the Merchandizes belonging to his Imperial Majesty's Subjects, but they shall be at Liberty to sell them at the current Price: The same Liberty is granted to the Spanish Subjects in the Emperour's Dominions.

35. If the Effects of some of either Parties Subjects, should be confiscated, and that some Goods belonging to any other Person should happen to be among them, they shall be restored to the Owners, &c.

36. His Imperial Majesty's Ships and Subjects shall be allowed to carry and bring from the *East-Indies* into all the King of *Spain*'s Dominions, all sorts of Fruits, Effects, and Merchandizes, provided it appear, by Affidavits of the Deputies of the *India* Company established in the *Austrian Netherlands*, that they come from the conquered Places, Colonies or Factories of the said Company, in which Case they shall enjoy the same Privileges granted to the Subjects of the United Provinces, by the Royal Letters of the 27th of *June*, and 3d of *July* 1662. Moreover his Catholick Majesty declares, That he grants to the Imperial Subjects whatever has been granted to the States-General of the United Provinces by the Treaty in 1648, both with respect to the *Indies* and any other thing applicable to the said Treaty, as likewise to the present Peace concluded between their Majesties.

37. As to what relates to the Commerce of the *Canary-Islands*, the Imperial Subjects shall enjoy the same Advantages with the *English* and *Dutch*.

[To be Continued in our next]

Remonstrance of the General Assembly of the Clergy of France, as presented to the King, against the New Tax of Two per Cent.

SIRE,

THE Clergy of *France*, who have always esteem'd it their Glory to give your Majesty, and the Kings your Predecessors, Effectual as well as publick Proofs of their most profound Submission and Obedience, find themselves constrained to accompany the new Homage, which they have the Honour to pay you this Day, with just Complaints and most humble Remonstrances.

The Edict which your Majesty has been pleased to publish, for raising *Two per Cent.* upon all your Subjects Estates, seems indeed not to include the

46. New York's First Newspaper, Established by William Bradford in 1725

with the composition, because by so doing I avoid any tendency of the paper to warp while drying. It is also well to apply a second coat of the composition after the first coat is dry. When this flong is to be used, the face upon which the mold is to be produced is preferably smoothed with sandpaper; but this it not essential. This face is then slightly dampened with water or with the composition by means of a sponge or otherwise (humidifying) and it may then be covered with one or more sheets of tissue or other suitable paper, damp or dry. (At the present day many foundries in England still paste one tissue on dry mats, producing extra humidification thru the wet paste.) Then it is preferably rubbed with French chalk or other suitable material which will absorb superfluous moisture. The flong thus prepared is placed upon the type or in a frisket or frame, and is then surrounded by heated air (a kind of scorcher) for a few seconds, so as to just soften the composition and render it plastic. When in this state it is pressed upon the form by means of a platen press. The mold is thus taken and becomes at once fixed.

"It will be understood from the foregoing description that my flong is a dry flong with the composition or paste on the face. When the flong is used the blotting or other paper does not contain moisture, but the composition or paste, after being slightly dampened, as above described, becomes sufficiently softened (humidified) by the heated air or by contact with the form (when this is heated) to enable a perfect mold to be taken by the press. The special composition or paste which I preferably employ for facing the bibulous paper consists of treacle or other saccharine liquor, glue, flour, whiting, borax and water. I do not limit myself to any particular proportions, but I recommend that the amount of treacle used should be about one-twentieth, by weight, of the combined weight of the other ingredients employed, exclusive of water."

Eastwood then describes in length the proportions of his paste. His patent claims were:

(1) A flong for producing matrices or molds for stereotyping, consisting of a thick sheet of dry bibulous paper having on its face a dry composition, substantially as hereinbefore described.

(2) A flong for producing matrices or molds for stereotyping consisting of a thick sheet of bibulous paper having a normal unimpregnated interior and having on its face a coating of a dry paste composed of saccharine liquor, glue, flour, whiting, borax and water in approximately the proportions specified.

(3) A composition for coating the bibulous paper or flongs used

for producing matrices or molds for stereotyping, the said composition consisting of treacle, glue, flour, whiting, borax and water in approximately the proportions specified.

Thus, thru Eastwood the dry mat appeared on the market. The first product was given to the foundries in England in 1887, and after having applied for his second patent the new dry mat was introduced.

In October, 1895, an American cold type stereotyping outfit (the Potter) was advertised in trade journals as ready for shipment, and a stereotyping expert stated that "now country printers can do their own stereotyping," meaning that the monopoly of making stereotype plates only in the large foundries in the big cities could be accepted as over and done with. "No beating of type to spoil the face, nor heating of type to make it soft and elongated. The molding is done on scientific principles and in about one-twentieth of the time required by the old papier-mache method. The manufacturer supplies the matrix, with full instructions for use. The form is laid on the molding machine, the matrix is placed on the form and by the rotating of a heavy iron cylinder the matrix is pressed into the form and the mold is made. This mold is then taken from the form, placed on a hot plate to dry, and is then put in a casting box, into which hot metal is poured and the cast is made."

An advance step in the making of stereotype dry mats was made in 1895 by Hermann Schimansky of Berlin, Germany. He contended that dry mats made in accordance with the specifications of prior inventors were so constituted that the free spaces which were to remain white in the printing were filled up at the back of the matrix by covering with pieces of cardboard, as otherwise the hot lead would press down the very thin matrix in these spaces during the casting. Schimansky's invention (patented in 1899) was supposed to obviate this drawback and consisted in using perfectly dry matrices of vegetable fibre which were characterized by great porosity produced artificially, so that the impression of the type to be stereotyped takes place by simply destroying the porosity at the pressed parts, thereby rendering the mold directly suitable for the casting. Thus Schimansky claims he obviated the manipulation of covering up ("backing up") the free spaces, as his mat retains the original thickness at all free places which are not impressed. Schimansky recommends for the making of his mats all kinds of vegetable fibres—such as wood, cellulose, hemp, cotton or flax. In order to obtain the porosity of the mats, the inventor proceeded as follows: The fibres are first immersed in sodium carbonate and then in an acid, for example vinegar—thereby developing as a gas carbonic acid, which effects the loosening of the mat. In this manner the porosity of the mat is obtained by loosening alone. Presumably the parts of resinous matter clinging to the fibre dissolve. In order to bend the fibre to form a mat, the fibrous material is treated in a long-sieve (Fourdrinier) paper machine. Finally these mats are coated on one side with a thin coat or layer of starch paste, to which five per cent of glycerine has been added, in order that the adhesion of the metal to the vegetable fibre may be obviated in the casting. The matrix thus produced ready for use may be kept in stock in any quantities in printing shops and used at once when required. Schimansky gave his dry mat the name "Porosin Matrix."

All of these improvements did not permit of obtaining a matrix of sufficient depth and faultlessly smooth surface, since the Eastwood as well as the Schimansky mat did not possess a surface which could receive sharp and sufficiently deep impressions from the type without tearing. On the other hand, the mats were not firm enough to allow the formation of sufficiently deep interstices at the blank spaces of the type which could resist the pressure of the poured in metal on repeated casting. Another drawback of these first dry mats was that the texture of the paper employed made itself appear on the cast plate.

Johann Egyd Weigl of Vienna undertook in 1901 to remedy these drawbacks by using a different process, which he claimed produced a plastic and impressionable dry mat which would neither crack nor tear, and having a perfectly smooth surface. Weigl's mat was practically a wet mat made almost identically in the same manner as a wet mat, namely by pasting different sheets and layers of paper together with different pastes, then drying same and stereotyping with this mat as with the cold process. The single sheets were thoroughly bound thru calendering and after drying formed a single indivisible matrix. Weigl manufactured his dry mat by brushing a sheet of supple, plastic cardboard with a paste of vegetable glue, glue of albumen and alcohol to which was added glycerine and calcium chloride, laying on a gauze-like fabric prepared in mucilage of gelatin and pressing thereover a sheet of unsized paper, the outer side of which unsized paper was coated with mucilage of carrageen-mass and albumen glue and pressing thereon several sheets of tissue paper. It is very easy to understand that such a manufacturing method would tend to make the price of the mat out of all question.

[143]

The patent rights upon the Schimansky invention were acquired and the manufacture of such dry mats carried on by a paper factory in southern Germany. The results, however, obtained in the beginning with the new dry mat did not warrant the making and selling of the product on a commercial scale. The factory simplified the manufacturing process, finally making a good dry mat, which it sold to German and foreign newspaper offices and which is still being marketed as the "Porosin" mat. Schimansky's dry mat was adopted by the great German daily "Lokalanzeiger" of Berlin, and based upon this success the inventor made a trip to the United States with the intention of disposing of his American patent. Several paper mills were more or less interested; Schimansky however returned home without having met with the hoped for success.

Results of These Dry Mat Experiments: Although both Eastwood's and Schimansky's inventions were not satisfactory in a commercial sense, they certainly influenced a large number of paper makers to experiment with dry mat manufacturing, and finally led to the excellent present day product.

Several German firms (Claus, Niezsche, Benesch, Rosenthal, Geissler, etc.) took up manufacturing of dry mats as a side line in their paperboard mills, and in due time the results of their pioneering work made the dry mat their principal product. For many years Germany was the only source of supply for dry mats, the product going to all countries in Europe and overseas. Karl Kempe of Nuremberg was the first (1882) to sell ready-to-use paper mats to the printing trade.

THE TIMES

THEATRE-ROYAL, DRURY-LANE.
THIS EVENING, THE HYPOCRITE.
To which will be added, a new musical Romance, to be called
THE NINTH STATUE, or The Irishman in Bagdad.

THEATRE ROYAL, COVENT-GARDEN.
THIS EVENING, KING RICHARD III.
To which will be added, THE FOREST OF MONDY.

TO-MORROW, THE STATE LOTTERY BEGINS DRAW.
ING.—THE WHOLE IS TO BE DRAWN ON THAT DAY.

LONDON, TUESDAY, NOVEMBER 29, 1814.

Our Journal of this day presents to the public the practical result of the greatest improvement connected with printing, since the discovery of the art itself. The reader of this paragraph now holds in his hand, one of the many thousand impressions of *The Times* newspaper, which were taken off last night by a mechanical apparatus. A system of machinery almost organic has been devised and arranged, which, while it relieves the human frame of its most laborious efforts in printing, far exceeds all human power in rapidity and dispatch. That the magnitude of the invention may be justly appreciated by its effects, we shall inform the public, that after the letters are placed by the compositors, and enclosed in what is called the form, little more remains for man to do, than to attend upon, and watch this unconscious agent in its operations. The machine is then merely supplied with paper: itself places the form, inks it, adjusts the paper to the form newly inked, stamps the sheet, and gives it forth to the hands of the attendant, at the same time withdrawing the form for a fresh coat of ink, which itself again distributes, to meet the ensuing sheet now advancing for impression; and the whole of these complicated acts is performed with such a velocity and simultaneousness of movement, that no less than eleven hundred sheets are impressed in one hour.

That the completion of an invention of this kind, not the effect of chance, but the result of mechanical combinations methodically arranged in the mind of the artist, should be attended with many obstructions and much delay, may be readily admitted. Our share in this event has, indeed, only been the application of the discovery, under an agreement with the Patentees, to our own particular business; yet few can conceive,—even with this limited interest,—the various disappointments and deep anxiety to which we have for a long course of time been subjected.

Of the person who made this discovery, we have but little to add. Sir CHRISTOPHER WREN's noblest monument is to be found in the building which he erected; so is the best tribute of praise, which we are capable of offering to the inventor of the Printing Machine, comprised in the preceding description, which we have feebly sketched, of the powers and utility of his invention. It must suffice to say farther, that he is a Saxon by birth; that his name is KŒNIG; and that the invention has been executed under the direction of his friend and countryman BAUER.

By the *Hamburgh* mail we learn, that a note which was understood to be of great importance was delivered into the Congress on the 10th inst. It was sup-

---

7. London "Times." Facsimile of the Issue of November 29, 1814, the First Newspaper Printed on a Cylinder Press with the Aid of a Papier-Mache Matrix

48. An Armed Neutrality (1850)

CHAPTER SIX

STEREOTYPING IN NORTH AMERICA

In Europe, where stereotyping was first invented, and where for centuries all activities relative to improvements in the old methods and the inventing of new methods were centered, there has been, compared with other phases of the printing art, a dearth of recordings concerning one of the most important printing innovations, namely the art of stereotyping. Here in America the same condition prevailed. The entire literature dealing with stereotyping in America consists of three practical handbooks, i.e., manuals, including a few historical notes in their prefaces. Even in encyclopedias dealing with printing one finds but short articles on stereotyping. Thus it has been a difficult task to assemble data pertaining to the invention, adoption and development of the stereotyping art in this country. In fact, the main sources of information can be extracted from occasional trade journal articles, from letters exchanged between printing plants, controversial articles, criticisms of stereotyping, and such information as may be gleaned from patent publications. Only by recording excerpts from this sparse material can one obtain a picture of the development of stereotyping in America.

Many are the practical American stereotypers who could have described the host of interesting events of their times, but more than 100 years have passed since the introduction into this country of papier-mache mats, and it is almost half a century since dry mat stereotyping first appeared on this side of the Atlantic ocean. It is almost an impossibility to find such "old timers" still alive in our midst. Despite many efforts to ferret out whatever personal documents they may have left behind, it was not possible to secure such material. Practically everything we know was handed on by word of mouth and hardly anything was recorded in writing. Some recent happenings in the stereotyping field, however, have been learned from stereotypers still active in plants throughout the country. Therefore the writer has compiled his material from letters, patents, catalogues, price lists, instruction sheets and so forth, and thereby is able to present a fairly accurate picture of what has, up to our time, transpired in the field of stereotyping in America.

The first printing in America was done in the year 1540 by the Jesuits in Mexico, the first book being a religious work entitled "A Manual for Adults."

The first printing press in the United States was erected and operated in Cambridge, Mass., in 1638 under the charge of Stephen Daye, and the first book he published was the "Bay Psalm Book" in 1640. For this press the colony was mainly indebted to the Reverend Jesse Glover, to whom some gentlemen of Amsterdam also gave "towards furnishing of a printing press with letters, forty-nine pounds and something more."

In 1745 an attempt at stereotype printing was made in Philadelphia by Benjamin Mecom, nephew of the great Benjamin Franklin. Mecom cast plates for several pages of the New Testament and made considerable progress toward the completion of the book, but he never finished it.

Isaiah Thomas, in his "History of Printing in America" (Worcestor, 1810) made the following note: "The ingenious Jacob Perkins of Newburyport, Mass., has lately invented a new kind of stereotype for impressing copper and other plates. From the plates so impressed most of the bank notes of Massachusetts and Newhampshire are printed at rolling presses and are called stereotype bills."

Glover, a wealthy dissenting clergyman, bought his good printing press and type fonts in England in 1638 and started for New England with them. However, he died on the trip, but his widow brought this, the first printing press, to America.

There are conflicting statements as to whom belongs the honor of having first introduced stereotyping in America. It has been claimed that an Englishman named John Watts was the first, arriving in New York from London, and starting a printing shop at 15 Murray Street in 1809. Watts spoke French and it appears that the stereotyping process he used was a combination of the Didot and Stanhope systems. In 1812 he made stereotype plates, and in 1813 a book was published, entitled "The Larger Catechism. The first book ever stereotyped in America. Stereotyped and printed by J. Watts and Co., New York. June, 1813." In 1815 he moved his little plant to 154 Broadway. In 1816 his name disappeared from the City Directory, he having sold his foundry to B. and J. Collins, a couple of Quaker printers. Watts left America and was traced to

Austria where from 1820 on he conducted a stereotyping shop until his death.

In "The Typographical Miscellany," printed in Albany, N. Y., in 1850, Joel Munsell reprints an article which was taken from "The Long Island Star" of October, 1811. The article is about Francis Shield, a typefounder, and says: "Mr. Shield is also in possession of the art of taking stereotype plates, and has specimens in his possession."[1]

It has been contended that David Bruce did not go to England to learn the stereotyping art until 1812, and thus it would seem that Francis Shield was the first man to bring stereotyping to America. However, in the light of thorough research it can be accepted as a fact that to David Bruce belongs the honor of introducing stereotyping in America.

The Bruce family of printers and typefounders were descendants of John Bruce, a farmer, of Wick, in the county of Caithness in the far north of Scotland, to whom on November 12, 1770, a son, David, was born. David went to sea, and before nineteen summers had passed over him he had seen a great part of the northern hemisphere. His family had meanwhile moved to Edinburgh, and there in his nineteenth year David apprenticed himself to a printer. Having acquired a thorough knowledge of his craft, as his work proves, he is next found in 1793 arriving in New York, a city of 40,000 inhabitants, something less in importance than either Boston or Philadelphia, where he found employment as a pressman on a daily newspaper. Next year, 1794, he was working for Hall & Sellers, successors to B. Franklin and David Hall. David Bruce sent money home to bring his brother John to Philadelphia, but in the meantime John had gone soldiering against Bonaparte in Egypt, so his parents sent George Bruce, aged fourteen, in his stead. George reached Philadelphia on June 26, 1795. The two Bruces were not without friends. David had known Archibald Binney in Edinburgh, and when Binney and James Ronaldson and David Ramage arrived in Philadelphia on one ship in 1795 they soon found David Bruce and his young brother. Binney & Ronaldson set up the first permanent typefoundry in 1796 (which finally developed into the American Type Founders Company), and in the same year Ramage opened the first shop for building printing presses. Here were got together five young Scotsmen who afterwards achieved both wealth and

---

[1] "Typographical Miscellany", by Joel Munsell, page 114.

fame, although their combined cash capital was less than $600. George Bruce was put to learn bookbinding, but not liking his employer he ran away to sea. Returning soon to Philadelphia, his elder brother persuaded him to apprentice himself to Thomas Dobson, printer. After two years, in 1798, Dobson's plant was destroyed by fire, and an epidemic of yellow fever prevailing, the brothers left the city and walked across New Jersey to New York City. Not finding employment there, they walked to Albany, where they worked for Webster Brothers. In 1799 they walked back to New York City. In that year the first American printer's union, the Franklin Typographical Association, was formed in New York, of which David Bruce was elected vice president, while George was secretary. The young union formulated a demand for higher wages. Compositors and pressmen were getting $6 a week of seventy-one hours. They demanded $7 and got it; nothing was said about the hours, but overtime was price and a half.

In 1803 and for two years thereafter young George Bruce's name appears in "The Daily Advertiser" as "printer and publisher for the proprietor." What David was doing we know not, but both had married, and George was already a widower. In 1806 there was a printing outfit, with one hand press, to hire. The Bruce boys hired it, and began to print Lavoisier's "Chemistry" in a small room in a building on the southwest corner of Pearl and Wall Streets. Their friends in Philadelphia, the prospering typefounders and the prospering press builder, gave them credit for types and materials. Their work was better than New York publishers could get elsewhere. They also prospered, and in 1809 removed to 27 William Street, where they kept nine wooden hand presses busy. When the publishers failed at times to keep them busy they published books on their own risk. It would seem that honest industry, working more than eight hours a day, had little trouble in getting ahead in those times when the city was literally "little old New York." The Bruces were well read, studious men. They would select a standard book to print on their own account. They would then ask publishers and booksellers throughout the land to agree to take and pay for certain quotas, printing the bookseller's name on the title pages of his quota. In this way they would have a sure venture. Among others they issued a series of Latin classics and a New Testament and a complete Bible. There was thus no lost time in the shop—no nonchargeable hours. Compositors and pressmen working for $7 obtained good board and lodging for $2.50; working twelve hours a day, with

49. M. W. Isaiah Thomas, Esq., P. G. Master of Massachusetts
and Author of the History of Printing

50.

occasional overtime, with few holidays, and everything shut down close on Sundays, there was little opportunity to squander their earnings.

In 1812 David Bruce, Sr., went to England to learn the art of stereotyping, recently revived under the auspices of Earl Stanhope. The earliest and best method of stereotyping was from plaster of Paris molds. We do not know what prompted David to learn stereotyping, but probably it was the advent in New York of one John Watts, who brought a knowledge of stereotyping to this country, and issued the first book from stereotyped plates in America in 1813. Watts, disappointed in his venture, went back to England, and shortly after his return went to Holland and Germany, selling the secrets of the process. David Bruce, Sr., found the English stereotypers secretive. He saw their work and got in touch with some of the workmen, and discovered enough of the process to put it in practice in New York. While away he kept his brother partner advised of his progress and of his visit to his relatives. These interesting letters are now in the Typographic Library and Museum in Jersey City. Unable to buy any of the apparatus used by the two English stereotyping firms, David had to design and have made in New York his furnaces, molds and other appliances. While these were in the making another obstacle presented itself: both the existing typefoundries refused to cast the high spaces and quads necessary to the clay process. Fortunately for the Bruces, in that year, 1813, two brothers, Edwin and Richard Starr, skilled typemakers employed by Elihu White, had a desire to become master typefounders. They had accumulated a typemaking outfit, and had finished a set of nine point (bourgeois) matrices. Lacking capital, they were willing to take the Bruces in as partners. A font of nine point types and other accessories were cast, and in 1814 David Bruce made two sets of plates for a complete Bible. One set was sold to Mathew Carey of Philadelphia, the other was used to print several editions of the Bible, which the Bruces disposed of profitably. Before a year had passed a disagreement arose. The Starrs were bought out by the Bruces to save their investment. They tried to sell their outfit to the two existing typefoundries, but it was so incomplete that they could get no offers. Thus they had the nucleus of a typefoundry with no knowledge of the art, and no skilled employees. How they surmounted this unfavorable condition we do not know. Doubtless they found a skilled workman, or more than one, and George Bruce began to perfect himself in letter punch cutting. In 1815 they issued a few leaves of specimens of body types, adding to them gradually. They sold their profitable printing business to two employees. In 1816 their type and stereotype foundry was in Eldridge Street. George managed the typefoundry and David the stereotype foundry. In 1814 David invented the first plate shaving machine. The English stereotypers were leveling their stereotype plates by holding them against a revolving disk equipped with knives. By their method they could not regulate the height of the plates. Bruce's flat bed planer went into use everywhere and is today more than ever an indispensable machine in electrotyping and stereotyping establishments.

In 1818 the Bruces erected a building on Chambers Street, which was the home of the typefoundry until 1895. In 1820 David retired, purchasing the White Hill Estate. He was then fifty years of age. George in the same year sold the stereotyping equipment and concentrated on typefounding. In six years he had become the leader in that art and industry. He died on July 5, 1866, aged eighty-five, leaving his business to his surviving son, David Wolfe Bruce, who carried it on until his death in 1895, leaving it to three heads of departments, who eventually sold it to a competitor.

David Bruce, Sr., died in Brooklyn at the home of his son on March 15, 1857, aged eighty-seven years.

A large number of printers followed in the footsteps of the Bruces in installing stereotype foundries. The following merit closer mention:

Tillinghast King Collins was born in Philadelphia on October 14th, 1802 and died there in 1870. He lost his father at an early age, and before he was thirteen years old entered the printing office of the celebrated Mathew Carey. He remained with this great publisher but a short time and was then apprenticed to James Maxwell, from whose office he graduated with high repute as a skillful compositor and pressman. He then removed for a time to Washington, D. C., and upon his return to Philadelphia he entered the office of James Kay, the law publisher. In 1833 he united with Robert Wright in opening a printing office with only one hand press. This partnership existed about two years, when Mr. Wright retired, and Mr. Collins removed his office to 1 Lodge Alley, now 705 Jayne Street, where he formed a new partnership with his own younger brother, and the firm, under the name of T. K. & P. G. Collins, soon became known for the superiority of its typography.

To the practical part of his special business Mr. Collins paid much attention, and the patent roller-boy for hand presses, and the immovable rules which surround the blocks on which certain stereotype plates are placed, are due to his inventive talents.

In 1810 Cadwallader David Colden published a paper presented to the American Medical and Philosophical Register in that year, in which he reported a new method in printing he had discovered.

Colden was an American lawyer and a nephew of the naturalist Colden, was born near Flushing in the State of New York on the 4th of April, 1769, and after having completed his studies he practiced law in New York in 1791. He soon attained high rank in his profession and was made a member of the legislature.

In 1818 he was elected Mayor of the City of New York, a member of Congress in 1821, and a State Senator from 1824 to 1827. He was then elected Lieutenant Governor of the State of New York, and died in Jersey City, N. J., on the 7th of February, 1834.

The new method of printing described by Colden in all its steps in the article he submitted to the Register, was later known by the term "stereotype," and it is a curious fact that the stereotyping process at that time claimed to have been invented by M. Herhan of Paris and practiced by him in that city under letters patent granted by Napoleon, is precisely the same as that described by Dr. Colden. It appears that when Benjamin Franklin went to France he communicated Dr. Colden's "new method of printing" to some artists there, and that it lay dormant for about sixteen years when Herhan, a German who had been an assistant to M. Didot, the renowned printer and type founder of Paris, but then separated from him, took it up in opposition to M. Didot.

Experts in Paris examined M. Herhan's method of stereotyping and described it to be exactly what Governor Colden had invented. This fact established, there can be no doubt that Herhan was indebted to America for the celebrity he attained in France.

There is no evidence that Colden's process was practiced by stereotypers in America.

In the latter part of the year 1815 Jedediah Howe of Connecticut, hearing of the success of the Bruce brothers in the newly invented art, came to New York and commenced a stereotype foundry on Thames Street. Mr. Howe obtained his fair proportion of the limited and uncertain stereotyping business of that early day. But in the course of eight years other foundries started and an exceedingly keen competition followed. Mr. Howe was thence induced to remove his establishment to Philadelphia, which he did in August, 1823. The late Lawrence Johnson was already there, having commenced **a** stereotype foundry about the year 1820.

Adding type-founding to stereotyping, Mr. Howe formed a partnership with Mr. Johnson (which continued until the death of the former in 1834). Although partners, the two foundries were carried on by the new firm as if they were separate establishments.

The publishers of Philadelphia had, previous to the arrival of Mr. Johnson, sent their orders for the few books they ventured to subject to this process to the stereotype founders of New York. There was a reluctance to incur the extra expense of casting after setting up the types, for at that time this caused a double expenditure and capital was hardly abundant enough to afford such a locking up for future benefit. Nothing, perhaps, could more forcibly show the necessity of such a process as stereotyping than the nature of the rude, imperfect and expensive system which preceded its advent. Only half a dozen years before, Mathew Carey of Philadelphia had set up in type all the pages of a quarto Bible and Testament keeping the forms continually standing in a fireproof room and printing editions as sales demanded. It is probable that this enterprise cost Mr. Carey four or five times as much as the price of a set of stereotypes for the same work, and yet we believe the venture was a successful one in its material results. It may interest printers and type-founders to note that about a dozen years ago these old forms of type were sold as metal to Mr. Isaac Ashmead, and that from the minion side notes he collected several casefuls of good type, the unexposed portion of which still retained much of the original hardness and sharpness—a fact reflecting great credit on the manufacture of Messrs. Binney and Ronaldson, from whose foundry the fonts were purchased.

Bibles and school books were the first to be stereotyped, and then gradually came books of great and continued popularity, including the English classics in prose and verse, and the books of popular authors like Washington Irving and J. Fenimore Cooper.

The slow and cautious manner, however, in which American publishers availed themselves of this new invention was rather discouraging to the beginners. Gradually, however, the booksellers were led into stereotyping, though at first not very profitably, for the first large work stereotyped by J. Howe for W. W. Woodward—"Scott's Commentary on the Bible," in five quarto volumes—proved so heavy an undertaking that Mr. Woodward broke down under it and

52. George Bruce

51. David Bruce, Sr.

[157]

53. The Stereotype Plant of David and George Bruce, 15 Chambers Street in New York City

left the plates on the hands of Mr. Howe to his great embarrassment.

Mr. Johnson was more fortunate in stereotyping a book not very dissimilar in character and magnitude, "Henry's Commentary on the Scriptures," undertaken by Tower and Hogan, and carried on successfully to a remunerative result.

On the death of Mr. Howe in 1834 John Fagan, who had been employed in the stereotype foundry for some time, purchased, enlarged and continued the establishment.

Lothian, George Baxter: A celebrated type-founder of New York City, one of the experimental pioneers in machine type-casting and type-rubbing, and also in the present method of kerning type. He was the son of Dr. Robert Lothian of Scotland, who made an ineffectual attempt to establish a foundry in New York in 1806, but failing, sold his material to Binney and Ronaldson of Philadelphia, and died shortly afterwards. The son, George B. Lothian, remained for some time with a bookseller in Philadelphia, where he became much interested in the theatre and appeared in public in a round of Scotch characters. In 1810 he was employed by John Watts of New York, the first stereotyper in the United States; but Lothian's singularly irritable temper and license of speech led to a difficulty which resulted in his being committed to jail. He afterwards worked for Collins & Hanna as a stereotype finisher for about two years, leaving that employment to establish a type foundry in Pittsburgh, Pa. Failing in this undertaking he returned to New York, where his material was purchased by D. & G. Bruce, who also furnished him with employment. This engagement he abandoned in order to study for the stage, but was compelled to relinquish that pursuit on account of his defective verbal memory, although otherwise he was remarkably fitted for the theatrical profession. In 1822 he manufactured type for the Harpers and others in partnership with Alfred Pell, but this connection was soon broken by a personal encounter, and Lothian's interest was purchased by Mr. Hagar. In 1829 he was again manufacturing successfully and proposed a partnership with James Conner, a man of remarkable self-control; but in one of the preliminary conversations upon their affairs Lothian used such exasperating expressions that Conner broke off the arrangements and nearly pitched Lothian out of the window. The Harpers continued to employ him, bearing with the eccentricities of his temper on account of the excellence of his type, and Mr. Hagar also undertook a partnership with him in 1840, but this connection, the last attempted by Lothian, was ruptured in less than half a year. Domestic sorrow was added to Lothian's business misfortunes: his wife and children died, and in declining health his mind was seriously affected. He died in 1851 attended by a single female domestic. He left a handsome competency, judiciously bequeathed.

Perkins, Jacob: A distinguished American inventor, regarded as having introduced one of the greatest improvements in the art of plate-engraving. He was born in Newburyport, Mass., in 1766. Apprenticed at an early age to a goldsmith he soon exhibited his inventive genius by introducing a new method of plating shoe buckles, and was quite successful in their manufacture. When only about twenty-one years of age he was employed by the State of Massachusetts to make dies for copper coinage. He next invented a machine for cutting and heading nails, patented in 1795, and shortly afterwards turned his attention to that branch of industrial art in which he afterwards gained so great a reputation. Copper had been, previous to this time, the only material used for plate engraving, steel having been used but in one instance, in England, in 1805, in a print in a book entitled "The Topographical Illustrations of Westminster." By the invention of Perkins a steel plate engraved by the method used in copper plate is hardened so as to transfer the design by pressure upon other plates of softened steel, which can in turn be hardened and used to transfer the design to an indefinite extent. A peculiar style of note, with a stereotyped check, invented by Perkins, was, in 1808, by a special Act of the State of Massachusetts, directed to be used by all the banks in the Commonwealth as a thorough protection against counterfeiting; and it was used in some New England banks until a very recent period. His substitution of steel for copper and his invention of transfers were especially applicable to bank-note engravings, and in 1814 Perkins removed to Philadelphia and became associated with the firm of Murray, Draper & Fairman. Asa Spencer, also connected with the same firm, shortly afterwards succeeded in applying lathe work to bank-notes, securing what was at that period considered an absolute protection against counterfeits. The directors of the bank of England had endeavored, in 1800, to furnish notes secure from imitation; but forgeries had multiplied, and in 1818 they offered liberal propositions for competition. Attracted by this opportunity Perkins went to England, accompanied by Mr. Fairman and a number of experienced workmen. Unfortunately for his success a London wood engraver succeeded, after a number of efforts, in making a wood-cut copy of one of Perkins' pieces of lathe work, and he was therefore compelled to withdraw from the contest, and the manufacture of the notes was awarded to Applegarth & Cowper in 1820. Perkins, however, obtained the privilege of making the notes for the Bank of Ireland, and for this purpose entered into partnership in London with the distinguished engraver Heath, a connection which continued until the death of Perkins in 1849.

James Conner was born April 22nd, 1798, near Hyde Park, Dutchess County, New York, died May 30th, 1861. He was the founder of the Conner Type Foundry of New York, which since his death has been conducted by his sons under the firm name of James Conner's Sons. After serving an apprenticeship to the printing business in a New York City newspaper office, he worked for some years as a journeyman printer, chiefly in book stereotyping offices, beginning his labors as a stereotyper in the office of Mr. Watts, who in conjunction with Mr. Foy was one of the first, if not the first, to stereotype successfully in the United States. Subsequently he started a stereotyping establishment in New York, to which an extensive type foundry was afterwards added, and he prepared plates of a number of valuable standard works, some of which he sold while others he published on his own account. Later in life, after an adventurous career, his business attention was concentrated on his type foundry and he made strenuous efforts to increase his variety of faces as well as to improve the facilities for manufacturing type. A biographical notice of Mr. Conner, which appeared in "The Printers" of May, 1859, gives the following account of some of his experiments:

"Among these, elaborated by the process of chemical precipitation, was the casting of letters from an electrotyped matrix. Previous to Mr. Conner's successful efforts in this direction, Messrs, Mapes and Chilton, chemists, had experimented to produce a facsimile of a copper-plate which Mapes wished to use for his magazine. Ascertaining the perfect success of the experiment under other hands, he was anxious to have their battery tried on a copperplate. It was, to his and Mr. Chilton's joint delight, successful, and a very favorable report was inserted in many of the European scientific periodicals. So gratifying, in fact, were the results of the experiments made in this direction, that improvements were suggested from time to time.

"In the course of his experimenting, Conner took a Long Primer

Italic capital T, and inserted it through a piece of stereotype plate. This was attached to a copper wire by soldering, some zinc was attached to the other end of the wire; a weak solution of sulphuric acid was made and placed in a vessel; a solution of common blue vitriol in another apartment; then the matrix and the zinc were placed in their respective apartments, and the process of extracting the copper from the sulphate, through galvanic action, commenced, and the copper obtained was thrown on the intended matrix.

"Conner and his assistants then took a small cut of a beehive, and setting this also in the same way, obtained a perfect matrix, which is now in use at Conner's foundry. These successes encouraged him to other experiments on a larger and more valuable scale. Mr. Conner, therefore, ordered a fancy font of type, which he originally had cut on steel, selecting therefrom a perfect alphabet, points, and figures, and then shaved a stereotype plate on both sides. This he lined off into sizes, equal to the matrices he desired to make. He then made the necessary openings through the plate, and inserted the types designed to be precipitated on, which he cut off and soldered on the back. This proved a highly successful experiment, as it gave him a perfect set of matrices at one precipitation. This plate is still to be seen at Mr. Conner's establishment, as originally made, and is regarded as a great curiosity—being supposed to be the first alphabet thus made, in this or any other country."

One of the most extensive and successful type founders in the United States was **Lawrence Johnson,** born January 23rd, 1801 in Hull, England. He was apprenticed to the printing business in the plant of John Childs & Son at Bungay, England, at so early an age that he had served an apprenticeship of seven years before he emigrated with his parents to the United States, where they arrived in 1819, landing in New York. Here he worked with extraordinary diligence as a compositor in the printing office of Mr. Gray, often protracting his labors sixteen or eighteen hours per day. About the year 1820 he became deeply interested in the comparatively new art of stereotyping and with a view of obtaining a knowledge of it he worked for some months with B. and J. Collins of New York, after which he removed to Philadelphia, where, with but a small capital and limited experience he established a stereotype foundry. Despite numerous difficulties he built up and conducted a large and prosperous business as a stereotyper, and after this had been successfully prosecuted for more than ten years he added type founding to his previous calling.

55. T. K. Collins

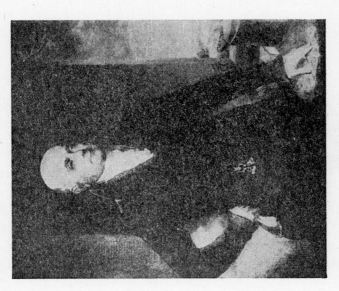

54. Jacob Perkins, Esq.

57. Thomas MacKellar

56. James Conner

[164]

In 1818, or soon after, a type and stereotype foundry was established in Boston and another in Cincinnati, principally thru the enterprise of the late **Elihu White,** who, having the means of multiplying matrices with facility, took this method for the extension of his business. Others followed his example and type foundries were established in Albany, Buffalo, Pittsburgh, Louisville and St. Louis, with several additional in New York, Boston, Philadelphia and Baltimore. The business, in fact, was overdone and failures and suppressions took place as competition reduced prices of types.

An interesting article appeared in "The Long Island Star" (Brooklyn) on the 23rd of October, 1811. The original issue is conserved in the archives of the Long Island Historical Society. Chronologically it belongs in this chapter, and reads as follows:

"Interesting to Printers."

"We have the satisfaction to inform the Printers of the northern and eastern sections of the United States, of the establishment of a manufactory of Printing Presses in the city of New-York, by Mr. **Francis Shield,** from London. Mr. S. has made two common presses since his arrival, one of which is in the office of the Long-Island Star. They are highly approved by the best judges, and have never been exceeded, if equalled, by any manufactory in our country. Mr. Shield likewise makes very neat and accurate Chases, Composing-sticks, Rules, &c. &c.

"The improvements in the printing-press made by Earl Stanhope (which are now getting generally into use in England) are but little known in this country. They are detailed in Stower's Printer's Grammer, published two or three years since. The Press is entirely of cast iron—the plattin covers a whole sheet, which is impressed at one pull—the increase of power is such, that the strength of a child is sufficient for the heaviest form—they are entirely detached from the side of the room, the lightness of the pull not requiring a brace, and they take up much less room than the common press. We have never heard of more than two of these presses being brot into the United States, one of which is now owned by Messrs. Bruce, of New-York. This press is imperfect in some of its parts: but enough may be seen to satisfy any printer that the principle is correct, and a very great improvement.

"Mr. Shield is also in possession of the art of taking Stereotype plates, and has specimens in his possession. A particular account of this art may be seen in the book abovementioned. His manufactory is, at present, at No. 14 Beekman-slip; but a new building is now erecting in First-Street, to prosecute the business on a more extensive scale. Orders, postpaid, are received by Mr. John Tiebout, No. 258 Water-street.

"We are happy to add to the above, the interesting information, that the Type Foundry of Messrs. White & Co. of Hartford, Con. is shortly to be removed to New-York; we may therefore expect the printers of this section of the union to be less subjected to impositions than heretofore. This foundry has recently produced type of a peculiarly beautiful cut, and well adapted to service. New-York, we may confidently expect, will soon rival her sister cities in these first of all arts.

"We should not omit to mention that a Printing Ink manufactory has been some time established by Mr. R. Prout, No. 278 Greenwich Street, who makes ink of the best quality."

The experiments of **Starr & Sturdevant**, under the patronage of the Boston Type and Stereotype Foundry, an incorporated company, promised at one time to be very successful; so much so that at one period they had in operation several machines of their construction, and felt encouraged that they would be able to overcome every difficulty and soon present to printers if not perfectly solid, at least reliable, merchantable type. But they were disappointed, and after the loss of a large portion of their capital they abandoned altogether the use of machinery and fell back to the old system of hand casting.

Thomas MacKellar was born in New York in 1812. At the age of 14 he entered the Harper Brothers printing office to learn the craft. He moved to Philadelphia in 1833 and became the foreman of the stereotyping department of L. Johnson & Company's type foundry. The business of stereotyping was then in its infancy in this country and many obstacles had to be overcome. Nevertheless, the imprint of this establishment soon began to appear on many standard and popular works published in Philadelphia and elsewhere. In 1854 MacKellar became associated with Lawrence Johnson, and when Johnson died in 1860 a new firm was founded bearing the name MacKellar, Smiths & Jordan.

Thomas MacKellar was not only one of the foremost stereotypers of his time, but was a popular poet as well, as evidenced by his works such as "Droppings from the Heart," and "Rhymes Atween Times."

Mr. MacKellar's remarkable poetic ability is shown in the text of the specimen books issued to the trade by the Johnson Type Foundry, wherein he elevated the certainly prosaic theme of a business catalogue into a work of art. His method of interesting his prospective customers in stereotyping was unique, being contained in the catalogue in the form of an imaginary visit to the stereotype foundry of his concern. It merits being recorded in this compilation on the history of stereotyping; the following is the text:

"Mr. Typograph, how are you, sir? Glad to see you. How is business with you? Plenty to do, and customers paying up? You are so prompt in paying us, that we have no doubt you have a noble set of customers. You wish to add to your stock our new things? All right, sir. You have a fine office already, but you want to keep up with the times, and give your patrons the best the type-founder can invent? That's the way, sir. The man on the lookout sees the sun earliest. Mr. Faithful, show our new things to Mr. Typograph, and take his order.

"You say, Mr. Typograph, that you have never gone over a type-foundry? We shall be happy to show you every thing.

"We will proceed to the stereotype department of our business.

"To you, Mr. Typograph, our composing-rooms present nothing new, except, perhaps, in the enormous size of our founts of plain type, and the great number of jobbing founts. So we will only say, that in ten years we have set up in these rooms and stereotyped more than eight hundred considerable works,—most of them consisting of a single volume, but some of from two to twelve volumes each,—besides a multitude of smaller books, tracts, &c. Among the rest we may mention two Quarto Bibles (one of them, published by Peck & Bliss, the grandest ever got up in America), Lippincott's two great Gazetteers, Dr. Kane's Explorations, The North American Sylva, Thiers' Napoleon, and Macaulay's England. Allibone's magnificent Dictionary of Authors and Books is not yet completed. After the pages have been set and carefully read, they are sent down to the casting-room. Let us go down and see how they fare there.

"In the electrotype-room, everything is as black as the brow of a coal-heaver: in the casting-room, all is as white as the neck of a belle. Take care, sir, or your coat will commit a larceny of our plaster. The form of type is laid on this stone, and nicely oiled: and then a mixture of plaster and water—doesn't it look like a good wife's buckwheat batter?—is poured over it, and gently rolled in. In a short time the plaster sets, and the mould is removed by screws as tenderly as a nurse handles a baby. It is then dried in this hot-tempered oven, and, after the moisture is all evaporated, it is laid in a pan and fastened tightly, as you see, and plunged into this terrible bath of a thousand pounds of molten type metal. Phew! you exclaim, what warm work! Yes, sir; but from that fiery sea of lead soon emerges the pan, and its hissing heat is gradually overcome by the water in the trough into which the pan is lowered. Now, caster, break it out. There, Mr. Typograph, is the plate, fixed,—immovable,—stereotyped. The mould is ruined; but the plate is comparatively immortalized. It is rough yet, and, like an uncouth boy, needs polishing.

"This next room is the stereotype finishing-room. Here the plates are carefully examined, picked, shaved, trimmed, and boxed, ready for the printer. Take a plate in your hand and examine it: it will bear inspection. You say it is far better than the untrimmed, uneven plates of English founders? We know that, sir; for we have often had to re-finish English plates imported by some publisher who imagined he could save a little by ordering a duplicate set of plates of a popular foreign book. A mistake, sir. Both in typefounding and in stereotyping the Americans have driven the foreigner from the field,—and in the only legitimate way, too: simply by surpassing him."

Up to this period the Stanhope plaster of Paris method of stereotyping was the one used in the foundries in the U. S. A. An article appeared about the year 1874 in an American periodical which described the process as operated in the United States, and at the same time contained criticisms offered by practical stereotypers. The following is an excerpt of the article:

"Several methods of stereotyping are now practiced. Many of the leading newspapers of England and America are printed from stereotype plates cast in moulds made of prepared paper: this mode is, however, very inferior and is not applicable to fine books.

"Matter for stereotyping is set with high spaces and quadrates. The forms must be small, containing about two pages of common octavo. A slug typehigh is put above the top line and another below the foot line of each page, to protect the ends of the plates from injury when they are passed through the shaving-machine. Bevelled slugs, in height equal to the shoulder of the type, are placed on both sides and between the pages to form the flange by which the plate is to be clasped by the hooks of the printing-block.

"Before the form is sent into the foundry the type must be carefully compared with the proof to detect any errors which may have

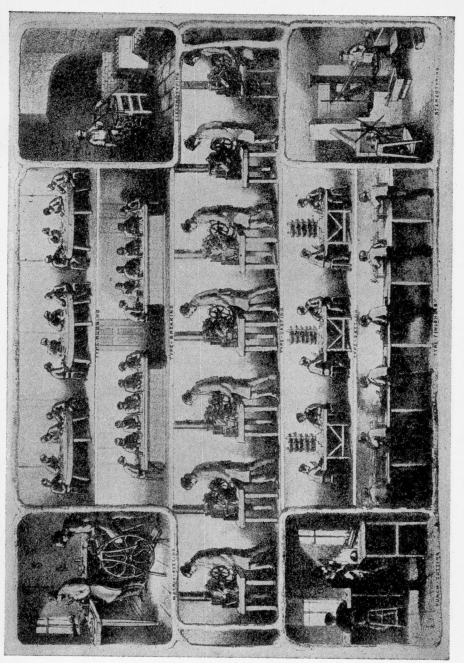

58. Printing Plant Operation in 1845

BOSTON STEREOTYPE FOUNDRY.

ESTABLISHED IN 1822.   INCORPORATED MARCH, 1850.

NO. 4 SPRING LANE, BOSTON.

Charles J. Peters, Agent.

Books of all descriptions Stereotyped or Electrotyped *promptly* and *faithfully.*

Publishers and Authors are referred to the numerous works that have been Stereotyped at this Establishment, from its commencement to the present time, as guaranties for our fulfilment of contracts with accuracy and good taste. By the employment of large founts of Type we are enabled to complete work, when required, with great despatch.

Extensive preparations have been made for applying the Art of

ELECTROTYPING,

and we are ready to furnish Copper Plates from all kinds of Type Work and Wood Cuts.

ADVERTISEMENTS AND ADVERTISING CUTS,

for Newspapers, Stereotyped or Electrotyped, on Wood or Metal bodies, and all kinds of Job Work executed in a tasteful manner.

☞ A Silver Medal and Diploma were awarded the Boston Stereotype Foundry, at the late Exhibition of the Massachusetts Charitable Mechanic Association in this city, for the best specimens of Electrotype work.

☞ The stereotype plates from which this work is printed are from this Establishment.

59. Advertisement. 1855

[170]

been left uncorrected. Care must be taken to lock up the form perfectly square and quite tight, to prevent the types from being pulled out when the mould is raised from the pages. It must be evenly planed down and no ink or dirt or incrustations from the ley be allowed to remain on the surface.

"The face of the type being clean and dry, and the bottoms free from particles of dirt, the form is laid on a clean moulding-stone, and brushed over with sweet-oil, which must be laid on as thinly as possible, care being taken that the entire surface of the types is covered. A moulding-frame, with a screw at each corner (called a flask), and fitting neatly to the form, is next placed around it.

"The material for moulding is finely ground gypsum, nine parts of which are mixed with about seven parts of water and well stirred up. A small quantity of the liquid mixture is poured over the pages and gently pressed into the counter of the types with a small roller, for the purpose of expelling confined air; after which, the remainder of the gypsum is poured in, until the mould is somewhat higher than the upper edge of the flask. In a few minutes the mixture sets, and the upper side is smoothed over with a steel straight-edge. In about ten minutes the mould is gently raised by means of the screws at the corners of the flask; and after being nicely trimmed at the sides, and nicked on the surface-edges to make openings for the metal to run in, it is placed on a shelf in an oven, and allowed to remain until the moisture has quite evaporated.

"The casting-pans may be large enough to hold three or four moulds. The dried moulds are placed in a pan face downward, upon a movable iron plate called a floater. The cover of the casting-pan, which has a hole at each corner for the passage of the metal, is then clamped to it, and lifted by a movable crane and gently lowered into the metal pot—containing, it may be, a thousand pounds of liquid metal,—till the metal begins to flow slowly in at the corners. When the pan is filled it is sunk to the bottom of the pot. The metal should be hot enough to light a piece of brown paper held in it. After being immersed eight or ten minutes the pan is steadily drawn out by means of the crane and swung over to the cooling-trough, into which it is lowered and rested upon a stone so as just to touch the water, in order that the metal at the bottom of the pot may cool first. The metal contracts while cooling and the caster occasionally pours in a small quantity at the corners from a ladle till it will take no more.

"The plates are carefully removed from the solid mass which

[171]

comes out of the pan, and the plaster is washed from the surface. If, after examination, the face is good and sharply set, the plates are passed over to a picker, who removes any slight defects arising from an imperfection of the mould. They are then trimmed and passed through the shaving-machine till all are brought to an equal thickness. The flanges are neatly side-planed, and the plates are then boxed, ready for the printing press.

"In England the plates are merely turned on the back, and consequently vary in thickness. This must be a source of continual expense and annoyance to the pressman. The flanges, besides, are very imperfectly made,—so imperfectly that they cannot be used on American printing-blocks; and English plates, when imported into this country, are therefore sent to a foundry here to be brought to an equal thickness and to be properly side-planed. The American shaving-machine and printing-block are scarcely known abroad, though far superior to foreign arrangements."

Another article, which we offer to the reader, also illustrates the attitude taken about 75 years ago by practical printers in reference to the new art of stereotyping, to wit:

"It is a noteworthy fact that though the art of stereotyping was known and practiced in Europe more than a century, the process was so awkward and imperfect that it interfered very little with the usual mode of letter-press printing. The Old-World people were slow in making improvements on the original rude and defective methods—a serious drawback to the use of the first stereotype plates being their want of uniformity in thickness, which caused both labor and vexation in the printing and disposed the old-fashioned pressmen to set their faces against the innovation. Comparatively few books were therefore stereotyped, and for a long period the art lay in abeyance.

"But when stereotyping was introduced into the United States our skillful and ingenious mechanics soon placed it upon a very different footing. Discarding the bungling turn-lathe, whereby the English were wont to shave their plates, the American stereotyper submitted at once a simple machine of easy operation, which did its office so well that during the more than 50 years which have elapsed since its introduction, scarcely any essential improvement has been found necessary. The early antagonism to the art of stereotyping was further abated by another very important improvement. This was made in the packing of the plates. Incredible as it may appear, when we consider the great proficiency of Europeans in most of the arts, their stereotypers awkwardly placed the plates in wooden racks, thus occupying large spaces for each work, and so encumbering the printing-offices as to preclude the reception of many sets of plates. The first set of stereotype casts of a Bible sent from England to Philadelphia for one of the religious societies of that city, may be remembered by the older printers as occupying the entire side of a moderate-sized room; and if the stereotype plates at present in the large cities were to be stored in this old-fashioned way, entire blocks of warehouses would be needed for the purpose. Packed in boxes, as they now are in the compact American method (likewise devised in the very origin of American stereotyping), a cellar or a vault suffices for the accumulated plates of a large publishing-house or an extensive printing-office.

"Though we derived stereotyping and electrotyping from Old-World inventors, the decided improvements made by our country-men entitle us to a large share of the general merit. The stolidity with which our cousins of Britain cling to their antiquated methods is amusingly illustrated by the following reminiscence. A prominent American sterotyper and printer, visiting London, called on one of the largest stereotyping firms of that city for a friendly confer-ence, and by chance saw in the yard of the establishment two of Hoe's American shaving-machines. They stood exposed to the ele-ments, crumbling to rust and ruin under complete neglect. Our countryman inquired into the reason of this strange disuse of such excellent machinery. The Englishman answered that such was the disinclination of his stereotype-finishers to adopt new improvements of any kind, and such also his own reluctance to urge his workmen against their will, that he had never had the machines placed in his foundry, and consequently they lay unused and decaying."

Genoux placed a wet or papier-mache mat on the market in France in 1830. The circumstances which lead to the introduction of this process in America rooted in England.

Though "The London Times" in 1856 had adopted a modern papier-mache process of stereotyping, it used the process, not for pages, but only for columns, which were fastened on the type-revolving cylinder of Hoe's press by means of V-shaped rules. In the same year a proposition was made to "The New York Tribune" by English stereotypers to establish a plant in New York and to stereotype the "Tribune" at so much per column. Nothing, however, came from these negotiations. Newspapers in New York and in other large cities continued to buy new outfits of type practically every three months.

When the War of the States broke out, circulation had increased so rapidly that it was impossible for either "The New York Tribune" or "The New York Herald" to meet the demand for papers, and Richard Hoe was negotiating with Greeley and Bennett for the construction of 20-cylinder type-revolving presses to meet the situation.

Meanwhile a noted steel engraver, **Charles Craske** of Norfolk, who was the proprietor of an electrotyping plant and well-known to all printers in America, practiced stereotyping by the clay process and had achieved a notable success with it. He then turned to experimenting with the papier-mache process in an attempt to apply it to newspaper pages. His experiments were carried on in rooms provided by "The New York Tribune," which paper had reached the point where it must have the faster presses already mentioned or set its pages in duplicate as had been the practice of "The London Times" before it adopted the papier-mache process.

In 1854 Mr. Craske made the first curved plate for a Hoe rotary press in the office of "The New York Tribune." The experiment did not bring entire success, however, inasmuch as the process was not permanently adopted at this time.

Craske's idea was to cast the whole page after the manner now employed, but in his experiments, covering over two years, he failed to make satisfactory progress because he attempted to cast the plates type-high. It was only when he reached the conclusion to cast a thin plate and then to compel press builders to change the cylinder that he succeeded in overcoming his difficulty. On August 31st, 1861 the Tribune commenced to print from curved stereotype plates of whole pages.

Data on Charles Craske appeared in a biographical sketch which appeared in 1894. He was born in London, England on February 22, 1822, and was educated in the well known Blue-Coat School of that city. He came to America in 1837 in his sixteenth year, and learned the art of steel and copper engraving, which he carried on in New York for twenty-five years. In 1850 he introduced a new method of stereotyping, that by paper molds or matrices. By this mode two important features were introduced, both of them new. One of them was that any number of plates could be made in rapid succession from the form, and the other was that, although the matrix was made flat, corresponding with the surface of a page, yet as it was flexible it could be placed in a casting box of any

60. a) Metal Pot, Drying Surface and Press
    b) Combination Finishing Table
    c) Casting Box
(From Miller and Richard's Miniature Foundry)

61. Charles Craske

desired curve and a plate obtained of that curve. In 1854 he stereotyped a page of the "New York Herald," and in 1861 he began regularly to make plates for the "Tribune." This proving successful, he shortly after made a contract for stereotyping the "Sun," "Times" and "Herald." The material used is a soft, wet and thick paper. The sheet is laid upon the form, beaten in with brushes, and then the form is put into a press where much power is applied. The page of type and the platen of the press are both heated, thus making the time for drying the matrix much shorter than it would be otherwise. When the sheet is taken off it is like a huge sheet of cardboard, somewhat scorched in places, where the type or indentations are to be found and where the spaces or projections are seen. After the introduction of this method, Mr. Craske carried on the business of electrotyping and stereotyping in New York City, but discontinued engraving.

At an outing of the (New York) Sun Employees Pleasure Association in the Eighties, an old stereotyper told of early days when it took four men all night to cast four plates. The following is the story told by this anonymous employee:

"In 1864 the four leading papers of New York City—namely, the 'Sun,' 'Times,' 'Herald' and 'Tribune'—were stereotyped by contract. Charles Craske, whose place of business was in Ann Street, employed all the stereotypers and acted as superintendent. The Sun at that time was owned by Moses S. Beach. His two brothers, Joseph and Henry, were with him, Joseph being publisher and Henry managing editor.

"Henry lived in West Hoboken and could be seen every morning at two o'clock wending his way to the Barclay Street ferry, dressed in trousers much too short for him and wearing brogan shoes and blue homespun socks which showed between the bottom of his trousers and the tops of his shoes. He carried a lantern and an umbrella tied in the middle.

"The 'Sun' at that time was a four page paper. Two pages, the second and third, were locked up in a chase at one time. They were rolled in the stereotype room, where the stereotypers had to take a matrix and cast two plates which constituted one side.

"Do I hear some one say, 'Only four plates a night and four men to do the work? Them were the happy days!'

"Permit me to say that the stereotypers have always had their troubles. It took at that time forty-five minutes to get two plates, and if the men were successful in getting the casts without breaking the mould they wanted to put a frame around them. As the matrix was being relieved from the plate it would very often break in several places and leave pieces stuck to the face of the plate. Needles were used to pick the paper out of the letters. Sometimes the places were dampened and the plate, being hot, would create steam, which assisted in removing the paper.

"Mr. Craske, who worked with the men at that time, always carried a cigar in his vest pocket, and every once in a while would bite off a large piece and chew it instead of the ordinary chewing tobacco. While trying to remove the pieces of paper from the hot plates (in order to save time) he would squirt a large mouthful of tobacco juice over them. The result was that every one had to stand aside and raise his hands to guard his nostrils from the offensive effluvia arising therefrom.

"In 1866 Mr. Bullock put his perfecting press on the market. The 'Sun' had one installed, but it was nearly a year before they got it running, the chief difficulty being with the delivery. The stereotypers were then called upon to make sixteen plates a night instead of four, which created a great deal of worry and excitement. Every effort was made to improve the matrix so that it would take the required number of casts and also to make better time in getting the plates to the press room.

"In 1868 Mr. Dana purchased the 'Sun' and the business was moved from the corner of Nassau and Fulton Streets into the building which it now occupies. The stereotype room was located on the top floor, where the steam tables stand at the present time. Wood and coal were used to melt the metal, and when there was a hard storm (the chimney being poorly constructed) it would smoke fearfully and fill the composing room with a cloud, causing tears to stream from the eyes of the compositors. The sweepings of the floor being thrown in the metal pot, a mixture of dirt, paper, old leather and woollen rags emitted a delightful odor, and Mr. Watkins one night in anger said, 'You stereotypers make more noise and stink than any other department in the office.'

"Four new perfecting presses were put in and new machinery was purchased for the stereotyping department. The matrix, instead of being beaten in by hand, was run through a mangling or moulding machine, thus saving one and a half minutes. The matrix has been improved further, so that instead of four plates a night, as in 1864, between five and six hundred plates are taken on Saturday nights at the present time. Instead of two casts twenty are now taken from one mould on the baseball edition, and instead of two forms eighty-five are sometimes moulded on Saturdays. If the present management continues to exercise the energy it has in the past, there is no telling how many casts may be required in the near future."

There has been little fundamental change in stereotyping newspaper pages since August, 1861 when the "Tribune" adopted the papier-mache process. "The New York Times" soon adopted the new process, as did "The New York Herald." Because of this process it was no longer necessary to add additional cylinders to the press. Pages could be duplicated to the number desired and several presses could be employed at the same time to print the same edition of the newspaper. Craske not only revolutionized newspaper stereotyping in America, but he also changed completely the construction of American printing presses. By 1880 45 daily newspapers in the United States were printing with plates made by this papier-mache process. They were distributed among the following states: Pennsylvania 10, New York 9, Ohio 6, Illinois 6, Massachusetts 2, Maryland 2, California 2, Missouri 2, Wisconsin 1, Minnesota 1, New Jersey 1, Kentucky 1, Indiana 1, Michigan 1.

It should be recorded that "The New York Sun" was stereotyped for a few months from clay molds on single columns, but on account of some of the columns breaking from their fastenings and injuring the presses they were discontinued. Later on the "Sun", following the example of the other New York newspapers, adopted the wet mat process.

An interesting example of early "stereotyping" (although the plate is not made of metal) on file in the Government Printing Office is a plate used in printing the Congressional Record in the year 1857.[1] A description of the method of manufacture with the formula of the material used has been written by Michael Shean, a former official who worked with the inventor on these plates in the late days of the use of the process. An extract from his description should be of interest:

"The composition entering into the production of the plates used for printing the proceedings of Congress during the years from 1850 to 1860 is as follows:

---

[1] John A. McLean, Superintendent of Plate Making, Government Printing Office, Washington, D. C.

5 pounds of Silica
2 pounds of Gum Shellac
5 ounces of Tar
1 ounce of Boiled Linseed Oil

"Silica, tar and boiled linseed oil are mixed thoroughly and spread out on the back of a flat stereotype melting furnace. This flat platen surface on the back of the furnace is always hot when the fire is burning for melting the stereotype metal, and on this the composition is kept in a soft or plastic condition.

"The gum shellac which is broken into fine particles is now added to the other mentioned ingredients, thoroughly mixing them together.

"The next operation consists of rolling the soft pliable composition into a fairly uniform sheet and cut into size according to the subject for molding and its dimensions."

Mr. Shean in his article then goes on to explain how the plastic material is pressed into the clay mold or matrix, being locked in a steel frame so that bevels on three sides and a flush head are molded on the finished plate.

Stereotyping had come to stay and practical printing experts began experimenting in stereotyping, and many were the improvements made in the art in the United States. It would be beyond the scope of this short book to make mention of the hundreds of patents issued to American inventors for improvements in the art; however, a number merit mention, partly on account of the age of the patents and partly for the benefits they afforded those devoting their labor to stereotyping. The wet mat process was considered the best method, and experimenting was done on the wet or papier-mache matrix.

It will be observed that this catalogue of patents is not restricted to those pertaining to the papier-mache process, but includes all the different methods of stereotyping dating back to the year 1819. While most of the older patents have no value now in a practical sense, they are considered of sufficient historical interest to entitle them to a place in this list.

It is interesting to note the increasing importance of the art with each succeeding decade of the century, as indicated by the number of patents issued. Previous to 1840 we find record of but two patents. From 1840 to 1850 but two patents are shown. From 1850 to 1860 there were eleven patents granted. From 1860 to 1870 there were eighteen. From 1870 to 1880 sixty were granted.

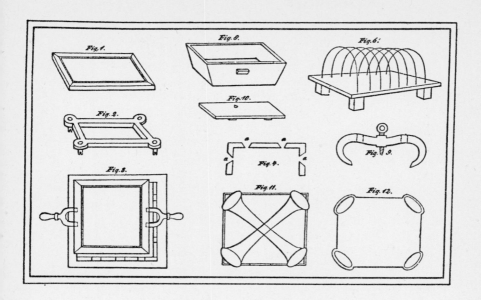

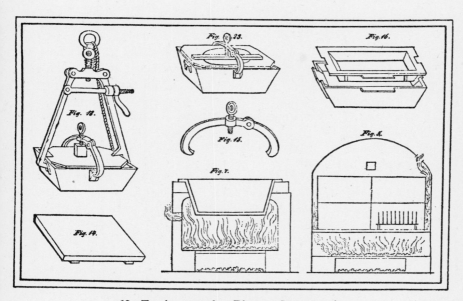

62. Equipment for Plaster Stereotyping

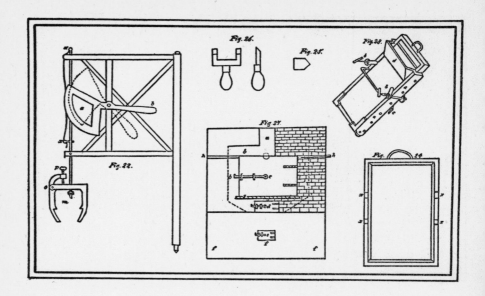

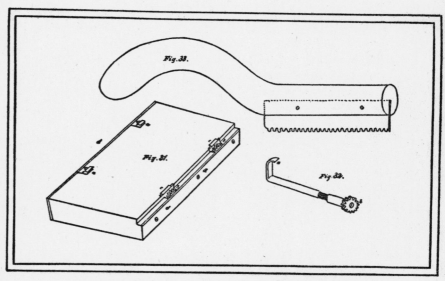

63. Equipment for Plaster Stereotyping

From 1880 to 1890 one hundred and sixty-three were issued, and for the first two years of the present decade the number is fifty-seven. If the remaining eight years are as prolific the total number of patents for the current decade will reach two hundred and eighty-five.

Clement Davison, Saratoga, N. Y., November 26th, 1844. A patent for an improved method of moulding and casting stereotype plates, also cutting, chiseling and finishing the same.

Charles Hobbs of New York City, September 2, 1851, invented a method of making stereotype plates. His patent covers molding and casting any given number of plates at one operation and making them more rapidly and more perfect than heretofore. He accomplished this thru exhausting the air from the plaster and from the type before applying the plaster to the type when making molds. Further, he saved material by making the molds with two faces, thus making one mold instead of two.

In casting the molds he stood them on edge with a body of stereotype metal above them, thus having the largest body of metal above the molds.

In his apparatus he cast ten to twenty times as many plates as could be cast in the ordinary way, and he had only to take off the top wedge and two side wedges in order to release the whole of them, whereas ordinarily the operator has to knock off all the metal around the edges of each cast before he can get at the plates.

In his apparatus the molds were stood on edge, and having two faces the metal flowed alike on both sides, thus the pressure of the metal was equal on both sides of the molds, which prevented them from breaking while they were cast. Finally, he cast with the metal at a much lower heat.

Hobart P. Cook, Albany, N. Y., August 3rd, 1852. Casting stereotype plates by the application of pressure upon the surface of the melted metal. The pressure forces the melted metal through a tube and upon the mould—the face of the mould being turned down to receive the metal making the casting.

John L. Kingsley, New York, June 14th, 1853. The nature of this invention consists in making moulds for stereotyping of India-rubber or gutta-percha, by mixing the gums with metallic or earthy substances, and by expelling all air from the mould while it is being filled, to render the cast in all respects perfect.

Wm. Blanchard, Washington, D. C., February 22nd, 1859. The improvement consists in casting stereotype plates, by immersing a metallic mould-plate, with a mould of matrix forms upon and adhering to it.

M. S. Beach, Brooklyn, N. Y., July 29th, 1862. The object of this invention is the production of a composite stereotype, of which one part is a stereotype or electrotype of the finer portions, made by any approved process, and the other part is made from papier-mache, or other matrix, which receives and embodies in itself the first-named part. Use is also made of a movable or adjustable bed or block made of type-metal or other similar, substantial and yet yielding material, upon which the stereotype is placed, and under which instead of under the stereotype itself, the underlays are adjusted.

Clemoire F. Cosfeldt, Jr., and **Thomas T. Pears,** Philadelphia, June 7th, 1864. In this apparatus the melting-pot is suitably fixed in a furnace. Near the bottom of the pot is a pipe for conducting off the melted metal; at the end of this pipe is a device for regulating the flow of the melted metal.

J. D. McLean, New York, June 28th, 1864. The object of this invention is to obtain a machine of simple construction, by which moulds or matrices for producing stereotype or electrotype plates for letter-press may be formed directly from dies, for the purpose of avoiding the labor and expense of setting up type, and casting or forming moulds therefrom, and the invention consists in the employment of devices for effecting such object.

Ariel Case, New Haven, Conn., April 24th, 1866. A stereotype block. The stereotype plate is mounted upon quadrats set up in a chase; the clamps which hold the edges of the plate are inserted among the quadrats.

Johnson of Philadelphia examined the new papier-mache process on the spot in France. He bought the rights to use the Genoux patent in foreign countries but refused to use the Genoux equipment. His objection was that it was too primitive. However, in the end he bought the equipment, stored it and made his own machines. Johnson's agent then left for London where he installed the wet mat system of stereotyping at "The London Times," owned by the Walter family.

Simon H. Mix, 1860. The nature of his invention consists in interposing between the type form (when set up to receive the plaster of Paris as a matrix) and the plaster of Paris or other material for the matrix, a very thin sheet of tin or other soft metal foil, and pressing the same into and upon the types and form so as to receive the exact impression thereof, and then placing thereon the material to form the matrix, the foil thus used to be left on the plaster of Paris mold when immersed in the bath of type metal, or to be stripped off before immersion as may suit the operator

M. Nelson in 1870. He bases his claim upon the use of a woven or knitted fabric coated with a composition impressed upon the types to produce the matrix, and then inserted the same in a mold provided with non-conducting material so that the metal would not chill but perfectly fill the interstices of the matrix.

He makes use of a fabric such as Canton flannel, and coats the same with a composition, either by a brush or by dipping, the former preferred. The composition enters into the surface, and the projecting fibers become the means for holding all particles of the composition, so that the matrix will separate from the types and none of the pieces of the composition remain upon the surface of the types.

The composition he employs is made of Paris white, well boiled flour paste, mixed to the consistency of cream, the white of an egg, introduced into about five pounds of such composition; the same is thoroughly mixed and applied as aforesaid, and allowed to dry, or nearly so.

When the matrix is to be made the sheet should be damp. This may be effected by the use of a sponge, and water applied to the back of the fabric. He also prefers to rub plumbago upon the surface of the fabric prepared as aforesaid.

The matrix is made by laying a piece of this fabric upon the face of the types, then a sheet of India rubber or other elastic material, and subjecting the same to pressure in a suitable press, which indents the fabric between the types and takes a perfect impression of the faces of the types, in the composition upon the surface of the fabric.

M. Galley in 1872 invented a mechanism to permit stereotypers in one plant to produce stereotypes at some other distant plant. He states that the object of his invention is, first, to do away with the necessity of the use of movable types, either in forms or parts of forms for letter-press printing, or in forms or parts of forms from which stereotypes are prepared for press; and second, to enable operators who are preparing matter for press in one locality to reproduce the same in other localities at the same time, either in the form of stereotypes or stereotype molds; also, to enable the operator, if he desires, to produce the mold or stereotype only at a distance. The first part of his invention consists in a mechanism which shall mechanically arrange and rearrange an alphabet or alphabets of dies, which dies shall form impressions in the material for a mold corresponding with the composition of matter desired in a stereotype; and in the same or similar mechanism with a substitution of female dies and other appliances, changes and attachments made necessary by such substitution of dies, and the work to be done, as shall enable the operator to produce directly the stereotype instead of the mold. The second part of his invention consists in working a machine by means of electrical connections, when such machine is used for preparing matter for letter-press printing, either in arranging types for press, in making molds formed by a mechanical arrangement of dies, or in producing directly by mechanical means a stereotype.

Willard S. Whitmore of Washington, D. C., in 1881, in his invention relating to paper molds or matrices for casting stereotype plates, proceeded as follows: Instead of making his mat up of alternate layers of unsized paper and sheets of tissue paper pasted together, and in order to remedy the drawbacks of pulling in wet mats, Whitmore constructed a new composite mold which was formed of a sheet of unsized paper, covered same with a layer of paper pulp which had never been set by drying. He formed the plastic pulp by adding to it in a watery state a little glue, gum or other adhesive agent. The water was then squeezed out by pressure, when the pulp was laid upon a heavy piece of unsized paper which had received a coating of paste made of starch, flour or some albuminous substance and allowed to stand a while under light pressure, so that the paste could combine more thoroughly with both the pulp or plastic and the heavy stereotype paper. The advantage Whitmore claimed for his mat was greater plasticity, toughness and economy, requiring but one layer of pulp, while the old wet mat required three or four layers of paper.

Benjamin B. Huntoon of Louisville, Ky. in 1881 took paper from the common or poorest stock, but of extra thickness; and in order to prepare it for his purpose he first subjected it to heat sufficient to char or carbonize it, or by dipping it (a sheet at a time) in molten metal, or by baking it (after slight dampening) upon a steam-chest under slight pressure, or by moistening it with acid, and when this moisture had sufficiently evaporated to leave it but slightly soft and pliable it was ready to receive the impression,

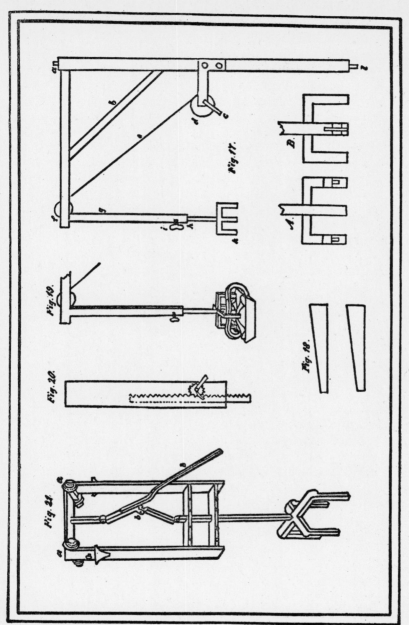

64. Equipment for Plaster Stereotyping

65. Rivett Patent Flong or Matrix Machine

which was made by passing it thru an ordinary printing press provided with suitable type in a cold state, either with or without a paper backing; but if a backing was used it was only intended to assist in removing the matrices from the type. The process of drying was accomplished by means of a steam heated surface.

George Damon and **Elias Peets** in 1888 produced a metal-faced mat with a papier-mache backing. Their method in detail was as follows: By means of the type they first took an impression in papier-mache, thus forming a matrix. Stereotype metal was then poured into this matrix and an ordinary stereotype plate formed. The plate was then coated with melted wax, and before the wax had entirely hardened powdered plumbago was dusted over the whole surface. The plate thus prepared was immersed in a copper solution and a film of copper deposited upon its face. The plate was then placed upon a beating table and a sheet of dampened stereotype paper laid over it, which was beaten into the irregular copper surface. Thereupon a thin coating of pipe clay was spread over the entire surface, which was then removed from the depressed surfaces (which occur where paragraphs or blanks are found in the type), and into these depressions were then placed small strips of compressed, properly cut stereotype paper, and over the whole were then laid in succession and beaten in several additional sheets of moist stereotype paper. This plate was then smoothed and dried, when the copper coating with its backing of paper was stripped from the plate and was in condition to be used as a matrix, from which any number of stereotype plates were produced.

Charles M. Gage of Massachusetts invented a rather novel mat in 1888. He destroyed the most essential property, the basic fundamental of a paper mat, namely its elasticity. In accordance with his invention his matrix board was made of sheets of paper composed of vegetable fibre, preferably two or more of these sheets being heated with a solution composed of shellac, borax and water. The sheets of paper were dipped into this solution and thoroughly dried. Hereby the elasticity of the fibre was destroyed. Then there was pasted to this matrix board a finishing sheet of paper made of a strong long vegetable fibre, which had been coated with paraffine or wax. The non-elasticity of the matrix permitted, according to Gage, of maintaining a perfect impression for an indefinite period of time.

W. Mears, 1883. His patent consists in the following: First, treating thick porous or bibulous paper with a solution of gun cotton, not quite saturated, or collodion, applied either by a brush or by immersion, the latter being the preferable mode of treatment. The effect of this treatment is to impart to the paper the quality of being easily impressed upon the form to be reproduced in stereotype and of retaining the impressions received into it without change.

Second. Backing up the paper so saturated with gun cotton, as above described, after placing it on the form preparatory to making the impression of the matter to be reproduced in stereotype, with a layer of paper saturated with shellac or any similar gum soluble in alcohol, to be thoroughly dried before using.

The necessary pressure to fix into the prepared paper the form to be stereotyped being applied, it will be seen that the excess of alcohol and ether contained in the solution of gun cotton is forced thru to contact with the gum, thus combining with it and cementing the second layer of the paper to the matrix, the compound thus formed at the same time absorbing most of the moisture remaining in the matrix paper proper. The pressure being removed, after a few minutes exposure in the open air, or if great haste is required, drying in an oven, the matrix is ready for the casting box.

Walter B. Carr and **Augustus G. French** of St. Louis invented certain new improvements in matrix boards in 1892. Their invention, made to dry a wet mat without heating the type, consisted in forming a matrix of semi-porous blanket, and forming an impression sheet on one of its faces. Their mat consisted in only one sheet of manila or other ligneoux fibre, one side of which was finished so as to give it the properties of woven paper, while the other side was left in its original semi-porous state, thus making the impression sheet a part of the blanket, which parts up to that time had been applied separately in use. No paste was necessary as the mat consisted of only one sheet.

Louis G. Timroth of Brooklyn, N. Y., invented in 1896 a chemical paste which was to do away with one of the great drawbacks of the wet mat. He claimed that his mat could be rolled for mailing, be stored and kept for an indefinite length of time without liability of souring or otherwise deteriorating. He also claimed that no backing was necessary and that his mat permitted reproduction of the finest possible lines, such as were found in halftones, which could not be produced by methods hitherto employed. His paste consisted of water, alum, flour, ocher, rosin, ground cloves, sugar, starch, gum arabic and white glue.

When during this period the dry mat cold stereotyping idea was being discussed, the advantages claimed for the same led to many experiments in rapid drying of wet mats on the part of stereotypers who were opposed to the new cold process.

It was tried to produce quickly drying paper matrices by means of easily volatile fluids, for instance alcohol, but this method had the drawback that the alcohol of the wet mat evaporated too soon, and consequently the mat became dry before it reached the steam table, whereby it lost its binding power and instead of forming a solid coherent mass it was loose and liable to be separated sheet layer for sheet layer.

A number of experiments were made to shorten the stereotyping process, one of which was rather novel. In 1884 **Charles A. Skene** of Kansas invented a process to obtain stereotype plates for printing purposes directly from matrices made by telegraph or typewriting machines, and thus obviate the necessity of having to prepare type forms in order to obtain a cast, thereby saving the time, labor and expense of composition, distribution and makeup that are necessary prerequisites to the operation. In order to carry his process into operation Skene took a thin sheet of soft paper and coated it evenly on both sides with a brush that was dipped into a pasty mixture of glycerine and plumbago. When the paper had thoroughly absorbed the mixture it was passed between heated rollers until its surface became perfectly smooth. The paper so prepared was placed in a common typewriting machine and the writing proceeded with as upon ordinary paper. Skene expected the types to make impressions on the paper sufficiently deep to form a mold or matrix in which a stereotype plate could be cast in the ordinary manner for use on an ordinary printing press. He stated that "it will be obvious that a telegraph printing machine may be thus employed in preparing the mold or matrix, and operated from a distant point, which will be found of great practical utility." His hopes were not realized and no practical use was made of his invention.

This idea of typewriting and also of linotyping directly on a prepared paper matrix has been followed up by different inventors; as late as 1922 machines for this kind of work were invented and patented. It appears, however, that for many years to come such attempts will prove futile because of the many millions of dollars tied up in equipment which can hardly be scrapped before such new ideas have been tried out in practice a score of years and have proven beyond a shadow of doubt the claims made for them by their enthusiastic inventors. Machines have been invented to do away with the use of type altogether by punching the types on some substance which acted like a matrix and became a mold from which stereotype plates could be cast, for instance punching upon teak wood. This process was impractical as it did not permit of correction.

The invention of mats made of celluloid by Emile Janin of Paris has been described earlier in this book. These celluloid stereotype plates, made in accordance with the invention of Janin, were also introduced into the United States. In 1882 a stereotype foundry in New York City situated at the corner of Fulton and Gold Streets, started to make these very thin and black plates. In 1883 a company was organized in New York City with a capital of $50,000 under the name of Celluloid Stereotype Company of America. Thru purchase of all existing patents this company held a monopoly on the use of celluloid for celluloid stereotyping purposes.

The low weight of the celluloid offered considerable mailing advantages; the material was heated up to 257° F., acquired plastic qualities, and was readily molded. Metal plates were easily imbedded in the warm plastic celluloid, which acted very much like putty when cooled. The business of making these plates began promisingly but never did it become the great success the American company had envisaged and hoped for. After engaging for several years in this business the corporation dropped the manufacture of celluloid plates for the stereotype industry.

A. N. Kellogg of the Western Newspaper Union invented a celluloid plate, the lightness of which further reduced transportation costs and for a short time gave it a world wide sale.

It is interesting to follow the development of the dry mat method of stereotyping in America. In 1890 Ferdinand Wesel, Sr. of New York, paternal manufacturer of stereotype machinery, was in London where he found newspapers using a German made dry mat quite successfully. Wesel proceeded to Germany, visited the foremost manufacturers of these dry mats and secured the sales agency for these products for America. At first Wesel had but little success with them, principally on account of opposition on the part of the stereotypers.

The mats were tried in New York with scant toleration—although they were used abroad with success. Wesel made a hand-power matrix roller for slow speed molding, hoping entree could be made thru book and job printing plants. Among those who experimented

66. Brush Beating

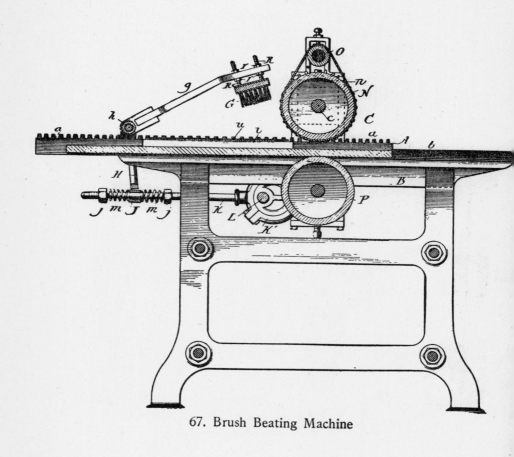

67. Brush Beating Machine

at that time were the J. B. Lyon Co., Albany, N. Y. and Burke & Gregory, Norfolk, Va.

Undaunted, Wesel still had faith and continued to import a few hundred sheets at a time, and later some thousands, because there were always a few venturesome souls in the West willing to try the mats. However, as a business proposition the matter might have died had it not been for the persistent faith of the late Colver who founded the NEA at Cleveland. He used them continuously wherever they would fit the subjects and where speed was needed. He also persuaded managers and editors of the Scripps-McRae League to use them for "starters"—keeping 25 to 50 sheets always on hand for emergencies. Their "beats on the streets" compelled opposition newspapers to lay in a supply for "starters," among whom were the "Cincinnati Times-Star", "Indianapolis News", etc. Thus, for a number of years there was a flow and a use for dry mats in this country.

The shrinkage of the early mats was but a trifle as a vexation. It was made a talking point to sustain a prejudice against the dry mats. The chief defect was the "pulp pattern" which appeared on the cast plates and which showed on the printed pages with a gray tone—not sharp and black as were the wet mat pages. Hence, some newspapers used the dry mats for "starters" to reach the street quickly and followed with wet mats to finish the rest of the run. Others finished the entire runs without change.

At the time of the fight between Jeffries and Johnson at Reno, Nevada on July 4th, 1910, there was no steam drying table nor matrix roller in the whole state of Nevada. Colver of the NEA had to have mats to send out from Reno and here is where the dry mat served him for his "beats." A Wesel hand-power matrix roller was shipped from New York to Reno with express charges almost as high as the cost of the machine, but it saved the day.

Later on the Wesel Company sold their agency to the "Pittsburgh Press." Here the stereotype foreman, Alfred Birdsall, started his experiments in dry mat making. The mats not being coated, the face was uneven. Birdsall attempted to remedy the drawback by pasting one or two tissues on the dry mat, but this method did not meet with success. In 1910 Birdsall invented his own coating, started a "Dry Mat Service Co. Ltd." in Pittsburgh, and in 1912 advertised that over 50 newspapers in the U. S. A. were purchasing the new dry mat. With the advent of imported coated dry mats no more was heard of the Pittsburgh mat.

The American Type Founders also imported and sold mats for

a short time, the price asked for one dry mat of newspaper size being $1.00.

In 1908 the mechanical superintendent of the "Daily Mail" in London, Charles F. Hart, until recently the mechanical superintendent of the "New York Times," advocated the use of dry mats for all newspaper work. "The Daily Mail" was the first daily newspaper in Great Britain to adopt dry mats exclusively, using the imported German "Padipp" mats made in Dippoldiswalde, Saxony. Indirectly, thru Mr. Hart's endeavor to have an English manufacturer provide English products to an English newspaper, L. S. Dixon, paper maker of Liverpool, engaged in the manufacture of dry mats as a side line, marketing his product under the name "Dixotype" mats.

In 1909 Henry A. Wise Wood of New York visited the plant of "The London Daily Mail" where the working of German dry mats was shown him. Wood decided to engage in the dry mat business in the United States, and some time later, in 1911, made an arrangement thru Gerald Wetherman, agent for the "Padipp" mat in England, for the sales agency of this German dry mat in America. Wood continued the sale of this dry mat until the World War made imports from Germany impossible.

These facts have been challenged. An exchange of two letters, published a short time ago, one written by that veteran stereotyper of America, Bertel O. Henning, and the other by Oscar C. Roesen of the Wood Newspaper Machinery Corporation, shed light on this interesting controversy as to whom the credit is due for having first introduced, i.e. imported the original German dry mats into the United States.

Henry A. Wise Wood, the renowned inventor of the Autoplate machines, stated in an interview that he was the first one to import the dry mat into this country. We give condensed reports of the two aforementioned letters. First B. O. Henning: "The first dry mats were imported to this country about 1900 by Ferdinand Wesel, or perhaps a little earlier. Messrs. Henry and Benjamin Wood came into the dry mat picture about 1911-1912 when Charles Hart was on the London Harmsworth papers. Hart, with his Western courage, tried and used successfully dry mats and at about this period the Woods began to import them.

"Thereafter, there were more dry mats used and other importers engaged in the business of supplying. Little by little, small newspapers went on a sole dry mat basis. However, their printing showed the gray tones and occasional sinks which could be detected easily from the staid, dependable wet mat printing. As time went on, improvement in the facing occurred and then "as over night" (about 1924) newspapers went on the dry mat basis very rapidly because the dry mat was able to meet the printing excellence required.

"Whoever overcame the pulp pattern or mottled facing of the early dry mats deserves particular credit. But it might be reasonable to suppose that this one and that one contributed a little here and there over the period of years with the incredible support of the newspapers whose every plant was a working laboratory.

"It is a significant fact that it required 12 years by Wesel and 12 years by Wood and others before publishers felt safe in discarding steam tables. During the last 15 years intense concentration has been shown in the manufacture and use of the dry mat with considerable refinements during the last five years.

"You can verify by research the dates of Wesel's introduction of the dry mat and his tenacious efforts to keep it from dying at birth. Consult his early catalogs and printed matter concerning it. Henry L. Bullen wrote most of it and had the engraving (wood cut) made of the mat roller referred to. No doubt the data is in the Typographic Museum at Columbia University in New York.

"S. H. Horgan, the authority on photo-engraving and graphic arts history, might recall the facts as he was close to Bullen at this early period."

Mr. O. C. Roesen: "I asked some of the older members of the Wood Newspaper Machinery Corporation as to the facts contained in the communication you received from Bertel O. Henning. They all agree that Mr. Henning's statements are substantially correct as to Mr. Wesel, Sr., being the first to import dry mats into this country, but in such quantities that they were only used in an experimental way and due to the many defects were many times followed-up by wet mats.

"There is no question but that Henry A. Wise Wood and Benjamin Wood, his brother, were the first ones to import dry mats in large quantities into this country, and it was their foresight and tenacity that put the dry mat into practical operation in the various plants in the United States. The Wood Flong Corporation was the first company to erect a mill and manufacture dry mats in this country."

In April, 1913, Carl Raid founded the Flexitype Company in Cleveland, Ohio, sole agents for the German "Flexitype" dry matrix which was manufactured in Saxony. John Breuer, stereotyper and demonstrator of this new dry mat, invented the necessary equipment for handling these dry mats, namely a scorcher and a humidor. Within a year's time many newspapers taking three to five casts from a mat had been won over to these dry mats exclusively. The advent of the World War ended the contracts, and after disposing of its stock of mats the company went out of existence.

The World War, having put an end to the business of importing German dry mats into America, Benjamin Wood, convinced of the fact that the dry mat was here to stay, decided to engage in the manufacture of this product. With the aid of American chemists, in whose experimental laboratories all makes of dry mats were analyzed, a dry mat manufacturing process was found, and in 1917 Wood, as first in the United States, began producing dry mats on a commercial scale. His products are sold under different names such as Metropolitan, Marathon, Speedmat, Standard, etc.

After several years spent in Europe learning thru actual practice all details of a number of dry mat manufacturing processes, and also studying dry mat stereotyping methods, Geo. A. Kubler of Akron, Ohio, founded in 1923 the Certified Dry Mat Corporation of New York City for the manufacture and sale of dry mats. The product this company put on the market is known as the "Certified" dry mat. The corporation and its chemists improved the ordinary dry mat thru eliminating the gray tones and blisters usually found in dry mats in the beginning of their manufacture, and by applying special raw stocks and facings overcame the great drawback of the mottled "elephant hide" screen marks on the mats. Upon the advent of these improved dry mats the metropolitan newspapers turned their attention to experimenting with dry mats, and the first metropolitan newspaper, "The New York Times," after conducting exhaustive tests with this Certified mat, went over from wet mats to dry mats entirely. From then on other large and small papers followed suit so that today practically all of the American stereotyped newspapers use dry mats exclusively.

The Morley Button Manufacturing Company, manufacturers of pasteboard and plastic buttons, turned over a number of their idle machines for experiments in the making of dry mats. After thorough research work they developed a product adapted for newspaper and syndicate stereotyping work and placed it on the market under the denomination Morley dry mat.

The Burgess Battery Company, making in their plant in Free-

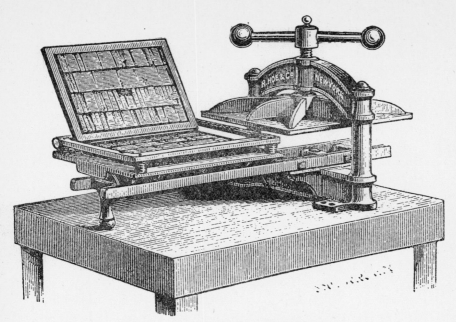

68. Press for Stereotype Moulding

69. Matrix Rolling Machine for Newspaper Work—Papier-mache Process

70. Stereotype Matrix Rolling Machine

71. Wesel Improved Hand Matrix Rolling
Machine

port, Ill. pasteboard boxes for their well-known batteries, also turned their attention to developing a dry mat. They met with success and formed an affiliate company, the Burgess Cellulose Co. to manufacture and market their product.

A number of other American manufacturers experimented in the making of dry mats; they encountered innumerable difficulties and after having sacrificed considerable sums of money abandoned dry mat manufacturing entirely.

The new mat made friends and made adversaries. As soon as American stereotype foundries learned of the newly invented dry mat there arose, as is usual with a new and novel product, a wide divergency of opinions concerning the qualities of this novel innovation. For instance, in 1893 "The American Bookmaker" reported as follows: "From time to time during the past two years we have heard of the new method of stereotyping invented in England, and in which the matrix does not need to be dried off the type by heating the form but is removed while the type is still cold. The processes were kept secret, but they were understood to be the use of papier-mache not as wet as formerly, a different facing from any previously used and a current of cold air over the back. We hear that the results are by no means marked. The forms take as long to be finished properly as electrotyping would require, the pages stand no more impressions than before and the plates are brittle. The requirements here are such that the greatest speed must be attained, and if there is a difference of one minute to each page by different processes this would be sufficient to throw out that which is slow."

Shortly after, it appears that samples of the new dry mats were received in the United States, tested in several foundries, and the following verdict arrived at in the same trade paper: "The cold process of stereotyping from which much was hoped as a means of taking matrices for daily papers, does not seem to have yielded the results expected. The pages took a long time to make, were soggy and moist when the metal was to be poured in, and the generated steam beneath the hot fluid was often sufficient to injure the plate. It is to be hoped that some method will be devised by which the plate can be made quickly without involving the necessity of heating the type, which suffers thereby and becomes permanently lengthened, sometimes to the thickness of a cardboard. Otherwise the papier-mache (mashed paper or wet mat) process seems the perfection of simplicity."

The new dry mat process of stereotyping met with an attitude of watchful waiting on the part of the newspapers in the United States. As stated before, samples of these different European-made dry mats were tested in American newspaper offices but without arousing any enthusiasm or desire on the part of the stereotypers to adopt same in place of the well proven wet mat method.

In December, 1897 "The Inland Printer" reported on a new dry mat invention which later proved to be Schimansky's mat. It was described as a dry, spongy sheet of paper pulp with a prepared surface on one side. This mat was molded under a mangle, perfectly dry, and then without being dried in any way placed in the casting box and supposed to be good for eight or ten casts. In 1899 Mr. Partridge, head of the stereotype department of the A. N. Kellogg Newspaper Company of Chicago, offered to send samples of this dry mat to stereotypers who were willing to try same, provided they made reports of their tests. In September, 1899, a number of stereotypers reported on their tests and the general opinion was that the mat was not satisfactory. In the first place, it could not be run dry as it broke, and could only give a very shallow cast. Some stereotypers tried pasting tissues on this mat when facing it, and in that way got fairly good results but ran into trouble with shrinkage, etc., and found that these so-called dry mats showed no advantage over wet mats in labor or in saving of time. In 1899 "The New York Tribune" experimented with these same mats, and while they were able to mold them they were not able to produce casts that they could use.

In the same year it was reported from London that a "Dry Stereotype Company" was formed which claimed to have regular customers in England, but none in London proper. They claimed to have a perfectly dry flong which was ready for the casting box immediately after being molded, without drying in any way. It was also claimed that these same mats had been used in Berlin for a year. Again a search showed that the mat in question was the Schimansky mat.

Hardly was the new dry mat suitable for use in U. S. A. stereotype foundries than American inventive genius turned to the improvement of the product. As was the case with the wet mat we also offer a record of some of such improvements.

Shortly after Eastwood had made his first invention, Friedrich Schneider and Arnold Schott of Philadelphia in 1888 invented certain new and useful improvements in stereotype matrices. The invention was made to provide a mat from which an impression could be made at any time in a dry state, no drying or hardening being required, that would be so durable and strong as to resist the pressure of the quantity of metal on the blank spaces. To attain their purpose the inventors made a semi-dry mat. The invention consisted of a matrix composed of a sheet of fabric (cotton-batting, flannel, lint) coated and partly impregnated with a semi-dry plastic mass and provided with a backing of pulp. This plastic mass was made of glue, syrup, glycerine and a powder (alum, flour, chalk, asbestos powder). This plastic was coated on a sheet of fabric and on this sheet another of very thin fibrous paper, for example Japanese vegetable-fibre paper, was placed. This mat was pressed upon the matter to be stereotyped and a sharp, clear impression of the type in the fibre paper and plastic was produced.

The matrix remains on the type and a sheet of wood pulp or any other pulp is placed upon the matrix, which sheet has been impregnated or saturated before being applied with a mixture of two parts of powdered dextrine, one part of starch and one part of asbestos powder mixed with cold water and boiled and stirred until it has the consistency of cream. By re-applying the pressure the pulp is caused to adhere firmly to the matrix and to stiffen the same, so that when the hot stereotype metal is applied it does not press down the matrix at the blank spaces. The matrix is removed and subjected for a few moments to a current of hot air for the purpose of hardening it. The improved matrix does not warp or shrink and the impressions are not injured or marred by hardening the matrix. The inventors claimed that "By means of our improved matrix, stereotypes can be made very rapidly, as the matrix need not be dried on the type and the type and matrix need not be heated as has been necessary heretofore when using composition or wet paper for stereotyping. There is no need of separately backing the spaces with plaster of Paris, or compositions, or cutting them out as has been necessary heretofore."

"By using our improved matrix the type is not injured by heat as it is by the old method of stereotyping. As we do not heat the type no time is lost by waiting for the cooling of the type in order to procure a second or more moldings. A saving in time is effected, from 6-10 minutes."

A dry mat method, which was supposed to do away with all auxiliary apparatus, was invented in 1898 by Jose W. Phoebus of Wheeling. Phoebus constructed a one sheet or one piece dry mat.

The face surface of the mat was coated with a sizing of diluted glue by means of a high pressure spray and when dry was not more than 1/3000th of an inch thick.

This dry mat was used in an absolutely dry state, no humidoring, no wetting, hence no steam table, no scorcher, no dryer, in short a total absence of heat or moisture at any stage of the making of the matrix. Furthermore, Phoebus' invention provided means of molding the mat whereby the pressure upon the type was delivered evenly throughout the entire form, the pressure being direct and gradual (similar to the action of direct pressure molding presses), thereby avoiding such injuries to the type as were caused by ordinary brush beating or by the roller processes. Phoebus describes one of the apparatuses he uses for the molding of his bone dry matrices as a form of a press in which the pressure on the mat is secured by means of a suitable fluid under pressure, such as air or water. Phoebus uses as support for the chase with the tightly locked type form a flat table. In connection with this table he employs a stationary slab which is hollowed out at its inner side to form the fluid chamber, which lies immediately over the type form within the chase. The edge of the fluid chamber, formed at the inner side of the slab, rests directly on the edges of the mat, which overlaps the chase. The mat forms a gasket or packing between the contracting faces of the table and the slab, thereby preventing leakage of the pressure fluid at the points of contact. The type form is placed on the table, the mat placed thereover and the hollow slab is clamped to the table. The fluid is then introduced under pressure thru a fluid supply pipe fitted to the slab, communicating with the hollow fluid chamber, and when compressed air is employed for mat molding it distributes itself throughout the fluid chamber, exerts an even pressure over the entire upper surface of the mat, causing the latter to be forced into the type faces, thereby producing the mold. When this impression has been secured a cut-off valve in the pipe is closed, the slab removed and the mat released for immediate use. The molding can also be effected by hydraulic pressure thru the pipe into the fluid chamber, but in this case a rubber sheet is placed over the mat to prevent it from becoming damp.

In 1900 Friedrich Schreiner of Plainfield, N. J., offered matrix paper for "cold type stereotyping." To quote from his prospectus: "Our Patent Cold Process Matrix Paper consists of a Plastic Face Sheet and a gummed Back Sheet. In making a Matrix the back of the Face sheet should be rendered moist with a wet sponge and

72. Modern Mat Roller

73. Modern Direct Pressure Molding Press

then as soon as the sheet feels soft it must be beaten in slightly with Brush, it may also be pressed in or rolled in. Then the gummed side of the Back Sheet is rendered wet with a thin paste and with the coated side laid upon the already beaten Face sheet, and united to the same by beating, or pressing, or rolling in. Then the Matrix is lifted from the type form and dried upon a hot plate." This mat paper was designated a "cold type matrix paper." It was used by a few stereotypers for baseball starters, but with the advent of the German dry mat Schreiner's matrix disappeared from the market.

A novel although commercially not applicable departure from the hitherto universally used method of making dry mats was invented in 1912 by Glenn S. Williamson of New York. In his specifications Williamson states that matrices have been heretofore molded from paper or other suitable fibrous material, previously impregnated with such condensation products of phenols and formaldehyde as may be rendered infusible by heat, the condensation product being transformed during or after the act of molding into hard and infusible condition.

Williamson finds that matrices of the above general character may be rendered more resistant to the effects of molten stereotype metal at high temperatures by using in conjunction with the above named phenolic condensation productions, certain structureless salts or compounds (silicates of alkali metals and the corresponding aluminates), which although soluble in water are refractory at the casting temperature of stereotype metal, say 550° F.

His procedure consisted in impregnating with the described liquid condensation product, then baking for an hour at about 70° C. The sheet is then dipped in a 50% solution of sodium silicate, thoroughly dried at normal temperature and then baked for 15 minutes at 70 degrees. The sheet is then faced with thin paper, as for example sizal paper, pasted on with sodium silicate solution, and is also backed with from one to three sheets of similar light, strong paper, also applied with sodium silicate solution. The compound sheet thus prepared is then dried and molded. Sample matrices prepared by the above methods withstood the action of type metal introduced under pressure and at temperatures of 550° F. and upward without necessitating extensive so-called "backing up" which has for its purpose the reinforcement of the blank or projecting areas of the matrix.

During all this period dry mat manufacturers experimented on the simplification of manufacturing their product. The resultant methods have remained secrets of the individual factories.

To make dry mats by hand instead of on a paper machine was tried and the procedure generally followed was to use a hand sieve, scoop up the pulp, shake same, thereby felting the pulp. The material was then mixed with an alkaline solution and thereupon the sieve holding the sheet was dipped into an acid. This freed a great amount of carbonic acid, which inflated the sheet which was dried in the open air or in lofts. This method was too slow and too costly to be commercially practiced.

An experiment was a method of stereotyping designated as "Graphotyping," a process of coating a plate with a mineral substance bound with glue, producing a film, and after this film was hardened it was coated with a fatty, resinous pigment, and the interstices deepened thru brushing same with water. For the printing of music, so-called "Pyrostereotyping" was practiced. The characters were burnt into wooden plates with a heated steel tool and then stereotyped in the usual way; or a machine similar to the modern sewing machine with a heated needle was used. Other innovations that appeared in the course of time were known as Lottinography, Monotyping, Cellulotyping, Cellography, Ikonography, Tachytyping, Gelationography, Photostereotyping, Gypsography, etc., etc.

"The Inland Printer" reported in January, 1894, on a new cold process of stereotyping which was offered under the name "Multotyping." The inventor, a stereotyper (the name is not given), instead of using ordinary matrix papers used asbestos paper, which he claimed could be molded in a dry state and placed in a casting box immediately after molding. However, all asbestos papers available had very rough surfaces so that plates cast from such mats were not very satisfactory. He therefore found it necessary to paste one or two tissues on the asbestos papers and to dry the prepared mat in a roaster. This stereotyper explained that it would no doubt be a very simple matter to find a manufacturer who made asbestos paper with a smooth face, and promised to report later on such sources of supply, but no further mention can be found of his process.

In 1911 in an article entitled "Development of the Dry Matrix" a claim was put forward to the effect that America had priority in the invention of the dry mat.

"Considerable discussion has occurred of late concerning the 'dry' matrix method of stereotyping, the alleged lack of inventive genius of Americans in perfecting mechanical improvements of this kind, and of our newspapers not making the proper use of such a revolutionary invention as the 'dry' matrix when it has been so far completed as to have proven entirely practicable in the strictest of tests.

"Among those taking part in the discussion have been eminent English and American authorities who have given credit for the development of the 'dry' matrix invention to Germany and England, leaving America only the satisfaction of knowing that Charles F. Hart, who they term 'the father of the dry matrix,' is an American, who before locating in London and assuming supervision of the mechanical plant of the Harmsworth newspaper was connected with the 'Brooklyn Eagle'.

"Such experts as Alfred G. Hawkins, supervisor of the stereotyping department of the 'London Mail'; Benjamin Wood of the Auto Plate Company, New York; and Mr. Hart himself have expressed opinions on the origin and development of the 'dry' matrix, and have marveled at the slowness of American newspapers to adapt it to their uses.

"While it is readily agreed to by all who have looked into the merits of the 'dry' matrix that as a time saving device it deserves all the praise that has been given it, there is ground for exception to the assertion that the credit for its origin and its subsequent development belongs to either Germany or England. Investigation into this side-view of the matter will show that newspapers in forty of the largest cities of this country are using a 'dry' matrix process that has been developed under the direction of Colonel Oliver S. Hershman, publisher of the 'Pittsburgh Press',—the invention of Alfred W. Birdsall, mechanical expert of Mr. Hershman's paper. Attention was first drawn to this process when it was being tried out on the 'Pittsburgh Press' in the issue of 'The Fourth Estate' of January 1, 1910, and in the intervening time it has been put to every possible test and is declared an unqualified success. The Hershman-Birdsall success is the culmination of more than thirty years' work to eliminate the trouble and loss of time in the drying of matrices. The process was again detailed at some length in 'The Fourth Estate' of April 29, 1911.

"Probably the most critical test to which the Hershman-Birdsall process has been put was during the recent world's championship baseball games in New York and Philadelphia, when every city in the country wanted the news and each move of the game at the earliest possible moment. The Dry Mat Service Company served over forty clients and has received congratulations from every section of the country.

"Papers which used the cold mat say they were enabled to beat their competitors on the street with baseball editions by from ten to fifteen minutes. One newspaper made a record of starting its presses in two minutes and fifteen seconds from the time the form was closed, the plates being cast in the Junior Autoplate.

"Colonel Hershman has used the dry mat continuously in the past three years on all editions of his newspaper, daily and Sunday. However, only the last, or 'starter' pages, are put through by the cold process, on account of the dry mat being more expensive than the wet mat.

"After perfecting the process the Dry Mat Service Company was organized to give other newspapers the advantage of Mr. Birdsall's discovery. The dry mat was discussed before the American Newspaper Publishers' Convention in 1910 and a number of publishers, who had tried it out, at that time attested its efficiency. More than a hundred newspapers at once started to use the dry matrix paper, but as was to be expected, perhaps sixty per cent failed because the stereotyper had ideas of his own and would not follow the instructions given by the inventors.

"However, scores of papers have handled the cold process successfully. Many publishers sent their stereotypers, or went themselves to the plant of the 'Press' in Pittsburgh and saw the dry mat being used successfully on all editions every day.

"In addition to the interest in this revolutionary process for plate making, inquiries were received by the 'Pittsburgh Press' from the 'London Mail', from Stockholm, Sweden, and other continental papers.

"T. R. Williams, managing editor of the 'Pittsburgh Press,' to 'The Fourth Estate' says: 'There is no question in my mind but that the credit for the cold process matrix belongs to Colonel Hershman. The process has been used continuously for three years to secure quick press starts on all editions. Our customers have been steadily increasing in number, indicating that the merits of the proposition have gradually overcome the prejudices of stereotypers.'"

The disappointments and successes met with during the period of the introduction of dry mat stereotyping in the United States is best shown in the letters and reports written by the individuals and concerns who were for and against the new product. The writer

74. Old Model Hydraulic Molding Press

75. Modern Direct Pressure Molding Press

has in his possession copies of a great number of communications of this nature; it would be of interest to the stereotypers of this country to learn of their contents. To embody all this material in this book would not be feasible, but in order to shed light upon the introduction period the writer compiles the contents of a few letters.

An engineer in England wrote to "The Fourth Estate" on February 15th, 1913, as follows:

"Your struggles with dry mats to us here in England are nothing short of ludicrous. We cannot for the life of us see how any one can run a newspaper without one. Stereotyping in our office is a lost art; new methods and modern machinery have wiped out all of the alleged secrets of stereotyping." The writer evidently is referring to the secret pastes developed by stereotype foremen and used in the making of the wet mat.

In 1914 the chief stereotyper of "The North Star," Darlington, England, Mr. R. S. Johnson, wrote to 'The Fourth Estate' about the use of the dry flong, or mat, and stated that it had many advantages. Mr. Johnson writes as follows:

"Dry flongs have become very popular during the last few years, and it is gratifying to note that some of the North of England newspapers were amongst the pioneers to introduce dry flongs in their foundries.

"It is, in fact, some four or five years back that the 'Northern Daily Mail' and 'Sunderland Echo' proved to the publishing world of the North that dry flongs could be used with success, and now that reliable flongs are procurable, the dry process has come to stay.

"The chief secret in the successful working of the dry flong lies in the employment of slow, but powerful pressure, and especially with picture work, in the use of clean elastic moulding blanketing. This flong does not allow of hand-beating, machine moulding being necessary, and as it is worked to gauge, it gives uniform results.

"Dry flongs yield much better results even than wet moulds, with half-tones. The dry flong, which is tough, yet flexible, will, given good pressure in the mangle, cut right into the fine grain of the half-tone and retain every detail with continued casting, and again if the process blocks are in good condition, there is no cause for underlaying or overlaying the mould.

"I may say here that many stereotypers are 'called to book' for bad printing of pictures, when it has not been their fault at all, the fault being entirely in the process department. For picture work with

[213]

the dry moulds, it is essential to have the blocks a thick lead above type height, on metal mounts.

"For moulding I have my mangle, which is of the latest type and electric driven, set to take the orthodox moulding blanket, with a machine rubber on top, and as it gives it a soft and heavy impression, I find it works admirably.

"After I mould my page I pack it and put it on the hot press for a minute or so, with weights on to take any moisture out that may be in the flong. If you do not take this minute or two in drying, you are liable to lose many minutes in the casting of your plates.

"After the mould is dry you put your tail end on. The reason why I dry it first is, because the mould generally being moist, it shrinks, and the stereo brown not being of a shrinkage nature, it draws the tail of the mould like furrows in a field, especially if you cast your plate broadways on, when you have trouble with a vengeance.

"It takes us two minutes to mould, pack and dry a press page ready for casting, the packing being nothing to what it is with the wet flong. In casting it is advisable not to use too hot metal.

"In my present paper, where the dry flong was introduced a few months ago when our new machinery was installed under the new regimen, it has given complete satisfaction to all concerned, and it would be quite impossible to catch our early trains to Newcastle, etc., without it, now that our circulation is so greatly increased.

"I would impress upon all stereotypers who use or are about to use this process always to keep their flongs in a zinc lined cupboard so as to keep them from becoming too dry. When the mould is too dry and hard it has a tendency to crease when going through the mangle and should your lino. metal be very soft, it destroys the face, and again when too damp it very often buckles when the metal is poured upon it.

"Of course, a great deal depends upon the attitude of the 'management' towards improvements of this kind, and in my case I am fortunate in having a manager who not only is in thorough sympathy with anything likely to facilitate business and reduce labor; but, having had experience of dry flongs in his previous office, knows their value."

An article appearing in 1918 touched on the difficulties encountered in American stereotype foundries in the use of dry mats. It states that "the dry mat is in successful use in a large number of plants, more having adopted it in the past year than in any year since its introduction into this country. The leading distributor is selling 80,000 a month as against about 25,000 at the same time in 1917. The larger papers have not, with one or two exceptions, taken to it because they have reduced the time element of the wet mat process to an irreducible minimum, and because the dry mat is not quite so dependable when presses must start at a given minute. The liability of breaking in the casting boxes and of giving down under a large number of castings is greater than for wet mats. They are not willing to take such chances. All large papers use the dry mat in a limited way for starter forms and special purposes."

"Some papers have introduced the dry-mat process successfully with the first day's usage. Most of them, however, have had a period of 'grief.' Few stereotypers are able to anticipate all of its problems, or to adapt their departments instantly to its peculiarities. The change is not automatic as a rule. The specifications, rules, advice, and injunctions of the dry mat makers do not entirely obviate difficulties. The new process is a more technical one than the old one. A dry mat stereotyper must be a more skilled and painstaking workman. The entire crew, from the moulder to the finisher, must learn to be more exacting and thoughtful in its work. Slam-bang, devil-may-care workmanship will not do. Deficiency in this particular, due to the fact that the wet-mat process has become so well learned that experienced men can perform any part of it with their eyes closed, and their minds on the bar around the corner, more than the inherent problems of the process itself, is responsible for most of the troubles publishers have experienced. There is prejudice against it in many places; workmen believing it will lessen the labor required are resentful of the greater care required of them, and many are constitutionally opposed to things new and unestablished."

In 1917 an article appeared in "The Editor & Publisher" concerning dry mats, and the outstanding points raised in the article were that the first successful dry mat was made in Germany and brought to this country by Henry A. Wise Wood in 1911. The first newspaper to use the dry mat process was the now deceased "Bergen News" of Hackensack, N. J. "The Bergen News" was the first newspaper to operate a stereotype plant without the use of steam tables, and it had no steam tables in its plant.

"A few months later the dry mat was adopted by 'The Paterson Call' in New Jersey for exclusive use. 'The Call' was the first newspaper to combine the advantages of the dry mat with those of the Autoplate, and today operates one of the most efficient stereotype

[215]

foundries in New Jersey. 'The Call' had been using dry mats exclusively since May, 1911, and had not used a wet mat or operated a steam table during that time. 'The Call' originally paid 25 cents each for a dry mat.

"The American-made Wood dry mat was perfected and placed on the market in January, 1916. At that time there were a handful of papers using dry mats, and the rapid growth of that process is evidenced by the fact that there are now upwards of 100 American and Canadian newspapers that use the process for all work and have abandoned steam tables."

The American Newspaper Publishers Association on August 11th, 1917, for example, had published diagrams showing how dry mats save print paper without necessitating mechanical changes to presses or reducing the width of margins. In this bulletin the Association states that the average office not only saves enough annually in the cost of print paper to pay for all stereotype mats used, but earns a substantial cash bonus in addition thereto.

Other features of the dry mat process are a distinct improvement in typography, particularly in the printing of halftones, a saving of all time consumed by steamtables, the cost of operating them, a saving in labor, etc.

Mr. Benjamin Wood, the general manager of the Wood Flong Corporation, made the following statement: "The dry mat has met with considerable opposition from some misguided stereotypers and from manufacturers of steam tables and other antiquated newspaper equipment, but it is now a well demonstrated success and can be adopted by any newspaper with complete satisfaction and at a very trivial cost for equipment."

"The wet mat is dried on the form and the impression it retains from the type is deep. The dry mat is removed from the form immediately after being pressed into it and dried in a scorcher. The mold inevitably springs back to a greater degree than if it were held against the form when drying. Some stereotypers think this is an insurmountable delinquency of the process.

"The key to the success of the dry mat is humidification. Uniformity of saturation is absolutely essential, but not easy to bring about despite the very definite formulas. Stereotypers who know the formulas have to learn by actual experience just how to do it perfectly. They have to learn to know by the look and feel and action what the correct saturation point it.

"The dry mat process is hard on type because the molding ma-

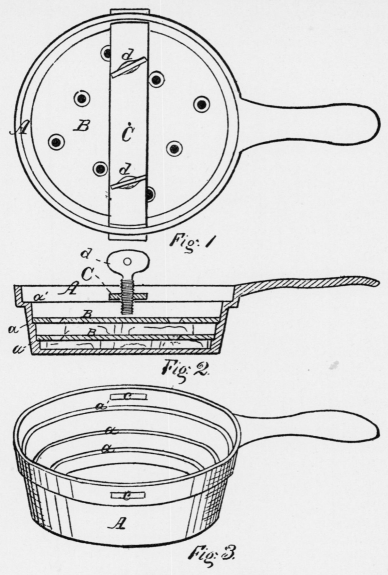

Fig: 1

Fig: 2.

Fig: 3.

76. Willbur Dryer (1867)

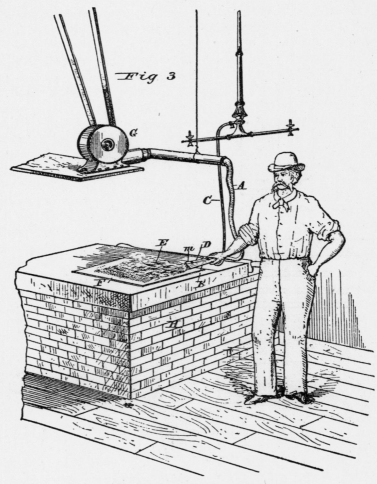

Fig 3

77. Johnson Dryer (1880)

chine pressure is very high. Italics with 'kerns,' delicate display type, and rules made from other than hard type metal suffer considerably. The amount of molding machine pressure necessary can be controlled considerably by proper humidification, as can most other like conditions.

"The superiority of the dry mat for flat work is pretty well established. It is now used for a large portion of the advertising and news mats being sent out."

The dry mat can, in the opinion of the writer of the article in the "Editor & Publisher", be successfully used in any plant where the proper machinery is in use, but where it is correctly adjusted to the process and where intelligent, painstaking and sympathetic workmanship can be secured in the composing and stereotype departments. In the absence of such conditions it will be only a partial success, if not a failure. If such a condition cannot be secured, however, the plant needs reorganization more than it needs the dry mat. It is very nearly a 50-50 proposition as between the dry and the wet mat, leaving the paper saving out of consideration. With that included the preponderance of advantage is considerably in favor of the newer process. On a straight comparative basis as a reproductive process, some of its advantages are discounted by disadvantage. But whatever the net result of such a comparison, the saving of $1.00 per ton of paper consumed, which is absolute, tips the scales in the but one obvious direction.

In 1899 Henry Kahrs of New York City, who had established a stereotype shop in 1875, published a pamphlet bearing the title, "Engraving Made Easy and Stereotyping Simplified, Being a Detailed Description of the White-on-Black and Granotype Engraving Processes and the Papier-Mache and Simplex Stereotype Methods." The first edition of this pamphlet was printed about 50 years ago, in 1890.

Kahrs' process consisted in writing or drawing on a sheet of bristol-board with a special ink made for the purpose, using an ordinary soft pen, and then casting a plate of type metal directly upon the writing or drawing. Unlike other methods there were no inter-operations between the work of the artists and the casting of the plates, the casting being done in a stereotype casting box; in fact, the operation of casting these plates was the same as in ordinary stereotyping, the only point in which it differed being in the preparation of the matrix.

His Granotype method consisted in using a red engraving ink,

[219]

and before the lines drawn with this ink were dry they were sifted over with a fine black powder of his own invention. If greater depth in the plate was desired a second application of the ink and the powder was made.

Other inventions made by Henry Kahrs were the Cold Simplex Stereotyping Process, the Hot Simplex Stereotyping Process, the Acme Dry Stereotyping Process, the Reverse Stereotyping Process, the Stereo Halftone Engraving Process, and finally the Kalkotype Method of Stereotyping.

The Kalkotype process is another way of making relief plates or line cuts by the use of a special form of papier-mache matrix board. The design to be printed is drawn in the mat with a lead pencil, then cut or engraved into the moist mat with chisel-like tools, one with a straight edge and one with a slanting edge, the latter making a sharp V-shaped cut. After the design has been cut into the mat the open spaces are filled out with space packing as done when stereotyping. Then the matrix is placed face up upon an iron plate, and a thick pad of cloth blanket laid upon the matrix with a heavy weight on top of all. The iron plate is heated to dry the mat and the gummed packing; the mat must be kept very hot up to the moment it is put into the casting box. The plate casting operation is the same as in ordinary stereotyping.

In closing this chapter, a letter on so-called "cold" mats is recorded. The following letter was written by Benjamin H. Anthony of the New Bedford (Mass.) "Standard Times" to the American Newspaper Publishers Association on March 20th, 1918:

"In reply to yours of the 19th, we never made a 'dry mat' but we were quite successful in the use of a cold type process, with a less wet mat than the ordinary one and one that did not require the use of any steam table. In fact, we did not own a steam table for a number of years but did put in one and now we have two because we believe that we get rather better results for halftone work than with the cold type mat.

"The history of our cold type mat is as follows: a man by the name of Schreiner, employed by the Potter Printing Press Co. of Plainfield, N. J., came on to install the process and was unsuccessful, but our stereotyper, named Riley, was fairly successful. He was never willing to divulge what he made the mat of but our pressman and his assistant finally evolved a formula that was so successful that they used to mix in their mats with the stereotyper's and the latter did not know the difference. The stereotyper is not now living, and I think his formula died with him.

"Our next stereotyper used the formula that our pressman gave him, and although I believe he modified it some I am not sure.

"The following is the recipe given me by our pressman:

Asbestos	.	.	.	.	2 lbs.	4 ounces
Flour	.	.	.	.	8	"
Dextrine	.	.	.	.	11	"
Gum Arabic	.	.	.		7	"
Starch	.	.	.	.	6	"

Stock for 50 Matrix

"The mat is to be made less wet than the ordinary mat and the shrinkage will be found to be quite uniform but nevertheless there is a shrinkage. I am under the impression that the mat is too dry and stiff to use successfully with a brush. It requires a matrix roller and is then stripped off and dried in a roaster (gas oven)."

The facts contained in this letter are verified by I. C. Wagner, mechanical superintendent of "The Norwalk Hour," Norwalk, Conn. He recalls that George Clark, father of the George Clark who owns the American Publishers Supply, who had charge of stereotyping at the Lynn (Mass.) "Item," and Joseph Riley of the New Bedford (Mass.) "Standard," and he himself, then working on the Cape Ann "Breeze" in Gloucester, Mass., were using dry mats on their regular editions back in 1894. Clark and Riley were using a dry mat they made themselves, whereas Wagner used a mat made by Schreiner of Plainfield, N. J. This mat was dried on a flat dryer with a heavy cover, and sand was used on the back of the mat to prevent the heavy cover from causing buckles and flattening out the impression in the mat. Wagner on the "Breeze" used the dry mats until 1898 when he left to work on the Manchester (N. H.) "News."

The writer is indebted to A. F. Brown of Chicago for the following interesting reminiscences on early dry mat stereotyping in our country:

"The success and general use of the Dry Mat and of the Junior Autoplate added greatly to stereotyping speed and, too, afforded a finer reproduction of halftones and the making of uniform plates and of a lighter weight. These enduring changes are in contrast to some earlier innovations brought in to meet the requirements of plate-making.

"The A. N. Kellogg Newspaper Co., leaders in ready print and job stereotype plate production and with branch houses in many Western cities, about 1888 introduced clay-process stereotyping at their Chicago 'Head House.'

"In the plant of the Iowa Printing Company in Des Moines, Iowa, the process was in successful operation on book work. The plant foreman came to Chicago, installed a clay department for the Kellogg Co., and later his younger brother joined him as assistant. The molding and casting, done in a separate room, was a sort of semi-secret process and the stereotypers promptly dubbed it the 'Mud Room,' the 'Mud Process,' and the operators came and went as 'Big' and 'Little Mud'—names that stemmed not so much from stature but rather from their forceful voices, overheard in frequent pow-wow. The plant of the Iowa Printing Company was one of the very earliest commercial stereotyping plants in the West. It was established in 1876 by Daniel Mills, as recorded by William C. Brinegar of Des Moines. The molding composition used, while suitable for book work, was less well adapted to large newspaper forms and later the department was closed.

"Thomas H. Jackson, employe of the American Press Association 'Head House' in New York City, reopened the 'Mud Room' and it continued in operation until the general use of fine screen halftones made the process obsolete. 'Mud' plates were out and the electro plate patterns returned to general use on the mat roller and the steam tables. The wear and tear on type fonts had made 'Mud Plates' a necessity and the metal used in casting was a specially hard alloy of stereotype metal which the operators smelted in their own metal pot."

" 'Zylotype' was another of the early processes. A zylotype department was also introduced in 1888 by the enterprising Kellogg Newspaper Co. to meet the needs of their mail order service. Thomas Hayes and William Breen came from New York City, installed the plant, and the process was in successful operation. It was an interesting and novel feature of the large Kellogg plant and received much attention. A thin sheet of dark, hard composition, Zylonite was placed upon a newspaper size form and, softened by heat, was by heavy hydraulic pressure forced into the type and a serviceable printing plate was produced. Mounted in column strips upon light, seasoned wood it met the requirements of the service. The process had large use on news-miscellany, on magazines and serial fiction matter. Later it was discontinued."

In retrospect: An article appeared in 1870, entitled "The Press of

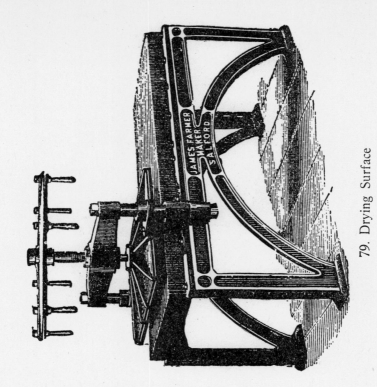

79. Drying Surface

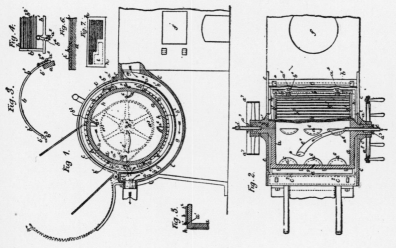

78. G. Pepe Apparatus for Drying Stereotype Matrices

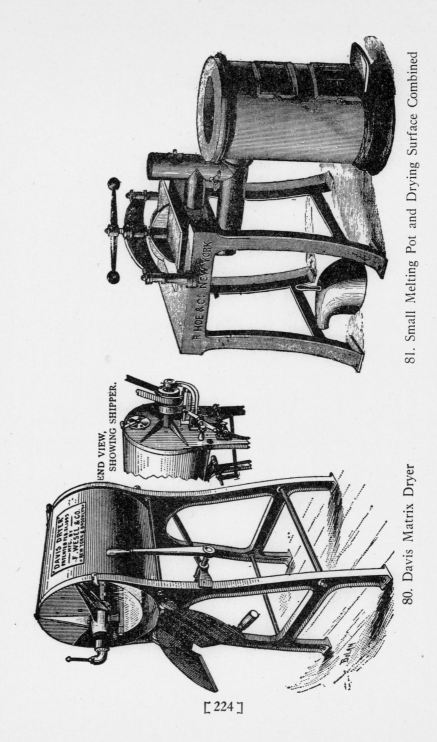

81. Small Melting Pot and Drying Surface Combined

80. Davis Matrix Dryer

END VIEW, SHOWING SHIPPER.

Today," in which the following statement was made: "The latest improvement in the processes of stereotyping enables the printer to reproduce the pages of a daily paper in duplicate with the labor of one hour." The number of pages is not mentioned in this article, but it may be accepted that 12 pages constituted the average size of the metropolitan newspaper of that period. Twelve stereotype plates in an hour! Today's production from a single Automatic machine is approximately 200 stereotype plates per hour!

While practically all of this chapter concerns newspaper stereotyping in North America, the increased use of stereotypes in magazine and book printing warrants some mention of this renewed phase of the art.

As stated previously, it was the stereotype that made possible wide dissemination of printed matter from almost the inception of printing. Yet, during the period from about 1860 to the early 1920's, stereotypes were seldom used in the United States for job, magazine and book work, having been largely supplanted by electrotypes.

In recent years, however, the combined efforts of the manufacturers of stereotype equipment, metal and dry mats, aided by those printers who realized the potentialities for stereotyping, enabled the trade to turn out stereotype plates of a quality capable of almost any kind of letterpress work.

Among the pioneers of stereotyping in magazine work is Mr. Arnold A. Schwartz of the Art Color Printing Company of Dunellen, N. J. He and many other printers and manufacturers persevered and experimented for years in order to develop stereotyping for printing of better than newspaper quality.

Today, practically all of the moderate priced magazines and books and even many of the so-called quality magazines and books are successfully stereotyped.

CHAPTER SEVEN

MACHINES

A HISTORY of stereotyping would not be complete unless it incorporated data concerning the origin and development of the many machines and accessory equipment used in the making of stereotype plates, beginning with the birth of the art on through the centuries to our day. In order to make this report reasonably clear, a repetition of some of the data already touched upon has proven unavoidable; however, for more minute details the preceding chapters may be consulted.

There have been four distinct phases in the art, namely the era of the macerated wet paper pulp, then the period of the plaster of Paris and clay processes. Following these the papier-mache or wet mat period, and finally the era of the dry mat. Each and every phase produced its special equipment and machines, and these will be described in the order referred to above. It must be remarked that a certain number of identical machines were and still are used in the operation of both wet mat and dry mat methods. To avoid confusion such machines will be dealt with where dry mat appliances are recorded.

(1) *The wet paper pulp process*, which is the oldest stereotyping method known (1690), was practiced with the aid of the following equipment: A chase and a galley used in the preparation of the form. For the molding, a brush such as was used later in the wet mat process. The drying operation necessitated an iron pan containing the form, and an iron crucible in which the pan was placed. Hot type metal was used to pour over the crucible and thus dry the mold. For casting, two wooden boards or two tin plates and a tin funnel for pouring the metal on the mold were used.

(2) *Equipment and machines used in the plaster of Paris and clay processes:* The preparation of the plates and ingredients used have been minutely described elsewhere in this book. The conditioning in the plaster method consisted of a special preparation of the composition, re-imposition of the pages, and locking up of the form.

[227]

The next step was the *molding operation*. The type material was locked in a form; then it was filled up with plaster by packing it in about the consistency of paste onto the surface of the type form, and rubbing it in well by hand. Before the plaster had set the whole was well brushed off with a stiff brush, which removed the plaster from the bowls of the letters. Then olive oil was applied to the mold.

The next step was the *casting operation*. A frame of brass or bell metal about ½" deep was placed over the form. Into this frame was poured the plaster of Paris which had been prepared in a special pot. The frame containing the molded plaster of Paris mat was then placed in the baking oven and roasted to a brown tinge. At the same time a dipping-pan and a floating-plate were placed in the same oven on a bottom shelf in order to have them acquire the same heat as the mold. The dipping-pan was placed into position, the floating-plate was placed inside the mold on the top and the lid fastened.

The metal was dipped out of the dipping-pan and then poured on the mold. Later the mass was cooled in a cooling trough for about 20 minutes. Then the pan was placed on a knock-out block and the plaster chiseled off the plate. Thus we find that the equipment used for the plaster of Paris operation were the following:

A metal pot
An oven
A dipping-pan
A floating-plate
A crane
A cooling trough
A molding frame
A block

(All of these items are shown in illustrations No. 62, 63, 64.)

The metal pot was square and deep, and large enough to permit the casting or dipping-pan to be immersed; it was placed near a wall in order to allow the fixing of a crane for lowering and raising the casting pans. The oven was installed adjacent to the metal pot and was furnished with several iron shelves to permit the taking of several molds at one time. This oven ordinarily had brick on three sides and on the top was a square opening bricked in, and the flue of the furnace was carried around the sides and back of the oven in order that the heat from the fire could be utilized. The whole of the front of the oven was used for the door so that the casts

82. Sta-Hi Vacuum Scorcher

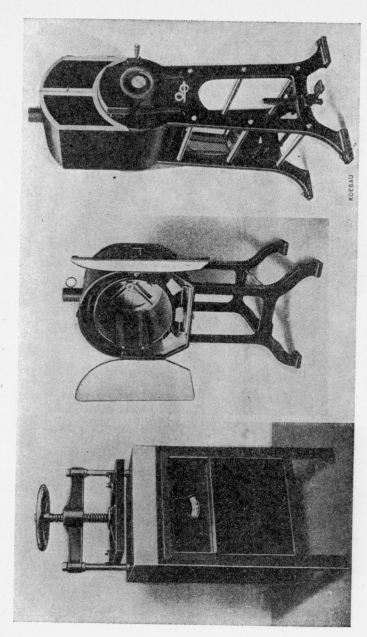

83. German Mat Dryers

could be placed in and removed easily. An iron shelf was placed in front of the oven on the same level as the bottom shelf to enable the stereotypers to slide the dipping-pans and floating-plates to the edge of the metal pot. The dipping-pans were wide at the top and tapering toward the base. On the sides were sockets to admit the clamps of the crane chain when it was swung. The floating-plate was of iron and fit loosely into the dipping-pan.

To the crane was connected, at the end of a chain, a ratchet with a wheel having extended spokes. Thereby the dipping-pan when connected by the clamps could be raised or lowered.

The cooling trough used for cooling the dipping-pan and its contents was placed at the side of the metal pot. It generally was about 4 feet long and 2 feet wide and stood slightly below the top of the metal pot. Four iron bars ¾" thick and 2" wide were fixed across near enough to each other to allow two dipping-pans to be placed on them at one time. Two or three pieces of thick flannel were wrapped around these bars in order that the moisture could be gradually communicated to the hot pan.

The molding frame in which the plaster matrix was first taken from the form was of the appearance of an ordinary chase, but the four sides facing the type were bevelled inwards so that when the plaster hardened, it had proper and equal separation on all sides.

The block upon which the casting pan was placed upon cooling was about 4 feet high and 3 feet wide, somewhat similar to a butcher's block. Upon this block the mold was knocked out of the pan, the corners of the cast struck off with a mallet, and the plate released.

(3) *Machines used in the papier-mache or wet mat method:* The wet mat is made of several thicknesses or layers of paper attached one to the other by means of a paste. Various wrapper and tissue papers are employed. For many years wet mats were made in the individual foundries by hand; later on machines were devised to achieve more uniform and speedier manufacture. One of these machines was devised by J. G. Rivett, mechanical superintendent of the Western Newspaper Union, who called his apparatus the Rivett Patent Flong Machine. This machine produces in a continuous automatic manner stereotype wet mats laminated in any number of sheets at one operation. It is capable of turning out from 300 to 400 completed wet mats per hour. This machine was made in various numbers of units to produce wet mats in any number or combina-

tions of laminations. However, the price, between $5,000 and $6,000, had so limited the sale of this machine that there are not more than five of them in use in the United States (See illustration).

W. C. Handley, New York and Cleveland stereotyper, also invented a wet mat-making machine, and sold many of his machines at about $1,500. With this equipment the roll must be re-run for each additional tissue. However, it produces a very fine wet mat, and the price being comparatively low more of these machines were in use at one time.

Zeb E. Aiken and Frank L. Rainer of Tulsa also invented a wet mat machine embodying a plurality of bed rollers.

There are still a number of stereotyping plants in the United States using large quantities of wet mats, and in some of these foundries wet mats are still made by hand with the aid of simple practical contrivances devised in the individual plants.

Conditioning: In the beginning, wet mats were placed separately between damp blankets with a board and weight on top. In this simple manner the finished wet mats were conditioned. Later on the practice of placing them in humidors was followed in order to conserve the moisture in the mats and thus facilitate the molding operation. If these mats were dry, the operator would not obtain proper depth in molding and the mat would be liable to crack when being dried in the heating apparatus before casting. The conditioning devices will be explained in the dry mat machinery section.

Molding: In 1829, Genoux who in that year perfected the wet mat stereotyping process, used a brush for molding; then tried to obtain his molds by making impressions with the aid of sort of a roller, proceeding as in taking off a simple proof. However, the molds he made with his roller were so shallow and so poor that he quickly reverted to the brush beating method.

From then on the molding of the wet mat was performed in all plants in the following manner: the wet mat was oiled to prevent the matrix from sticking to the type form. The mat was placed on the face of the type, the tissue downwards. It was then covered with a damp wrung cloth, and the molding was done by beating the mat with a hand brush. The operator began at one end of the form and advanced to the other in order to expel the air from the surface of the type. This beating operation was the most difficult process the stereotyper had to master. The handle of the brush had to be held in such a manner as to enable the bristles to fall positively flat on the back of the mat. One hundred and fifty mats per day was a record performance. At first papier-mache mats of one column were beaten; later the mat was taken from the complete page in one operation.

The brush beating method of molding mats by hand was temporarily displaced by brush beating machines. Mr. Derriez of Paris invented such a machine in 1899, and others appeared on the scene. However, the most practical machine of this kind was the one developed by C. S. Partridge of Chicago, upon which he received a patent in 1889.

A short resume of the text of this patent states that the inventor advocates replacing not only the brush beating by hand but also the roller or mangle. The patent reads in part as follows:

"In making papier-mache matrices for use in the production of stereotype-plates it is customary to beat the soft matrix material, after it has been laid upon the form of type which is to be reproduced, with a bristle brush until the material has been forced into the hollows, recesses and interstices of the type and into the blanks or open portions of the form and an accurate impression of the type-form has been produced in the matrix. The beating is continued until the material has penetrated the interstices, &c., to the depth requisite to avoid shallowness of the sunken or non-printing portions of the type, it being desirable that such portions shall be so much below the printing portions in the stereotype as to avoid "smutting" in printing therefrom. This beating operation requires considerable time, and is laborious work for the operator. Another method is to pass a pressure-roller over the matrix while it is on the type, a thick felt blanket or other cushion being interposed between the matrix and roller, so that the pressure of the roller will force the soft material of the matrix into the hollows and spaces of the type-form without uncovering the faces of the type. This method is quicker than the other and less laborious, but it is subject to serious objections. It is impossible by it to make a sufficiently deep mold without increasing the pressure to such a point as will injure the type, and to avoid this it is quite common to finish the mold by beating it with the hand-brush after it has been rolled. Where this is not done a shallow mold is produced, the stereotype-plates from which cannot be worked on printing-presses using very soft impression-blankets without smutting.

"In this invention I have sought to produce a machine which will perform the operation of beating the papier-mache evenly and with results approximately those obtained by hand, and which will avoid at the same time the evils found in the pressure-roller method of taking impressions from the type."

With the advent of workable molding machines of the roller construction, brush beating fell into disuse. Molding by machine is carried out in identically the same manner where wet mats as well as dry mats are used. Hence these machines will be explained later on when dealing with dry mat stereotyping equipment.

After molding, the wet mat is dried in order to drive out the moisture used in making and conditioning the mat.

Drying: In 1829 when the new version of the wet mat press was brought out by Genoux, and this mat began to supersede the plaster of Paris and clay methods of stereotyping, the drying operation was a simple one. The mat was placed on a hot iron plate and the moisture driven out. In due time less crude methods were thought out by individual stereotypers in the course of their daily work. An example is the so-called drying plate. This was constructed of iron and resembled a long, thick iron slab, and was placed upon the smelting furnace. It was hollow to permit the smoke to pass from the flue of the smelting furnace to the chimney. At one place was fixed a press for drying the molds. The platen was adjusted by a strong upright screw having a wheel at the top. As time passed, the need for a better drying method became pressing. Stereotypers objected to the use of dry heat for the baking of the mat as it sometimes destroyed the type by rounding the bottom. In 1856 a machine for drying the mats was invented by James Dellagana of London and installed in the plant of the London "Times." (It should be recalled that the firm of Dellagana Brothers were the most successful stereotypers of their day, and the proprietors of the mighty London "Times" handed to this firm the production of all the stereotype plates used at the "Times.")

The procedure followed in drying wet mats on the table was to place a double thickness of blanket on the mat and screw the press firmly down. M. Rusaud of Lyons, France, in 1836 was the first to use woolen blankets on the mats in the drying operation. The steam was turned on and after 10 to 15 minutes the press was unscrewed, the blanket removed and the mat left to dry for about 10 minutes. Then the mold was carefully separated from the form.

Robert Hoe of New York visited the "Times" plant in London and examined these steamtables. Upon his return to the United States he promptly started manufacturing steamtables, and put the

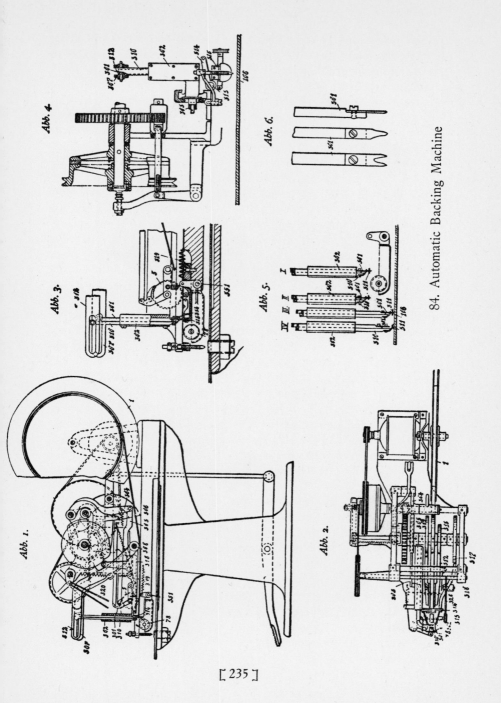

Abb. 1.

Abb. 2.

Abb. 3.

Abb. 4.

Abb. 5.

Abb. 6.

84. Automatic Backing Machine

86. Fremont Frey Humidor

85. Stereotype Melting Furnace. Papier-mache Process

first one made in this hemisphere on the market in 1867. The first steamtable, however, was imported from England and installed in the plant of the "New York Tribune" in 1861. In this plant Charles Craske and L. Collins were experimenting with the papier-mache mats. The story has it that the steamtable was installed in a room directly above Horace Greeley's office, and that due to a leak, hot water dripped down and scalded the famous editor's bald head. Mr. Greeley was so incensed that steamtable operations had to be suspended for several months.

Mazall and Hartnet of Boston in 1874 invented a combined steamtable and steam jacketed drying oven to cut down drying time from 13 minutes to less. Pearce and Hughes of London in 1880 invented a new method of drying a wet mat by removing the matrix from the face of the form while it was in a moist condition, and then confining the mat between a layer of heated plate and blankets with a perforated flat plate on top.

A novel method of drying wet mats was thought out by an American, W. J. Johnson, in 1880. His patent shows that his improvement relates principally "to drying the matrices employed in stereotyping the 'form' in newspaper offices. These matrices were composed of paper pulp and other similar materials, and after an impression of the type or form is taken, they are usually dried in the ovens or by steam-plates preparatory to casting the stereotype for use on the press."

"In drying matrices of this kind in the usual manner it has been found that the depressed portions or parts between the types known as 'blanks' do not dry as rapidly as the raised portions or parts corresponding with the types, thus causing delay in preparing or casting the plates at a period in the process when time is of the utmost importance."

To overcome this difficulty was the object of the above mentioned invention, which consisted in applying a jet of flame or current of very hot air directly to such parts of the matrix as require to be more thoroughly dried after coming from the ovens or hot plates.

In 1870, A. Chase patented an invention relating to the drying of stereotype matrices in a vacuum, and to the combination of a vacuum chamber and accompanying chambers above and below it, so arranged as to provide a vacuum, heat and condensation of vapor, for the purpose of drying the said matrices at a minimum expenditure of time, temperature and power as nearly as may be. It was especially adapted to the rapid and economical drying of papier mache stereotype matrices at a temperature which would not injure the type.

In 1872 the same Alonzo Chase patented a method in which the matrix was removed from the form while still in a moist condition and laid, back downward upon an iron bed, its face being then covered with a layer of sand which filled up all the intaglio parts of the matrix, and served the same purpose as the type in preventing the face of the matrix from becoming distorted during the drying operation which followed. The use of sand in this manner proved to be objectionable because it always adhered, to a greater or lesser extent, to the face of the matrix so that its removal therefrom after the mat was dried, required some time and labor and the element of time was then and is today of the greatest importance in the operation of stereotyping.

When steamtables were first put into use, gas was used for heating. Later on the pneumatic steamtable was developed and certain makes used electricity for heating.

In 1890 M. J. Hughes invented a combined furnace and hot water casting box. In his preamble he states that heretofore the most popular method of drying the molds on the face of the type or form was by the use of live steam, with its ever-leaking and expensive attachments used in connection with the chest of the drying table or casting box; and when steam was not accessible gas, gasoline or coal oil was generally substituted, and many seriously objected to the latter because the heat derived was what is termed "dry," and if not supplied with care would result in serious injury to the type by overheating in the drying process. Even steam with too great a head or heat would prove injurious. In every instance the two most important and expensive parts of a stereotype outfit—viz., the casting box and the furnace—were separated and used apart for their respective purposes. However, this last improvement—the combination of the metal furnace and the casting box through the use of hot water—was undoubtedly a most excellent one, resulting in economy, simplicity and practicability to an extent never before obtained.

The object of his invention was to dispense with these separate appliances by utilizing the casting box, which has a hollow bed or platen, for the reception of the water to be heated by the same furnace which melts the metal for general stereotyping purposes.

T. Bradwell and S. K. White in 1883 invented a machine in

which they combined the casting, sawing, shaving and drying operations all in one.

There exist a great number of different kinds of drying machines; the illustrations Nos. 76 to 83 show different types.

When the wet matrix has been completely dried, the casting and finishing operations take place. Since all of these operations are identical whether wet or dry mats are used in a plant, these machines will be explained in the section dealing with dry mat machinery.

To sum up: It has been shown in the preceding text that the equipment employed in the wet mat stereotyping method are:

A paste pot
A sieve to strain the paste
A beating or molding brush, or a roller
A smelting pot or furnace
A steamtable for drying the molded matrix
A casting machine
A plate trimming saw
A planing machine
A routing machine
A beveling machine

(4) *Dry mat machinery:* Dry mats are made of cellulose pulp often mixed with highly refined alpha pulps and treated with certain chemicals and earths to insure resistance against intense heat and against many other influences encountered in their use in the stereotype foundry. They are integral, homogeneous units, not laminated nor pasted together as is the case with wet mats.

Moistening: Just as is the case with wet mats, dry mats must be moistened with water and kept moistened to make them soft and more plastic in order that they take the type impression more readily and accurately and with greater depth.

At the time the dry mats made their first appearance they were conditioned or moistened, in the same way as the stereotypers humidified their wet mats, that is they were placed between wet blankets and boards and weighted down.

Following the universal practice of old time wet mat operators to invent and perfect individual, closely guarded paste formulas, each stereotyper thought out a special contrivance of his own to moisten, i. e., condition the mats delivered to his plant in a dry state. In most cases these dry mats were placed in boxes or closets containing pans filled with water; the moistening was affected through absorption of the evaporated water by the mats.

The first and basic patent taken out on a humidor was granted to J. Fremont Frey of Indianapolis in 1913. This conditioner was, for many years, the most used of all conditioning apparatus, as it insured complete and uniform distribution of moisture. In this humidor the mats are held in a vertical position by a wire comb and tray which are removable from the box. The inner walls of the box hold eight clay pads, each one removable. These eight clay pads are the reservoirs which supply the moisture to the mats. After soaking the clay pads for 20 minutes in cold water and replacing the racks in the box, the Frey humidor is ready for operation. It is imperative that no running water is allowed to strike the pads as the clay is soft and disintegrates easily. It takes 24 hours to condition mats that are soft; when mats are hard, owing to atmospheric conditions, they remain several days in the humidor, or until they are pliable. This humidor is made airtight through a tapered flange on the lid of the box, and it is necessary to moisten the pads but once a week.

The John Breuer humidor is constructed of either galvanized iron or copper. From a receptacle on top of the humidor, water is fed to numerous slits or blanks which line the walls, by means of wicking enclosed in lead tubes.

When the metropolitan newspapers adopted the dry mat in their plants there started a series of scientific moistening methods. Isolated rooms were constructed wherein hot water in the form of steam was circulated. These humidors were built by engineers who had solved similar moistening problems for the silk cloth and other industries. The fact that the plans for the construction of an entire room, called the conditioning room, were drawn on the order of the New York "Times" shows to what lengths installation of special humidors was carried. Why this particular plan was abandoned at the last minute is explained by the next paragraph.

About 1932, demands for delivery by the mat manufacturers of a perfectly finished mat began to become more and more insistent and by 1934 dry mats were no longer (except in very rare cases) conditioned in individual plants; this operation was performed directly at the mat factories.

The stereotyper who knows what moisture content is necessary in mats used under his particular climatic and plant conditions simply indicates the percentage of moisture he desires for his work, and

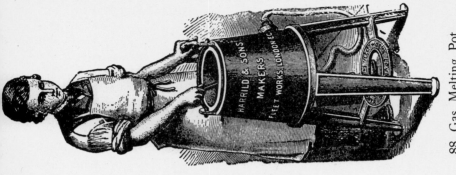

88. Gas Melting Pot

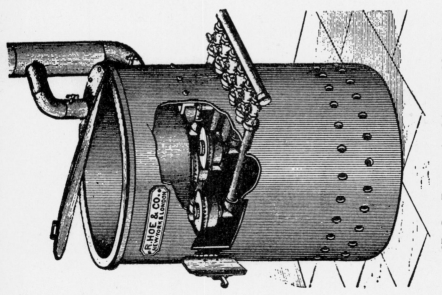

87. Gas Furnace for Linotype Metal

90. Asbern Melting Pot

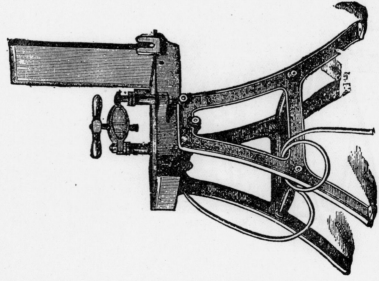

89. Casting Box for Gas Foundries

mats are moistened as per his specifications. This certainly is a far cry from the hit and miss method of moistening mats by simply placing them between wet rags or in tin boxes.

Roller Molding: The roller, or molding machine, displaced beating by the brush, and since such rollers were practically in universal use when dry mats appeared on the scene they were used from the very start of dry mat operations.

The first roller was used by Claude Genoux, who improved the wet mat in 1829. His roller was a clumsy, hand-propelled contrivance equipped with wooden rollers, a kind of adaptation of the old-time proof press. This roller did not work at all satisfactorily and shortly afterwards Genoux abandoned it and reverted to the brush beating method.

The next roller, of better construction, hand driven, equipped with soft wooden or iron rollers, was constructed by Rusaud in 1836; it, too, was soon abandoned in favor of the brush method.

The first practical roller, or molding machine (later known under the designation "calender"), was invented by James Dellagana in 1861. His English patent carried the number 1045, dated the 26th of April, 1861, and the roller was designated therein as an "apparatus for embossing and taking casts from matrices for stereotype or other purposes." It consisted of two heavy cast iron cylinders about 12 inches in diameter, mounted in a suitable frame, one above the other. The ends of the upper roll were provided with gear wheels which engaged the racks of a bed traveling between the rolls. The shaft of the upper roll extended beyond the frame of the machine and terminated in a worm wheel which was driven by a worm supported by brackets attached to the side of the frame. By means of tight and loose pulleys on the worm shaft, and suitable mechanism for shifting the belts, the roll could be made to revolve in either direction, thus moving the bed forward or back at the will of the operator. The purpose of the machine was to utilize steam power to perform the laborious work of molding. In operation the form was slid onto the bed of the machine and there made ready for molding in the usual manner. The flong was laid on and covered with a thick felt blanket, and the form passed through the rolls and back again. The depressions in the matrix were then packed and the form dried in the usual manner. The first Dellagana roller was used in the plant of the "London Times."

The first molding machine of this make used in the U. S. A. was by the "New York Herald," being purchased in London and a force of men accustomed to its use was engaged and brought to New York to run the roller. In 1906 this machine was still in use in the Herald stereotype foundry. Most of the men who came with it from England remained in America, becoming members of the New York Stereotypers Union No. 1.

The first machines, all made for wet mat molding, were not entirely successful. The difficulty with the Dellagana machine molds, seemed always to have been either lack of depth, particularly in the bowls of the type, or lack of sharpness of impression. It was found that the mat as ordinarily made for the brush process was not suitable for the machine because there was so much water in the paste and paper that it was forced through the flong by pressure of the roller, making the surface of the matrix rough and uneven; and, to add to the vexation, the paste soaked into the paper making the wet mat hard and difficult to impress. To overcome these difficulties various compositions were tried, one of which had for one of its ingredients an acid which acted on the paper as a solvent, reducing it to a semi-pulpous condition. In this state the mat was easily impressed but the depth so gained was largely at the expense of sharpness of impression. In other words, the paper was reduced by the solvent to a mushy condition. A better method of obtaining the necessary depth, and one which would not destroy or change the nature of the paper, was found in the use of a paste which, instead of soaking into the paper, would form a coating on its surface, thereby giving to the mat a somewhat wax-like quality which insured a sufficient depth of impression without subjecting the type to injurious pressure from the roller. There were various recipes for a paste which would fill the requirements noted, but the essential feature of all was the employment of as large as possible a proportion of a mineral or chalk ingredient.

The drawbacks inherent in the Dellagana roller did not deter others from making experiments on this new departure, and in due time others were constructed which definitely did away with the drudgery of the brush beating method of molding. A number of molders built on the same principle as the Dellagana roller were brought on the market in Europe and later on American manufacturers took over at the point where the European inventors and manufacturers left off. The result was a large number of practical molding machines.

With the invention of the cold dry mat process, however, difficulty was experienced with machines of the old design as the speed at which they were usually operated was too great to give proper results when this method of molding dry mats was employed. Also, owing to the different texture of the dry mat from that of the wet mat and the fact that the gears and upper lock were thrown slightly out of pitch when in operation—thus causing the machine to develop lost motion—there was a tendency to break off letters where parts of the plates overhung the type body.

The German dry mat makers, being the first to produce dry mats in quantity, were well aware that these detriments would hinder the rapid introduction of the use of dry mats, and brought the problems to the attention of their machine manufacturers. Rollers perfectly adapted to the molding of dry mats were the answer. The first heavy duty roller was built in Leipzig, Germany.

As soon as it became apparent that the dry mat was about to duplicate its European success in America, American manufacturers stopped importing European rollers and began the manufacture of these machines in the United States. The first rollers were built by the F. Wesel Company, the Potter Printing Company (Rapid Matrix Roller), the Wood Newspaper Machinery Corporation, and R. Hoe & Company.

The first roller was a hand matrix molding machine. The claim for this new invention, made by Mr. F. Wesel, was that it embodied one exclusive feature, namely that heretofore the bed of a matrix roller had been supported by stationary weights, and the roller track by the bed. This created abnormal friction and distorted the mold in the mat. The bed of the Wesel roller was supported by rollers the same as on power driven machines. The gearing insured uniform travel of both bed and roller; therefore friction was eliminated and the pressure applied uniformly and vertically, doing away with the cause of all distortions.

The final development in this kind of machine was the so-called heavy duty roller. These newest types of rollers are equipped with a variable speed motor which is instantly adjustable for rolling-in either wet or dry mats. The usual time of travel in one direction of the roller for wet mats is five seconds; for dry mats it is from 15 to 40 seconds. Today there are on the market a great many makes of rollers, both in America and in Europe; in England: Knowles, others are imported from Germany and United States; in Germany: Vomay, Voeban, Frankenthal, M-A-N; in America: Duplex, Goss, Hoe, Ostrander, Scott and Wood.

Direct Pressure Molding: in 1908 a description of a machine for impressing and drying stereotype matrices appeared in a trade periodical. It differs from the machines ordinarily employed, in that neither brush nor roller are used to produce the impression. The peculiarity of the invention is that the mold is made by direct pressure which is not exerted all over the form at the same time, but is brought to bear, first at the center of the form and then on the other portions, working from the center out to the edges, thus gradually expelling the air under the mat. The platen of the machine is made of sections, the central platen being pressed first, then the sections immediately adjacent to the middle sections are depressed and the pressure gradually extended until a perfectly clear impression of the entire body of the type has been obtained. After the several platen sections have all been brought into operation, the pressure therein is maintained by stopping the rotary movement of the cylinder of the platen until the impression has set, or until the mat is dried. The drying is accomplished by steam heat—the bed of the machine being cast hollow and heated in the same manner as an ordinary steam table. As the form is not moved until the matrix is dry, all danger of doubling the mat is eliminated.

This was the first reference ever made to a direct pressure molding press and such presses represent the latest innovation in stereotype molding operations.

One of the main arguments offered in favor of these presses is that they do away with the great drawback of rapid wear of costly type supposedly occasioned by matrix rollers. Furthermore, the makers of these presses guarantee die cast molds.

At first vertical pressure was adopted by building toggle presses in order to obtain the enormous pressure necessary for molding halftone blocks. After such machines had been in use for some time stereotypers complained that toggle presses did not prevent wear of type nor defective molding, because the gap between the two platens was always the same and because the thickness of the packing always varied and could not possibly be accommodated in each instance as exactly as required.

It was felt that only by introducing hydraulic pressure would it be possible to obtain uniform and exactly adjustable pressure independent of the thickness of packing. The result of this reasoning was the creation of the hydraulic matrix molding press.

The first toggle press in the United States for stereotyping purposes was built by Ferdinand Wesel of New York.

The first hydraulic press was built by Rockstroh and Schneider

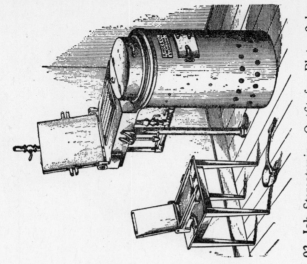

92. Job Stereotyping Outfit for Plates 9 by 12 inches and Smaller

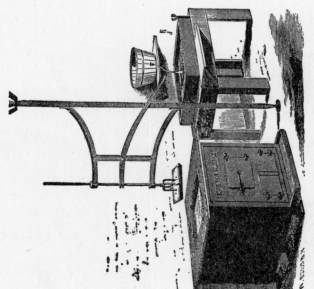

91. Melting Furnace, Crane, Casting Pan and Cooling Trough Used in Plaster Process

94. Curved Casting Box in Position for Placing Mould

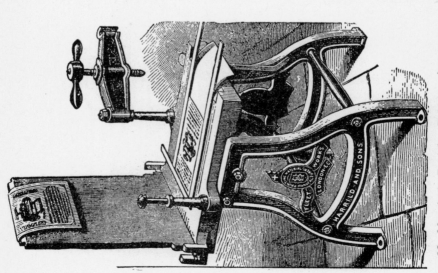

93. Matrix in Position Prior to Casting

of Leipzig in 1911. It had, as have all subsequent presses, a flat platen equal to the full size of the sheet, which descends over the whole surface at once.

A much improved hydraulic press was built by Koenig & Bauer in 1914 for 500 tons pressure, and was installed in a stereotyping plant in Copenhagen, Denmark. In the beginning the press head and frame were made of cast iron of a special alloy. Today all parts which are under stress are made of first class electro steel. Leather packing has been displaced by metal packing. The pillars between press cylinder and press head are today replaced by strong tie frames of full width, interlocked with each other. These presses may be used for hot or cold molding, and electrical heating is furnished.

The best known presses on the market:

In England: practically all presses used are imported from Germany and the United States; in Germany: Koebau, Vomag, Hydrotyp, Frankenthal, Winkler, M-A-N; in America: Directomat, Hoe, Ostrander-Seymour, Stereotex.

A few remarks about the use of these presses in the stereotyping industry are in order. The direct pressure molding press has, in Europe, displaced the heavy duty roller almost entirely. Rollers are used in small plants only. For instance, in Germany directly after the World War 118 direct pressure molding presses and 197 rollers were in use. Today about 80% of the molding machines used are hydraulic presses.

About 1926 the first European made direct pressure molding presses of modern construction were introduced into the United States. At once a number of American manufacturers seized upon the idea and started making American presses. However, the introduction of this molding system has been very slow in the United States, but in those plants where the presses have been in practical use for some time the statement is made that work finished on the roller cannot begin to compare with molding done by these direct pressure presses.

The late Major David Broderick was one of the country's foremost experts in the direct pressure molding of stereotype mats. For many years he had revolving in his mind a rather unique method for molding stereotype mats which would employ the use of air pressure. The stereotype chase in which the form is composed would have to be built with a suitable locking device so that when the mat is set in position on the form, it would create an airtight seal. Air pressure would then be applied of sufficient strength to make the necessary impression in the mat. This would eliminate the necessity for the cork blankets and other packing now used under the regulation roller and also under direct pressure molding.

Blanketing: In molding wet mats the standard practice in early days was to use a heavy woven felt blanket. When the impression was made, the felt molding blanket was removed and cotton drying blankets substituted under the steamtable. In some plants they used a cork blanket, which was coated with a pyroxilin substance, next to the mat and the felt on top of this.

When dry mats began to come into vogue, stereotypers still used a felt next to the mat. Usually it was a thinner felt than had been used on wet mats, and a cork blanket on top of this. It soon became evident that felt next to the dry mat gave too soft a cushioning and the felts were gradually eliminated.

The stereotypers began using cork next to the mat with a fibre or steel board on top and that is the general practice today.

With one particular make of mat it has been found necessary to use a rubber creeper next to the mat and the cork and board on top of this. In some plants they place a sheet of newsprint approximately .003″ thick or a sheet of mailing wrapper approximately .004″ thick next to the mat and the cork and board on top of this.

Direct Pressure Molding:

Cold molding: In the hydraulic presses for cold molding the standard practice is to have a rubber blanket or a combination rubber and fabric blanket attached to the head of the press.

Hot molding: For hot molding, where the mat is to be dried on the form in the press in which it has been molded, the usual practice is to use three or four Molleton blankets on coarse screen work for both molding and drying, and for fine screen work to use a layer of felt papers.

Hot molding for transfer: For transfer work, that is, where the mat is to be molded under direct pressure and dried under a steamtable, there is no standard practice. Each shop seems to have worked out a combination that gives them best results. For this kind of work Molletons are used, as well as cork blankets in conjunction with rubber blankets or in conjunction with felts. Usually the molding blankets are removed and the regulation drying blankets are substituted when the mat is transferred to a steam table.

The backing operation: After molding, the mat is backed, an operation indispensable with wet and dry mats alike. Gummed felt strips are placed on the back of the mat in particularly open spaces in order that the mat can withstand the weight and force of the metal in casting the plates, as otherwise the mat would give way in these open spaces and cause smudges in the printed pages. At first backing came in large sheets of felt, which were cut into strips as needed and a specially prepared wet paste was spread by hand on the back of each strip. Later on the felt was delivered already covered with paste, and then it became the practice to sell gummed strips cut to such lengths and sizes as desired. This backing operation is a tedious and sticky one; however, it is of great importance for the delivery of perfect printing plates and thus must be skillfully performed.

A number of devices to perform this backing operation by machine have been constructed. All of them involve the use of more or less complicated mechanisms, are expensive, and have so far not been able to compete with the accuracy of hand done backing.

A device protected by a great number of different patents is one invented in 1916 by Adolph Reisser of Vienna. We show only one of these machines in this compilation in order to give the reader an idea of the construction of such a backing machine.

In the preamble of his patent, Reisser states that the backing operation is bothersome, takes up a lot of time, which is of prime importance in the manufacture of plates.

The method of operation of one of his machines to perform mechanized backing is carried through in this manner: Pieces of felt board of one or more sizes and thicknesses are mechanically cut off or are taken from a magazine containing this felt board. They are attached to the back of the mat according to the size and shape of the space to be backed. In case of larger areas, thicker strips are used. The machine operates as follows: Several strips of such different widths and thicknesses as may be desired are brought into position so that with every stroke of the machine a piece of predetermined length is cut off and shoved forward to a gripper mechanism which carries the strip over a paste cylinder which is situated under a stamping device, which in turn presses the strip upon a space in the mat. This space may be suitably indicated by some kind of mark.

Another one of his machines works as follows: the strips to be pasted onto the mat are pre-cut to size and are deposited in magazines. Then with each stroke of the machine one or several sheets of backing are picked up, supplied with paste, and then pressed down onto the proper space in the mat.

Many attempts have been made to manufacture dry mats so constructed as to eliminate any need for backing. Such mats have been put on the market. However, inherent drawbacks such as losing control over the shrinkage and excessive hardness, deleterious to the type matter, and loss of necessary depth in molding, have prevented these pre-backed mats from being used in stereotype foundries. It would be useless to go so far as to explain how these mats are made. All of them are based on the addition of lithopon resins, astringent chemicals, filling earths and special adhesives. The old method of backing by hand still remains the one most employed and most efficient.

Scorching: Since molded dry mats are still moist they must be thoroughly dried preparatory to casting, as otherwise the heat of the metal in casting the plates, generally from 600° F. to 650° F., would create steam which would repel the metal from the mats and cause imperfect printing plates. The drying of the mats is done in roasters or scorchers. These machines at the same time help shape the mats to conform to the curvature of the cylinders of the printing presses.

The first dryers of dry mats to be invented were: The old Wesel flat dryers, the Pepe rotary dryer, the Davis matrix dryer of 1895; then followed the Wood semi-circular, the Cemer, the Clark, the Hoe, the Duplex tubular, the Centrifugal, and the latest type, the all automatic Sta-Hi vacuum dry mat former. The Sta-Hi takes the dry mat in its plastic state, vacuum shrinks it to minimum width, vacuum forms not only the solids of the types to uniform casting levels, but also vacuum forms perfect bolsters, and delivers the dry mat electrically baked at casting temperature in a minimum of time. A far cry from the primitive method of drying mats on iron plates placed over the metal pot. (See illustration No. 82.)

In 1885 a dryer was invented by G. P. Pepe of the "London Telegraph", where he was stereotype foreman. This stereotyper took out the first patent on a rotary scorcher. He dried a number of wet mats at one time through a combination of hot air and steam in a rotating device. It took just as long to dry the mats by this method as it did drying them on the steamtable. The improvement made by Pepe is to be found in the fact that the type was not subjected to such heat and did not expand as when using steamtables. Due to this novel process, a column of a newspaper shrank five lines in length and correspondingly in width. The form was set up longer to compensate for this. Pepe showed his paper extra profit

95. Pouring (Showing Arrangement of Gas Jets)

96. Adjusting the Casting Box Prior to Casting

in its five page ad section. The compositors had the advantage that their forms did not stick together.

Pepe employed a hollow drum, upon the exterior surface of which he arranged a number of hinged clamping frames to hold the matrices in contact with the drum. The drum is made with projections or ribs to act in combination with hollows in the clamping frames or vice versa. The drum is mounted in a casing with capability of revolving upon a hollow axle, through which steam is introduced into the interior of the drum.

At some convenient part or parts of the apparatus a fire is arranged and the products of combustion conducted therefrom through a flue carried partially or entirely around the exterior of the drum and near to the stereotype matrices clamped thereon. In the casing an outlet or outlets are employed for the escape of moisture driven out of the stereotype matrices. The fire or fires may be employed to melt the metal required to produce the stereotype, and with this object, one or more melting pots at some convenient part of the apparatus are arranged. In some cases Pepe dispenses with a special fire for the apparatus, and passes through the flue, around or partly around the drum, heated air or products of combustion obtained from other sources. Pepe claimed that by the use of his improved apparatus the production of stereotype matrices for newspaper and other printing was very greatly facilitated and cheapened, as the time employed in drying the same was greatly reduced, while by the peculiar form and action of the apparatus the buckling or unequal drying and shrinkage of the matrices was prevented.

His invention also enabled him to retain in position in the matrices the pieces of cardboard employed to retain the form of the white spaces, so that when the matrices were dried they required only little finishing. This effect was obtained by clamping the matrices on to the revolving drum with their backs toward the drum, the pieces of cardboard in the white spaces being also in contact with the drum and thereby held in position during the drying operation.

The technical superintendent of the "Daily News" in London in 1890 dried the wet mats quicker by putting them on a gas heated iron plate upon which a small amount of white sand was strewn.

Preheating: Preheating was done at first in a crude way; holding the mat over the metal oven, placing on a hot plate, holding it out of the window, etc. The importance of preheating emerged and devices were built.

A number of devices known under the designation "preheaters" are in use in stereotype plants in America. A preheater is a special stereotype mat preheating box designed to maintain mats at suitable casting temperatures during the interval which occurs from the time the mats are removed from the dryer or scorcher and the actual casting operation.

When a mat is taken out of the scorcher for even one minute, it begins to chill. It loses the high temperature to which it has been raised in the scorcher. As a result the first and sometimes as many as three casts taken from the mat must be discarded because of cold spots. To bring the mat back to the required temperature, to avoid cold spots in the plates, it is necessary for the casting machine operator to again place the mat in the scorcher to bring up the temperature of the mat. Even when this is done there is always the possibility that the temperature will not be just right when the mat finally is taken out of the scorcher for transfer to the casting machine.

To present a typical example of such a preheater, the one devised by C. G. Hamblen of Pittsburgh, Pa., is selected. His preheater is made of ⅛" cold rolled steel. Over all it is 4½" thick and 24½" long, with a 30 degree radius. It is divided into two compartments —storage in the front and heating in the rear.

The storage compartment, which will hold up to six mats, is 1½" wide and 16" high. The heating chamber has an opening of ½" and is 17½" high in the front and 20" high in the rear. In the center of the front section of the heating chamber there is a 2" hand size cut-out so that mats may be placed in and withdrawn easily from the ½" opening of the heating chamber.

The servicer is anchored to the outer rim of the metal pot, and because of its 30 degree radius, fits snugly against the pot. It is attached to the pot by two slotted, half-inch bolts, one vertical and one horizontal, making it possible to install or remove the servicer in a minute or two at the most. The servicer can be anchored at a position where it can be reached within arm's length by the operator of the casting machine.

Shrinkage: During the drying, and later on in the casting operation, the dry mat shrinks due to the loss of moisture; the greater the moisture in a mat the more it shrinks. When dry mats were first made in the United States of America they were a failure because they shrank in all sorts of ways—lengthwise and sidewise of the page. No two mats shrank uniformly. We know that before mats were made here, imported German dry mats only were used in America, and in analyzing their shrinkage it was discovered that the mats cut at the German mills from the mat web, shrank more in one direction than the other. Some were cut crosswise to the making of the web and some lengthwise. No attempt was made in any European country to benefit from the shrinkage in the mat.

After attempts at use by American newspapers the dry mat was condemned because of the undependable shrinkage. The German mat caused some pages to be longer and narrower resulting in pages of variable widths when cast in the plants. It seemed that no two pages could be cast of identical length.

It was found that the dry mat shrunk in one way with respect to its method of making, and that the stereotyper could rely on that shrinkage if he knew which way the mats had been made. It occurred to the stereotypers that they could get $\frac{1}{4}''$ shrinkage across the width, and that this shrinkage, properly controlled and used, would mean a saving in newsprint to the publishers. Due to this shrinkage it is today possible, without altering present makeup in any way, to print on narrower newsprint paper with uniform results. The margin of shrinkage is, when dry mats are properly manufactured and moistened, constant and uniform, and is always under the control of the stereotyper.

Shrinkages with dry mats may be had from $\frac{1}{4}''$ to $\frac{3}{4}''$ depending upon the width of the rolls on which the papers are printed. The ratio of shrinkage in width to shrinkage in column length is 2 to 1. Publishers can therefore obtain maximum shrinkage in width, which means maximum saving in cost of newsprint, and yet keep the extra work in the composing room down to a minimum. If the shrinkage in column width is 3% the shrinkage in column length will be approximately $1\frac{1}{2}$%. For example, a newspaper composes its forms 301 lines in length and 8 columns, 12 ems with 6-point rules in width. Such a form will measure $16\frac{9}{16}''$ in width and $21\frac{1}{2}''$ in length. Taking it for granted that this assumed newspaper wants a printed page 16" in width and 301 lines in length, the shrinkage in width is $\frac{9}{16}''$, which is 3%. The corresponding shrinkage in length with dry mats would therefore be $1\frac{1}{2}$% of 301 lines, or $4\frac{1}{2}$ lines. In order to print a column of 301 lines it would therefore be necessary to compose the form $305\frac{1}{2}$ lines. Through the shrinkage in the mat the actual printed page would measure 16″ in width and 301 lines in length.

Metal Pots: The metal used for making stereotypes has varied but little during more than 250 years. With the old (1690) wet paper pulp process it was made of antimony, tin and lead. The same metal combination is used in the plaster, clay, wet and dry mat stereotyping processes. There have been modifications in the quantities of these ingredients, the process of refining the metal has been greatly perfected, and the purity and cleansing of the metal has been greatly improved. The equipment and devices used in melting the metal and in pouring it upon the molds is the same as used in 1690, perfected however to a great extent.

The first smelters were simple ovens and a common ladle was used for pouring the metal. The plaster or clay process employed a metal pot that had to be square and somewhat deep, also sufficiently large to permit the casting or dipping pans to be immersed; it was placed near a wall in order to allow the fixing of a crane for lowering or raising the casting pans.

In the use of the wet mat process the metal pot was practically the same as heretofore, but was equipped with a large cover or bonnet made of sheet iron about three feet high, tapering at the top and having an outlet through an iron pipe into the flue.

With all processes the metal was carefully skimmed of all impurities, which floated to the surface, with a perforated scoop or skimmer. A few drops of oil or a piece of tallow was added to the metal as a cleansing agent. The proper heat of the metal was placed at 600° F., which is practically what it is today.

The old metal scoop has since been supplanted in larger establishments by metal pumps which were built into the metal pots, some holding up to 10,000 pounds of metal, or made in one piece with these pots. The heating was originally done with wood, later on with coal, and finally with high pressure gas or electricity.

One gas-heated pot, controlled by a Partlow burner, with a capacity of 2,000 pounds of metal, takes care of the flat casting. Another pot, electrically heated with a capacity of 10,000 pounds, supplies metal to the casting boxes for curved work. An interesting feature of this pot is a small motor controlling an agitation blade in the bottom, which, moving very slowly, keeps the alloy constantly in good mixture. Thermostatic control allows careful check on the temperature at all times with the standard formula

97. Flat Stereotype Casting Box for Paper
Process

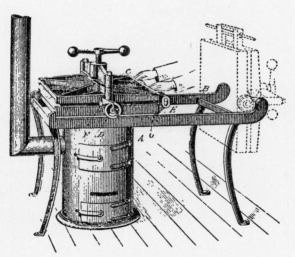

98. M. J. Hughes—Combined Furnace and
Hot Water Casting Box

99. Curved and Flat Casting Boxes

100. Hand Casting Box

being kept constant through careful supervision of the office of the Technical Director.

Casting: With the wet paper pulp method of 1690, the casting operation was performed in a very simple manner. A "flask" was constructed of two small wooden boards or of tin plates and the molded pulp matrix was locked between them. An opening was made between the two boards to provide a means of entry for the molten metal. A funnel was placed in this hole and the molten metal was poured in on the form. It was then immersed in a tank of cold water for cooling.

With the plaster of Paris and clay methods casting pans were used. The following is a typical example, covering practically all plaster and clay process casting methods: In the baked mold, at the moment it is taken from the baking oven, a small nick called a gate is cut into each of its four corners. To admit the molten metal the mold is placed in the casting pan. This pan is an oblong, square vessel of cast iron about 4" deep, the sides of which slope outwards at a small angle. On the bottom of the pan rests a plate of iron, the upper surface of which is turned smooth and level and the four corners rather rounded off to allow the molten metal to flow under it. The pan has a flat iron cover, the corners of which are rounded off to admit the metal. (Illustration 62 shows this pan.)

Many modifications of these casting pans for plaster and clay stereotyping were invented. However, the basic idea was always the use of a pan, and up to the advent of papier-mache wet stereotyping pans only were used.

One invention may be of interest: In 1867 J. M. Willbur of Ohio, patented an improvement in casting stereotypes by which he cast several plates at one time, using clay molds. He constructed a pan made up of different ledges, on which he placed a number of molds face downwards in the bottom of the pan. These molds have a sufficient number of creases in the sides to permit the molten metal to flow into and fill these molds. Then a plate or ledge is placed on these several molds, and on this plate again a number of creased molds are placed. Another ledge is inserted and several creased molds are placed on this plate, and so forth. Then the pan is closed with screws and the casting is performed (after heating the form to the temperature of the metal) by pouring the molten metal, sufficient to cover the topmost ledge. (See illustration 76.)

With the advent of wet mat stereotyping in 1829 the use of casting pans was displaced by casting boxes. When the dry mat was introduced in 1893 the same kind of boxes were adopted for that process.

The construction of such a box was as follows: It consisted of two thick iron surfaces, the top one serving as a lid. They are hinged to one another; these hinges are made by two protruding pins at one end, fitting loosely into slots on either side of the bed. By this means, plates of any thickness could be cast, the height being regulated by iron gauges placed around the matrix. The box is supported in a low upright frame by two swivels in the center. The lid and bed are held firmly together by a movable bar, which works loosely over a pin on one side of the bed, and when the lid is closed down may be swung around and securely clamped by a center screw. The mouth of the box is slightly bevelled inwards to permit the metal to be poured without spilling. These boxes were called flat casting boxes.

From 1829 on, many casting devices were invented but none of them succeeded in replacing these flat casting boxes.

Up to the beginning of the 19th century stereotyping was practiced almost solely for the printing of books. Newspapers did not print large editions. Therefore, stereotyping was not used in their plants. The forms were set up of cast type and the old fashioned flatbed presses printed from that type. When cylinder presses were invented (1813) stereotype plates made by the plaster method were curved to fit these press cylinders.

When wet mat stereotyping was introduced in the printing of newspapers, it became necessary to make curved plate casting boxes, and when the dry mat method of stereotyping appeared on the scene such boxes were also used.

The first intimation of using curved stereotype plates cast from a flexible paper matrix, i.e., the wet mat placed in a curved mold, is to be found in the patent which Jacob Warms of Paris obtained in France in 1849, who later protected his invention through DeWitte in England in 1850. This was the process that made web printing practicable.

In 1854 Charles Craske of New York cast his first curved plate, which he called a semi-cylindrical plate, in the following manner: The mat was fastened in a casting mold or box curved to the circumference of the cylinder of the press, and molten stereotype metal poured upon it. During the process the box stood upright, but while the mat was being placed into position it lay horizontally, a swivel mounting enabling it to be readily turned.

In 1863 John C. Macdonald and Joseph Calvery, employees of the "London Times," were granted a patent for "improvements in the manufacture and application of printing apparatus". The patentees employed the ordinary wet mat way of stereotyping, but they cast the plates in a tubular form, cylindrical on the external surface. In 1866 they were granted an additional patent on further improvements. From that time on, numerous curved plate casting boxes were constructed and placed on the market.

In one of these curving processes after the impression has been taken from the flat plate the mold is bent to the full extent of the required curvature to make the curved plate, and then the metal cast or deposited on or in such curved mold. This method shortens the curved plate dependent upon the thickness of depth of the mold and degree or extent of its curvature.

An improvement of these processes consisted in the "shell" being made flat in the usual way and then bent to the required extent of the curved plate. This more or less lengthens the shell according to the curvature and thickness of the shell and character of the surface, a smooth or plain surface not being so much affected as a deeply engraved one. In a third process the plate was made flat in the usual way and then bent to the full curve required. This also had the drawback of lengthening the plate to a degree dependent upon the curvature and thickness of the plate.

As time passed by the newspapers became larger and larger and stressed the need for more speed in all operations. Time saving became increasingly essential in the highly competitive field of newspaper production, and thus the slowness of the hand casting box methods became a problem. Engineers realized the time had arrived to devise the mechanical casting of stereotype plates to supplant or to be used in conjunction with the hand boxes. The slow working hand casting boxes are still in widespread use in smaller newspaper foundries, but almost all newspapers with a circulation of 15,000 copies or over have, in order to be able to compete, installed automatic casting machines. Of these latter there are two systems, the vertical and the horizontal machines. The vertical ones still retain the so-called tailpiece, whereas the horizontal ones have no tailpiece. These machines are either semi-automatic or entirely automatic. With the former the casting is done by hand, the subsequent treatment, however, is done automatically by means of different mechanical steps. The first machine of this kind was the "Citoplate" invented and manufactured by C. E. Hopkins and Ferdinand Wesel, both of Brooklyn, N. Y. Then came the "Compleo" caster, made by Koenig and Bauer in Wurzburg, then followed the Hoe, Duplex, Scott, Goss and the Autoplate Junior casting machines. Another semi-automatic casting machine, now obsolete on account of the sensitivity of its mechanism, was the "Rotoplate" invented by Egli.

The man to first invent an entirely automatic casting machine which proved to be successful in actual operation was Henry A. Wise Wood of New York. His first patent was taken out in the year 1900 and the machine was first used in the stereotype foundry of the "New York Herald." For his invention the Franklin Institute awarded Mr. Wood the Elliott Cresson Gold Medal on June 3rd, 1908. He designated his machine as the Standard Autoplate Caster. Since the time of the issuance of his first patent, Mr. Wood made a legion of improvements on his original machine. It is interesting to note that one of his first Autoplates is still in use in England. In order of their appearance on the market the Wood inventions comprised the Standard Autoplate, the Semi-Autoplate, the Junior Autoplate, single and double, the Senior Autoplate, and finally the latest of them all, the Automatic Autoplate. With Wood's machines the operation of casting is performed automatically from the time the mat is put into position until the finished plate is ready to be clamped onto the printing press. In lieu of the six and seven men hitherto employed, three or four men produce four plates per minute on a single Automatic. In the Standard Autoplate the casting is done against a horizontal cylinder or core, the interior of which is cooled by water. Below it is a frame or "back" carrying the mat. This back has an up and down movement of about six inches and when it is in its topmost position there is a semi-circular space between it and the core, equal in length, breadth and thickness to the plate which is to be cast. Molten metal having been injected into this space by a pump, there is a pause of a few seconds to permit of solidification, and then the back falls, bringing away the mat for another cast. Immediately afterwards the cylinder makes a half turn and presents what was previously its upper half to the mat for another cast. The first cast is taken with it as it turns, and is then pushed along from the top of the core against two rotating saws which trim its edges. Next it comes under a shaving arch, where it rests while its interior surface is smoothed to a proper thickness, and finally water is directed against its back to cool it without wetting its printing face. The Junior Autoplate is a semi-automatic plate casting machine. The casting is done against a

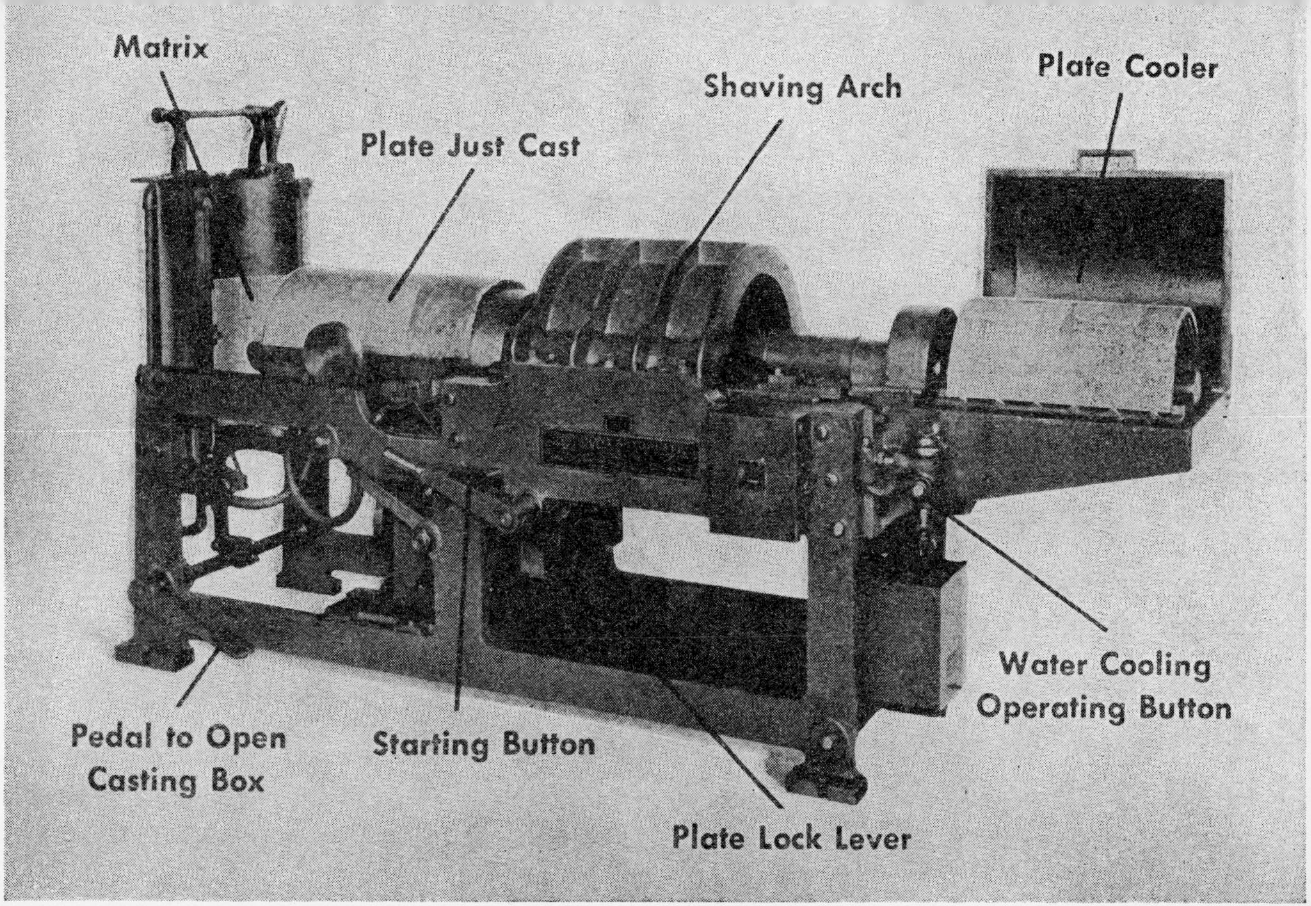

Plate Cooler

Shaving Arch

Plate Just Cast

Matrix

Water Cooling
Operating Button

Plate Lock Lever

Starting Button

Pedal to Open
Casting Box

101. The Pony Autoplate

102. Wood Automatic Autoplate Machine

vertical cylinder or core, whereas in the Standard Autoplate the casting is done against a horizontal core. The Junior Autoplate has been found more practical and has supplanted the Standard machine.

The latest development in the Autoplate machine is the so-called "Automatic". This casts four plates in one minute and this is the fixed uniform speed of the machine. It has no other speed. The machine requires no attention other than the insertion or removal of mats or the removal of plates and tails. The operator inserts a mat, presses a button, and then removes plate and tail. (See illustration No. 102.)

There are many other outstanding inventions in this field but our space is too limited to give due appreciation and mention to all of them. A few instances are as follows:

Another completely automatic plate casting machine is the "Multiplate" invented by Annard and built in England. The caster has a pump which is similarly constructed as in the Autoplate Standard. The machine is also a horizontal one, but the core is so made that it contracts under pressure. It takes the plate out of the casting receptacle or bowl into the boring, which then takes the plate to the part of the shaving bowl by means of an endless belt and deposits it upon a table.

A new development in the automatic casting machine field is the "Winkler" patent automatic plate casting machine. It is built in Switzerland and in Germany. A factory in the United States is now reported to be building the machine for the American trade. This machine embodies a number of patented features and new principles, which permit the production of perfectly true and solid stereotype plates without "tailpiece", without pumps, without subsequent shaving, without trimming or hand-finishing. In other words, after a short automatic operation, a perfectly finished stereotype plate is produced which is absolutely ready for the rotary press. The fundamental idea in designing the "Winkler" casting machine was to connect directly the casting box with the melting pot in such a way that the stereotype plate is cast without a tail but under the head of the whole contents of the metal pot by gravity, that is to say, at a pressure most suitable for obtaining a perfectly true and solid plate. The machine consists of (1) a melting furnace, (2) a hood with self-closing door, (3) one valve with automatic lubrication, (4) one pyrometer, (5) one enclosed driving gear with motor and starter, and one casting box comprising one casting shell, one core, one matrix clamping device, two rings and an automatic water-cooling arrangement for shell and core. The operation: Only work done by hand is setting the matrix (once only), starting the machine by foot pedal, removing the finished plate, everything else being done automatically by the machine. Other claims for the machine are economy of metal, economy of fuel (50% saving), low casting temperature, higher output, less floor space required and the use of exceptionally hard metal.

The same system is followed by Koenig & Bauer of Wurzburg and a number of other European machine factories. (See illustrations No. 99, 100, 103.)

Vacuum Casting Boxes: This section on improved casting boxes would not be complete without some comment on vacuum casting. It is not our purpose to discuss the relative merits of the various boxes. Almost all the manufacturers of casting equipment supply their boxes either with or without vacuum, and vacuum can be obtained on both or one side of the box. The Westcott and Thomson Company of Philadelphia has contributed greatly to this field, particularly in non-newspaper work. They supply only two-sided vacuum boxes for flat and curved casting. Other vacuum boxes are made by Duplex, Goss, Hoe, Ostrander, Scott and Wood. Some of the claims made for vacuum boxes are: Trapped air and gases are drawn through the mat, enabling the metal to set smoothly against the face of the mat, thereby giving better solids and sharper outlines to type and halftones. Vacuum holds the mat in place causing it to conform to the exact contour of the box and also prevents the mat from slipping out of place, a feature particularly important in making color plates.

Finishing: When the plates have been cast they are subjected to a number of finishing operations preparing them for their final destination, the printing press. These operations are performed by auxiliary machines: (1) a combination saw and trimmer or similar individual machines, used for sawing and trimming the plates. (2) Routers for removing any protruding areas of metal on the stereotype plate that might take ink and print. (3) Shavers, which smooth the interior surface of the plates. (4) Bevelers, which form the bevels by which the plates are clamped to the presses.

To explain chronologically: With the plaster and clay processes the contraction of the metal on the face as well as on the back of the cast was always spread unequally, and for this reason the plate had to be flattened before finishing in the ordinary way. This meant trimming the superfluous metal on the inside and running a small straight edge over the face, thus showing up the indentations. These plates were marked with a pair of calipers on the back, and they were knocked up to the required height with a planer or burnishing hammer. Then the back of the extremely uneven plate was planed to a uniform thickness on a specially constructed lathe. Then the plate was planed and beveled.

With the wet mat, after the plates were cast they were separated and trimmed by use of a circular saw. In the beginning this saw was worked by a treadle. Then the plates were planed to reduce them to the proper thickness by a planing machine. The early planing machines were operated by hand, later on by steam or electricity. Finally the plates were beveled. Then with a sharp chisel or gauge any metal that appeared unnecessarily high in the whites was chipped away. This was formerly done by hand, today it is done by a routing machine.

The dry mat process was introduced in 1894, long after the plaster, clay and wet mat processes had been in continuous use. The same operations as above described were performed for finishing the plates, but most of the old hand-worked devices had passed out of the picture and modern machines were used from the very start of the dry mat stereotyping process.

Among the pioneers of precision printing and plate making machinery is the former Claybourn Process Corporation, now the Claybourn Division of C. B. Cottrell & Sons Co. This company is responsible for many outstanding achievements in the printing and plate making field.

Out of their constant aim for better plates and better printing, they developed superior four and five color printing presses and multicolor proof presses. In order to make possible duplicate plates of quality and precision there was developed a 2,000 ton lead and mat moulding press, a combination flat rougher and shaver, a curved borer and shaver, a router, a proof press for curved plates, a gauging machine and many tools and accessories for finishing.

Printing presses: Before closing this chapter, a few words about the evolution of the modern printing press may be of interest, not only to refresh the memories of the master stereotypers, but to afford information to the students enrolled in schools where stereotyping and printing is taught, and also to the members of classes in schools of journalism.

The first press: Johannes Gutenberg, the inventor of printing, constructed a press to carry out his invention. As a model, he took

[269]

a common wine press. Gutenberg's press was a wooden screw press made of different parts, all of which could be taken apart. It consisted of two upright timbers with connected crosspieces at top and bottom and with two intermediate cross timbers. The lower one was the support of the form of type. Through the upper passed a large wooden screw, the lower end of which rested on the end of a wooden platen. After the form of type was fastened to this page it was inked by hand ink-balls made of wool covered with soft leather. A sheet of paper, previously dampened, was then laid carefully upon the type and the bed pushed to its place. A wooden lever was thrown into its socket and the platen screwed down, held for a moment and then raised. Then the bed was drawn out and the printed sheet removed and hung up to dry.

The basic principles of the Gutenberg press were preserved in all presses used up to the end of the 18th century. With his first press Gutenberg could make 300 impressions a day working constantly.

Later on in a period of universal revival a reforming hand entered on the scene. Today it appears incredible that with such primitive equipment in which carpenter work constituted the main element, so many splendid works, greatly admired still in our day, could have been produced.

A Dutch printer named Jansson Blaeu, who at the same time was a well-known mathematician and astronomer, undertook in the year 1699 the task of correcting the many faults existing in the old Gutenberg press. He performed his task with success, and after having constructed improved presses in accordance with his ideas, he installed nine of them in his own printing plant, baptising them in the names of the nine Muses.

His improvements consisted in passing the spindle of the screw through the wooden block which was guided into wooden frame, and from which hung the platen. He also invented a device for rolling the page in and out under the platen and improved the hand lever for turning the screw.

About 1650 W. Danner of Nuremberg replaced the customary wooden screw spindle with one made of brass. Later on both the foundation or the base plate, which was at first made of wood or of stone, and the mobile platen, were cast in iron. It was believed that owing to these improvements great strides in the art had been made. However, the platens were small and the impression could not be exercised at once over the whole area of the type form; only one-half of the form could be placed under the platen and then the pulling-bar drawn. After a second placing of the other half of the form a second stroke of the pulling-bar and only then was the printing of the form completed.

F. W. Haas of Basle, about the end of the 18th century, changed the existing presses to a great degree. He constructed almost all parts of iron and printed the type form in one stroke. The celebrated French printer, F. Didot, also constructed such an improved press.

The iron age of the printing press, i.e., construction entirely of iron, together with an improved stroke-mechanism, arrived at the beginning of the 19th century through the general adoption of Lord Stanhope's printing press. Stanhope's press was a hand press, giving its power by a combination of lever and screw, and was the first press made wholly of iron.

During and after Stanhope's time a great many improvements in the hand press were made. America produced two new presses: The Ruthven which differed from presses previously made in having the bed stationary while the platen was moved to and fro. The Columbian press, invented by George Clymer of Philadelphia in 1817. The crude and defective condition of the printing presses in use at the time, commanded his attention and the Columbian was the result. The strength of material and scientific combination of power of the press took off an amount of wear from the pressman never before achieved. Its elbowed pulling-bar, its diagonal connecting rod, which changed a horizontal movement into a perpendicular one and its main lever, applying its weight directly to the form, made it extremely popular at the time. The first press of this kind was constructed in London and was put up in 1818, and afterwards sent to Russia.

The final development of the hand press came in 1827 when Samuel Rust of New York perfected the Washington press. The iron frame was lightened and strengthened, the toggle motion was improved, and a screw regulated the pressure. With this improved hand press came the substitution of composition inking rollers for the leather covered ink-balls previously employed.

In 1822 steam was first used in America as the motive power to run a printing press; this was seven years before steam turned the wheels of the first locomotive in England. Daniel Treadwell of Boston built the pioneer power press. Its frame was constructed of wood, its mechanism was clumsy—but it worked. Another Yankee,

Isaac Adam, perfected the press, made it more practical, and in 1830 he put his press on the market. Isaac Adam "automized" the printing press. Automatically his press inked the type; automatically it drew the sheet between the type page and the platen for the impression; automatically it took the sheet now printed from the type page; automatically it "flirted", after registering, the sheet to a "pile" by a fly invented by Adam and still used on cylinder presses. About 1,000 sheets per hour was the maximum speed of this improved Adam press.

The use of steam, however, was still in the experimental state. Hand power from "crank men" who turned the large wheel was sufficient to print the papers of even the daily journals.

The Ramage press, a small hand press made of wood, was constructed by Adam Ramage the most celebrated of the early press makers of the United States. Later it was constructed with an iron bed and platen, the first of its kind in the United States.

Sir Rowland Hill of London, about 1825, first suggested the possibilities of a press which would print both sides of a sheet at once.

Englishmen constructed the Cowper, Hopkins and Cogger-Hager presses, Germany produced the Dingler, Koch and Hoffman, and France the Marinoni and Alanzet presses.

In 1790 William Nicholson of London took out a patent on a cylinder press, but this did not get beyond the drawing of plans. Suggestions rather than definite invention, but it helped other inventors.

Invariably inventors paid most attention to the mechanism of the pressure of the platen. After the Stanhope presses, which were practically indestructible, constructors turned away from the employment of screws and proceeded to other mechanical means.

Although the number of copies one man could deliver daily were relatively quite considerable, still the printing industry would never have attained the degree of perfection we today enjoy had the art been restricted to the hand press. When the editions of daily newspapers assumed ever-increasing proportions, mechanical genius was forced to cope with the problem. The mechanical printing press became a reality and with it a new era opened for the printing world.

The first inventor of the mechanical press is Friedrich Koenig of Eisleben, Germany. In 1810 he took out his first patent on a mechanically driven hand press, and in 1811 Koenig was granted a

103. German Automatic Casting Machine

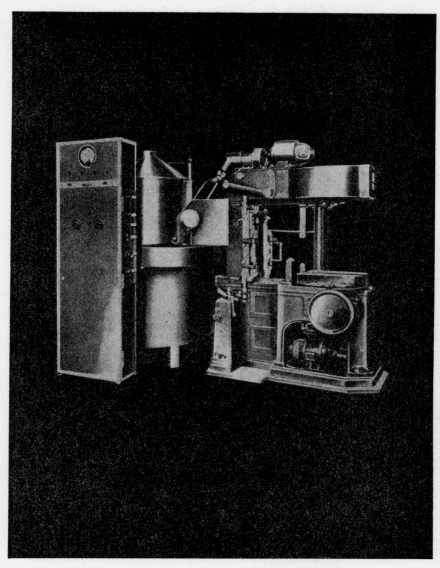

104. "Novoplate" Automatic Caster

patent on a cylinder press. The first machine of this kind was placed into operation in the printing plant of Thomas Bensley in London.

John Walter, publisher of the "London Times," took a great interest in the invention and commanded Koenig and his assistant Bauer to build a steam-driven cylinder press for the "Times." Cognizant of the bad temper rife among the workmen in the printing plant, they secretly installed the press in a house adjoining the plant of the "Times." When, on the 29th of November 1814, the printers came to work, they were told to wait under the pretext that the foreign mail had not yet arrived. At six in the morning, the hour when the printing in the plant usually started, Walter carried the first copy of a paper that had been printed on the new press into the room where the workmen were assembled. He reported what had transpired, warning the workmen not to commit any acts of violence against the new press as he had police on hand for protection of his property. The workmen then received full pay and were detailed to other work. The press printed 1,100 copies an hour, so that the whole edition of the "Times" was printed in three hours as against ten hours before.

Presses built for German newspapers by Koenig & Bauer following their return to Germany were destroyed by the printers.

This first mechanical printing press invented by Koenig and built in 1811 in London, was naturally a far cry from today's ultra-modern rotary presses. The form of type was placed on a flat bed which was carried under an impression cylinder that had a three-fold action. On the first part the sheet was fed at the bed upon the tympan and gripped. On the second part of the revolution the sheet received the impression and was removed by hand. On the third the empty tympan came up and received another sheet. Koenig also invented a most efficient device to roll the page, rolling the type to and fro in a reciprocating motion.

A press, built by Applegath and Cowper for the "London Times" and operated in that plant for over 20 years, was equipped with eight cylinders, and delivered 10,000 sheets per hour, each sheet imprinted on one side only. The cylinders were placed into the axis vertically and the ink was applied by means of rollers.

With the perfection of paper stereotyping the construction of newspaper presses pursued an entirely new course. By means of stereotyping it was made possible to take matrices of type forms, set by the compositors, to curve these mats and thereby obtain curved printing plates, and (an idea that Koenig had already expressed) print on an endless roll of paper.

The honor of taking the decisive step which brought the realization of this plan, belongs to the Americans. They built the first rotary printing press, and from that time on furnished the most important momentum and impetus which brought on all later improvements.

In America the first rotary presses were built in 1860; at the end of 1860 England followed and in 1870 Germany emulated these two countries.

The rapid growth of newspapers and their problem of increasing printing speed served as an incentive to inventors and engineers to find ways of perfecting and increasing the productive power of the printing presses. Important daily newspapers with large production were forced to employ several presses in the manufacture of these newspapers in order adequately to serve their readers with these large editions.

In 1832 Robert Hoe of New York sent his engineer, Sereno Newton, to London to inspect the Koenig presses, and on the return of his agent Hoe began the construction of cylinder presses on the same principle as Koenig but according to Hoe's own construction plans and his own new inventions.

When speed and greater production became the slogan, Hoe in 1847 built his first rotary press using stereotype plates, and designated the press as the "Patent Type-Revolving Printing Machine". A contemporary of Hoe's expressed the following thought: "Various experiments had convinced Hoe of the feasibility of casting stereotype plates with a curve. The process was brought to perfection by the use of flexible paper matrices, upon which the metal was cast in curved molds of any circle desired. Hoe placed these plates upon his type-revolving machine, upon pages adapted to receive them instead of the type forms. The newspaper publishers were thus enabled to duplicate the forms and run several machines at the same time with a view to turning out papers with greater rapidity."

Such an improved "Patent Rotary Newspaper Perfecting Machine" was constructed in 1863 for a London journal. A right to manufacture under his original patent was granted by R. Hoe & Company to M. Marinoni of Paris.

These machines were equipped with four to eight feeders. (See illustrations No. 124, 125.) The press was designed exclusively for stereotype plates and printed both sides of the sheet in one operation. Two impression cylinders and two form cylinders were placed side by side in a horizontal frame, the impression cylinders occupying the center with the form cylinders at each end. The two forms were secured to their cylinders and inked in much the same manner as on the type-revolving machine, the fountains and distributing cylinders being placed at the end of the press. A two-feeder machine printed from 4,000 to 5,000 perfected eight-page sheets of ordinary size per hour, or printed and cut from 8,000 to 10,000 perfected four-page sheets of ordinary size per hour. The machine occupied a space about 18 feet long, 8½ feet wide and 6½ feet high.

From the Centennial year 1876 up to our day, a legion of improvements in printing presses have been made in Europe and America. Important press manufacturers in the United States are Duplex, Goss, Hoe, Scott and Wood. In closing this chapter a short description of what a modern 1940 newspaper press performs is of interest.

THE NEWSPAPER PRINTING PRESS (shown in illustration
No. 127) WILL PRINT COMPLETE NEWSPAPERS AT
THE FOLLOWING RUNNING SPEEDS:—
840,000 newspapers of 4, 6, 8, 10 or 12 pages per hour, or
600,000 newspapers of 14 or 16 pages per hour or
420,000 newspapers of 18, 20, 22 or 24 pages per hour, or
300,000 newspapers of 26, 28, 30 or 32 pages per hour.

It should be with pride that stereotypers look at this modern giant, since paper stereotyping made possible such a miracle.

Presses on Wheels: A Western newspaper, named "The Frontier Index" was published on the frontier and was literally a press on wheels. Published at 25 different places along the line of the Western advance, it was founded at old Kearney, south of Nebraska Territory in 1866 and was printed on an old time hand roller press. "The Frontier Index" in the fall of 1866 was taken by three ox teams, driven by Mexicans to a temporary terminus of the Union Pacific Construction Company at North Platte. As soon as the site was laid out for this mushroom terminal station some 4,000 adventurers flocked there to live in tents and portable houses, and the "Index" did a land office business printing circulars, for which it charged $20 for 100 words. The next move was to Julesburg in January 1867. In 48 hours North Platte was depopulated after the exodus to the new terminus, and the "Index" was the first enterprise to reach that station. On one or two occasions when "The Frontier Index" was being moved, its wagon train was held up by Indians, who took no pains to conceal their disgust when they found that the ox carts contained nothing except the printing outfit.

CHAPTER EIGHT

INVENTIONS FOR ELIMINATING STEREOTYPING

THERE HAVE appeared a number of inventions of this nature, but so far, judged from practical tests, each and every one of these inventions has failed to accomplish the elimination of stereotyping. No doubt many inventive minds at the present moment are working on ideas to effect such elimination, and recalling the ultimate and lasting success of much opposed, and, during the time of their development, skeptically regarded machines, as for instance the typesetting machines, Linotype, Monotype and others, it would seem possible that stereotyping as practiced in our day will in some future time be entirely eliminated by better and cheaper methods.

So far the primary object of all of these inventions is to produce better printing, but at the same time they all aspire to completely do away with stereotyping. It appears that it will be of interest to stereotypers to become acquainted with the nature of the outstanding inventions, and therefore such details should be included in the history of the stereotyping art.

All of these inventions awakened considerable interest when they first appeared on the scene, and were given exhaustive tests in a number of the foremost newspaper stereotype plants. Practically all of these processes are based upon photostatic or offset printing methods, and all of the inventors claimed to be able to print with them finer screens on ordinary newsprint. Each and every one of these inventions is of a nature that calls for changes in present equipment; in fact, if they were to be adopted a great quantity of otherwise satisfactory machinery would have to be discarded entirely. The question that has instantly arisen has been: Are these new processes of such a transitional nature to warrant such a great sacrifice and such a great outlay of money?

The following details are given to show that the saving in the cheapest bracket of the cost of producing a newspaper is so small that the immense expense necessary for changes for these processes that are supposed to eliminate stereotyping, would not warrant any existing newspaper office, and not even one about to be established, in spending large sums to make such changes and incurring great losses through immobilization and scrapping of already extant machinery.

The mechanical cost of producing a newspaper is a relatively small part of the total cost of producing a paper. The cost of newsprint alone generally represents 15 to 20% of the total cost of producing some papers. Salaries in the editorial department, of the columnists, features and feature writers, and distribution of the paper after it has been produced, undoubtedly take up at least another 50% of the total cost. There is also some doubt, based upon careful examinations, whether the cost of operating a composing room, stereotype foundry and pressroom exceeds 25% of the total cost. This would mean that the total cost of the stereotype foundry in the average newspaper plant is certainly not over 10% of the total cost of producing the paper. If stereotyping were entirely abolished the saving would not be sufficiently great to make it attractive even to a new publisher who appears on the scene. Incidentally, whatever process would take the place of stereotyping would cost something, so that abolishing stereotyping would not mean saving the total cost of operating the stereotype foundry. (It is interesting to note that the cost of mats is equal to $\frac{1}{12}$ of 1% of the total cost of producing a newspaper.)

Among the processes that have been tested in America with a view toward eliminating stereotyping, the following are the outstanding ones:

(1) The Lenzart Process: The object of the Lenzart process is to provide cheap and better fine screen printing with, or within, super-embossed or straight type matter, in combination with printing from standard stereotype plates on existing newspaper presses up to and including the highest printing speeds. The salient points of this invention are summed up in the following statement:

The affinity of mercury (quicksilver) for some metals and non-affinity for others, and non-affinity for certain printing inks, make possible the printing of this plate. The nickel-plated printing area of the solid copper plate accepts the ink and refuses the mercury, while the copper non-printing area is amalgamated and accepts the mercury and not the ink. The amalgam area is constantly replenished on the press through mercury fed into the inking motion.

Operations in the pressroom consist of attaching a portable mercury feeding device which extends the length of one of the intermediate rollers of the press and drops thereon a row of minute

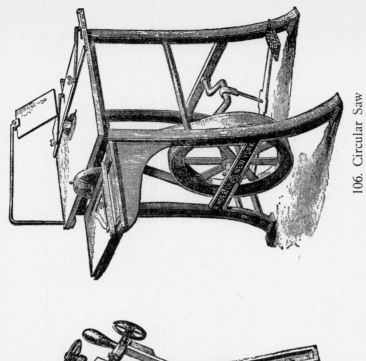

106. Circular Saw

105. Finishing Saddle

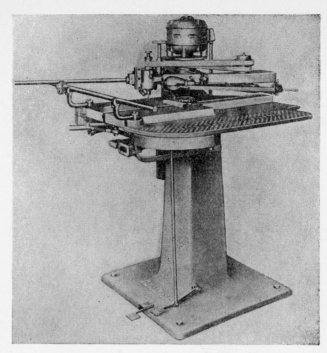

107. Radial Arm Routing Machine

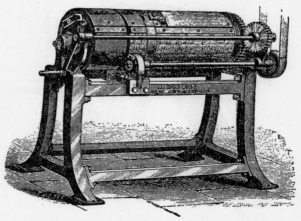

108. Dressing Table for Curved Newspaper Plates

mercury globules. These are ground into the ink by the inking motion and transferred to the solid copper plates by the form rollers. The mercury feeding device is driven by the press and synchronized to permit control of the amount of repellent used.

No press mechanism changes are required and the mercury feeding fountain is the only additional press device needed. No make-ready is used, and the change-over from stereotyping to Lenzart and back takes about the same time as change-over for color. Two or three minutes are required to clean and amalgam the plate after removal, over the enamel-resist by photo-engravers. Plates of solid copper conform in size and shape to standard stereotype plates and are locked on the press cylinders in an identical manner.

(2) THE TRIST PROCESS: This invention, made by an Englishman, A. Ronald Trist, covers a process built on the principle that when mercury amalgamates with another metal the amalgam will repel printing ink. This characteristic dates back to Albert's "Mercurography" of 1908. The inventor uses chromium surfaced steel plates from which he prints a rough surfaced paper with an ink containing a certain percentage of mercury. For such plates to work effectively on a fast running printing press the ideal ink must have an oil base with a free fatty acid content of 7.5%.

The Pantone (this is the trade name for the Trist invention) screen has a graduation from the perfect blackness of the solids to the highlights of the interstices, instead of the clear definition of the black lines and white interstices of the usual halftone screen. The use of an emulsion coated copper plate in mercury, eliminating the process of preparation of printing on metal, is made possible by applying the silvery emulsion to support of the same construction as the Pantone plate, namely the copper plate with chromium plated surface, since under these conditions desensitizing of the emulsion by the copper is prevented.

The inventor has exhibited specimens including many surfaces from strawboard and rough newsprint to fine silks and satins. He uses a halftone screen of 150 lines for all surfaces and declares that the speed of the press makes no apparent difference in the quality of the product. Newsprint reproductions run at 20,000 impressions an hour and at 1,000, impressions are similar in appearance.

(3) THE RENCK PROCESS: We quote from a letter by Ernest J. Smith, president and managing director of the Goss Printing Press Company of England, Ltd., written on March 5th, 1929:

"The process consists of providing a brass shell of the thickness and shape of a curved stereo plate as now used on rotary presses. This brass shell is bored, turned, polished and nickeled. It is then put upon a plate cylinder which is part of a transfer press.

"The transfer press that I saw in operation was just a matrix rolling machine with the roller covered with a rubber blanket and a type cylinder arranged in bearings (above this rubber covered cylinder) upon which the nickeled brass plate is fastened. This machine, of course, is only a makeshift and Mr. Sachs told me that the Messrs. Koenig and Bauer people are now making him a Pukka transfer press.

"The form, consisting of lino slugs and pictures, is placed upon the bed of the transfer press, is rolled up with transfer ink and a transfer is made of this form—first to the rubber covered roller, then from that to the nickeled plate.

"Having got the subject to be printed on the new plate, the plate is removed from the transfer press and the inked surface dusted in with wax asphalt and cleaned down with talcum. The plate is then placed in a muffle furnace for about half a minute. It is then taken out and all grease removed from the surface. It is then denickeled and, after being washed out, the surface is metallized with a solution of mercury salts. It is again washed and is then ready for placing upon the plate cylinder of the printing machine for printing.

"The ink used was one of ordinary news class but while printing it is necessary to spray the inking rollers with mercury to build up the resist to the ink that was created by metallizing the surface of the plate.

"This spraying with mercury is intermittent and it is proposed either to mix the mercury with the ink in the fountain or spray the ink as it is raised by the ink fountain roller so that the mercury will not be free but always sprayed into a closed vessel.

"After printing an edition, the brass shells have to be denickeled to remove the subject matter from which the last edition was produced."

(4) THE ALALGOGRAPH PROCESS: This invention is based on the same principle as the above methods. In this process, mercury is used as a treatment of the plate, after which the plate is burnished with a piece of chamois. A copper plate is used, over which the design is etched in the usual way. Control of the depth of the etching is the trick in making the plate.

(5) THE ALLTONE PROCESS: This is admittedly not a new proc-

ess; it is simply the refinement of methods and practices pursued in stereotype foundries for the past 50 years.

In essence the process is this: A zinc engraving $\frac{1}{16}''$ thick (.0625") is inserted into a suitable space left blank in the curved stereotype plate to accommodate the original engraving. Where such a procedure is to be followed, a mat of the page to be stereotyped is prepared as usual. However, before molding the mat is packed on the back in the area to be later occupied by the zinc engraving, with packing felt $\frac{1}{16}''$ thick. When the mat is molded this area is high on the face of the mat and consequently when the mat is cast in the curved box this area is low in the plate—low, that is, to the depth of $\frac{1}{16}''$ (.0625"), so that when the zinc plate is placed into position in this area the entire plate is of proper uniform height throughout.

The zinc engraving is curved in an ordinary electrotype curver. Electrotype tape is applied over the back area of the engraving which is fitted snugly into the stereotype plate before it goes thru the shaver. The pressure of the shaver is enough to insure a tight bond between the curved zinc engraving and the stereotype plate into which it is set.

While the inventors of the Alltone process and certain users of it claim that they are able to get better results in black and white, and particularly in color work, than are possible with regulation stereotyping means, these claims have not gone unchallenged.

(6) The Schoop Process is an invention of Professor M. V. Schoop of Zurich, a noted Swiss metallurgist, who has been decorated by the Franklin Institute for his contributions to the metallurgical sciences. This process is designed to rapidly reproduce or duplicate existing electrotype engravings, type matter and halftones. It produces a harder and more durable printing surface on the cuts. The process is mechanical rather than electro-chemical, and for this reason Schoop has invented a machine (in form of a pistol) that sprays the metal into forms, matrices and so forth by means of compressed air after the metal has been instantaneously melted by an oxy-acetylene flame and pulverized by the compressor.

Metals of various degrees of hardness, such as tin, lead, zinc, copper, brass, nickel, bronze and steel can be used in this process; and as this process is not of an electrolytical nature a wide range of matrix material is available. Besides the usual wax, celluloid, gutta-percha, etc., lead matrices which are made by the usual heavy matrix stamping presses are used. Without any further preparation these matrices are sprayed with any desired metal by means of the above mentioned apparatus to any desired thickness, whether to type high or to full plate thickness.

The size of the edition together with the kind of paper to be used determines the required hardness of the metal and the thickness of the coating. After a coating of hard metal has been applied a backing of soft metal may be sprayed on in the same manner, and furthermore, this backing can be carried on to produce any desired thickness of plate.

In like manner brass and bronze may be sprayed to full plate strength in order to produce dies for embossing purposes. Steel and copper engravings for printing bank notes, stock certificates, etc., are reproduced by the new Schoop process.

The planing and working of the back of the plates is done by the machines now in general use.

Stereotype matrices, both rotary and flat, are coated with hard metal by the Schoop process, and then put into the stereotype casting apparatus in order to add the necessary backing metal to produce the required plate thickness. In this way such stereotype printing forms obtain an extraordinary tough printing surface. They differ from the usual nickel stereos in that the hardening of the printing surface takes place on the matrix before the casting and not after the casting by means of electrolysis which requires a preparatory coating of copper. This copper coating quite naturally tends to spread the halftone dot and the type matter slightly since the cast lead plate always has the full dot and type strength. Furthermore, in this spraying process the copper coating is omitted entirely since the nickel coating combines readily with the stereotype metal without running the danger of peeling off the first coating or of any of the other electrolytical disturbances. In any case there is promised for the new process a tremendous saving of time.

This process has been used sporadically on a prominent Swiss newspaper but it has not yet been found in continuous operation in any other plants.

Another interesting invention is that of a mat made of alternating thin layers of lead and wax and matrix tissue, called the lead-wax mat. Although it is an ingenious process it is far too expensive in the manufacture.

A further invention covers the making of graphite celluloid mats molded with very low pressure. Any cardboard may be used instead of a mat. Through embodying a metal net in the celluloid plate shrinkage is completely avoided.

There was developed in Germany in 1935 a new synthetic gelatin film which is sensitized and exposed under a photo-composed negative, then washed out with a spray of warm water, which has the effect of sinking the letters in the film as in a stereotype mat. It is then dried with alcohol and sprayed with molten metal by means of a spray pistol. Thus a thin shell or plate is obtained, which may be backed with lead like an electrotype plate and mounted type high. Thirty-five minutes from the time the photo-composed film is handed to the operator the plate is ready for the press. This method has not been used for the reproduction of halftones and line cuts; so far type matter only has been reproduced.

Finally we record the invention of an electrolytical process permitting of the deposition of nickel directly on the wax mold and using the composite product as a printing plate.

A well known contributor to trade papers on printing subjects envisaged future newspaper making in a manner that would entirely eliminate stereotyping. His idea of the newspaper production in the future is the following one:

"A photo-composing department in which all type matter is set with a photo-typesetting machine, doing the work quicker and better than it is done today. Simultaneously with the typesetting the illustrations will be photographed in the photo-engraving department and the negative stripped into position and combined with the type. The resultant product will be a photographic negative or positive of the entire page. This will be printed onto a sheet of metal; will be chemically treated; will be planographic or slightly intaglio or relief in character, and will be immediately ready for the press."

A number of inventions that are seeking to make such a newspaper a reality have been made, and although they have not offered a practical solution of the problem they have received widespread attention and thorough examination in practical tests. We refer to such innovations as the Uhertype of Vienna, the Teletypesetter, Rutherford's inventions, further the Orotype of Max Ullman of Zwickau. Experts of excellent repute intensely at work on this problem, are, among others, Prozelt of Budapest, Arthur Dutton (Flickertype), Walton, Bawtree, Cornwall, August-Hunter, Bagge and Friedman-Bloom.

"The Times" of Blackpool, England was printed with the help of a photographic composing machine; the films were made and the paper printed by the offset method. Of course no mats were used. This experiment, however, was discontinued because the corrections caused too many difficulties and the insertions of last minute news entailed great loss of time.

Before closing this chapter, the writer would like to include in this compilation an article which will no doubt prove interesting reading to not only stereotypers but all members of the newspaper production crafts. Although it mentions a mat in a cursory manner, its contents place it, in a round about way, in the category of ways and means to eliminate stereotyping.

In 1874 an American printing craftsman, being of an inventive mind and also possessing a prophetic vein, envisaged the production of a daily newspaper in a way perhaps never before imagined by a printer. The genius in question proposed to show the world a method of printing a half million copies of a newspaper within a single second. Partly because the idea is even today of a novel nature, and also owing to the fact that this prophetic inventor mentions the use of a special mat, we embody his description of the process in this compilation. His mat is not made of paper stock as are today's dry mats; it is made of a cement compound composed of soluble glass, a chemicalized gum of powerful adhesive properties and a third substance of a purely organic nature. The latter is known only to the inventor.

The descriptive article carries the caption, "The Mechanical versus the Scientific," and reads as follows:

"Since Gutenberg, Faust and Schoeffer gave us the present art of printing, four and one-third centuries have passed away. The most enterprising of the newspapers of 1874 are composed and printed in the same manner and with the identical materials as were employed for the first Latin Bible of Mentz. Modifications have been made; of radical changes there have been none, though our demands for printed work have grown a million fold. While in other matters we have thrown aside the mechanical and adopted the scientific methods, in printing we have multiplied the old instead of creating the new. Yet we declare that while matter has its limit, the possibilities of science are illimitable. In printing, with its enormously progressive wants, why should we continue to do by slow and painful processes what science might effect in a flash? Think of the innumerable and expensive processes of printing, from the mining of metals for its type to the machinery for the finished newspaper. These alone prophecy a change. What is the nature of the change? If the printing of the future is to be done on scientific principles, what are they? What example can be given to convey the idea of a

[288]

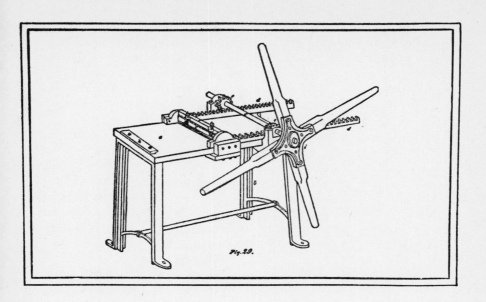

Fig.29.

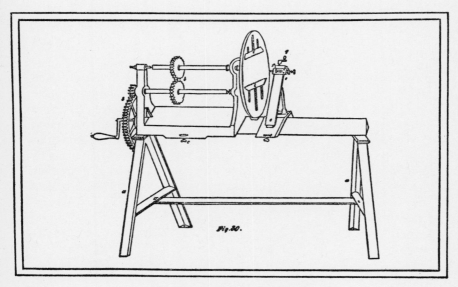

Fig.30.

109. Stereotype Plate Shavers

110. Power Shaving Machine

111. Autoshaver

possible radical improvement? It is the object of this paper to suggest the probable direction of such a movement. The change will certainly be no more wonderful nor more difficult than that which permits us to flash our ideas a thousand miles in a minute of time. It is to be brought about by force—force properly directed to its end. We do our writing by electricity; why not throw aside our ponderous machines and print our newspapers with it. With our present knowledge of the forces and of chemical changes and their results, we should be able today to print a half million of newspapers within a single second. The forces at our command do not stop to think whether they have one sheet or a million to contend with; they do the work. Nitroglycerine does not weigh resistance, it forces it. Steam power long since reached its zenith, and the struggles of the fast-machine manufacturers remind us that the limit of mere machine power is at hand. We can get more speed and more power for less weight, less room and less money and may, if we will, meet the requirements of the age, were they a thousand times greater than they ever will be.

"How is this to be done? No one can dare to say in one age, exactly and in detail what the usages of the next will be. All will depend on the wants which always, sooner or later, effect new discoveries. But as one age is necessarily the father of the next, we may by analogy arrive at a fair guess. As the past was the age of steam—artificial or mechanical force—so the future will be the age of electricity—natural force. The precise way in which it may eventually be used can only be suggested afar off. But the writer is satisfied that with our present knowledge of science, we should print at least one hundred thousand papers in the time it now requires for the printing of a single paper. The sun prints our photographs, electricity carries our messages; the printing of paper is alone the work of the machine.

"In suggesting a method, we have only to say that for our electrical effects and chemical changes we have selected forces and substances in a manner purely arbitrary, and only analogous to such as may be produced in some similar process. We are suggesting those possibilities and probabilities we have full warrant to suppose within our reach. In electricity and chemical change we have our forces which are infinite in power; in nature we have material equally infinite in its variety and capacity for combination. What matter then, if for illustration we choose one substance or another; the right one will surely be found. Whether or not we have for the moment substituted a plausible chemical combination, rather than given the exact result of our experiments, the reader may determine for himself.

"We are to make an eight-page or quarto newspaper, like the 'New York Times,' for instance. The paper is to be of good quality, but light and thin. The journal is to be made by the 'manifold' process. It will be printed therefore on one side only. The inside pages will be blank, which defect, if defect it be, will be more than compensated for by the other advantages of the system. All the co-operative papers in the country could be printed by it in one second. The reading matter will be very black and brilliant, sharply defined, indelible, and as cleanly as white paper. Smaller type than agate will be perfectly plain. The composition of the paper will not differ from that now in use. Type are not necessary to the process, for a written sheet will answer precisely the same purpose. It is only supposed that the uniformity and clearness of the present mode of composition will be considered preferable. The great feature of the process and the saving in it, will be, that whereas the morning paper of today must go to press at two o'clock, A.M., in order to get its edition off by six o'clock, the new paper will not go to press until two minutes before six o'clock, and will have the whole edition ready for delivery at six o'clock precisely. This is a saving of four hours, during which time all important news and telegrams may be set up, and the full and exact news of the world up to within ten minutes of six may, at farthest, be ready when the clock strikes. It was stated above that the paper 'would not go to press' until the time given. That was hardly accurate, for no press is used. The paper is set up in sticks placed on galleys and proved and corrected as usual. Any type now in use may be employed. A certain space is left on the plate for early morning news. The form being now as nearly ready as it can be made at present, let us go to the paper room.

"The paper is manufactured to order. In the vats of paper pulp there is introduced a small quantity of a simple chemical substance, which, under given conditions, decomposes instantly. This, practically, is the ink used in the process. It is white at this time, and is thrown 'in a lump' in vats of white paper pulp. With this exception the paper is manufactured in the regular way, is cut into sheets of the proper size and taken to the newspaper establishment. Here it is piled one ream upon another, until the amount of paper needed for the whole edition of the publication is in line. The paper rests upon a plain copper plate, coated with silver.

"To return to the form. It is now necessary to complete the making up, to get in the latest news and to print the paper. The rest of the type is placed, the whole is thoroughly planed down, and then comes the making of the matrix, a short, easy and simple process. A copper plate is chosen, the full size of the form. The surface of the plate is covered to the depth of a sixteenth of an inch with a heavy, insulated cement compound, composed of soluble glass or silicate of soda, a chemicalized gum of powerful adhesive properties, and a third substance of a purely organic nature, which need not be made known here. The plate is placed over the types, and is pressed close to their surface, so that on removing the plate the matrix appears stamped out clearly to the bottom of the coating (i. e., to the copper surface), and showing the metal through the stamped places. The process need not take more than three minutes. The plate, when removed, dries almost instantly, and is then placed with the stamped side down, upon the pile of paper. It will be readily understood, that all parts of the matrix-plate being covered with insulated material, except the parts 'stamped out' by the types, there is really no impediment to electrical force wherever the type mould appears on the surface of the plate. If, therefore, we apply the galvanic battery to the upper surface of the metal plate, it will be received at once and transmitted as soon as charged, through the matrix impression, to the paper upon which the plate rests. All the rest of the under surface of the plate being insulated, electricity can touch the paper nowhere but where the matrix permits. It is precisely as though a stencil plate were laid over a substance, while another substance was laid over to blacken it,—only the one is a mechanical and the other a chemical force. It has been stated that the pile of paper rested upon a silvered plate; what is now the course of the electricity? It must pass from the top to the bottom of the paper. It will pass through the prepared substance of the paper, blackening it into letters in its course, and when it reaches the bottom plate the edition of the journal will be completed. The electricity would pass were the pile a mile high. The spark cannot choose, but keep upon its direct path; straight and sure as the lightning flash, it will go wherever the hand of man chooses to direct it. In this instance a proper use of decomposing and conducting substance in the paper effects the end.

"This is all. If it is not simply enough explained, a little thought will make it clear. Without cuts the explanation of the matrix is difficult. But nothing has been stated not warranted in electrical science and chemistry. It is well known that the point of a needle will hold millions of sparks enclosing the electric force. It is upon this quality that we rely in order to make an exact, purely cut, clear impression, where the electricity, through the open stamped figure of the matrix, strikes the paper and blackens it, as lightning does the oak in its downward course.

"The ways in which the scientific printers of the future will employ methods, of which the above is a mere crude suggestion, are almost illimitable. In book manufacture it will produce a library per minute. If it should be thought better, the printer may take a roll of chemicalized paper and run it between two matrixed cylinders, both charged with electricity. By this means both sides could be printed instantaneously, for the paper could be so prepared that its two surfaces alone contain the decomposing mixture. As this would be a press without ink, and with no danger from offset, it could be run to five times the speed of the fastest of our present presses.

"In what way the new processes may be applied to colored printing, will also be an interesting subject for future printers. It is a vista almost too bright for realization, unless the mind be led to it step by step. For it is well known that the action of electricity can be made to seize and develop the most magnificent tints and colors within the bounds of natural things. The possibilities in this direction of elevating printing to a science, will bring about wonders which might be difficult of belief to those who have not observed the daring, original tendency of modern thought, and the boldness of experimental science. The motto of the coming age will be 'all things are possible.'

"It has been stated here that type were not necessary to the process under consideration any more than are presses or printing ink. It is simply that matrices may as easily or more easily be made without type. Why may not an editor write upon a plate prepared as described and use it just as the large matriced plate was employed. He would be able to give autographic comments on the latest news, place his column plate under the large matriced plate and have his hundred thousand edition printed and delivered with news matter and editorial comments, all within a short half hour.

"In commerce the matter might be largely utilized. The merchant may send out his autograph circular at an eighth part of the present cost. He need only write it on a varnished plate, place it on his pile of prepared note paper, apply the battery and the thing is done.

"Indeed the possibilities of the art of printing for the near future are illimitable. All that it needs is the practical, money-making, utilizing genius, of the sort that moves and generally rules the world, to get the process or analogous methods into practical shape for use.

"We have but rudely outlined the kind of change which eventually must take place. In its details no single method will become universal, but something at least as startling as the printing of half a million newspapers in an instant of time must come about, and it will come much sooner than most people imagine."

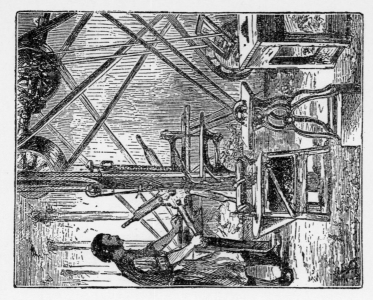

113. Planing and Beveling

112. American Beveling Machine

115. Shaver

114. Hand Planing Machine

CHAPTER NINE

RUBBER AND PLASTIC STEREOTYPING

BEFORE RECORDING the historical development of such stereotypes, a few words pertaining to possible innovations in the domain of stereotype mats—a glance into the future as it were—might be of interest.

Looking into the future, there is on the horizon a new possibility—as yet, however, not a concrete probability. I refer to the use of plastics in the making of mats; in other words, a dry mat made out of paper pulp but covered with some plastic material. (To avoid any confusion of ideas, the so-called "Plastic Mats" that are on the market at the present time are not made of plastics. They only carry the trade-mark name "Plastic.")

Definition of the term "plastic": A plastic is a synthetic polymerized "substance." It is thus not to be confused with the synonyms of plastic—flexible, pliable, etc.

The first forerunner of plastics we are today experimenting with appeared in 1868 when the supply of elephant ivory ran low and forced higher prices of billiard balls. An American manufacturer offered a prize of $10,000 to anyone who could find a substitute for ivory. A young New Jersey printer, named John Wesley Hyatt (of later ball bearing fame) spurred on by the prize, treated cotton celluloid, the first plastic. Twenty-two years of non-activity in the field—and then in 1890 Dr. Adolph Spittler of Hamburg, engaged in trying to find a white blackboard for schools, mixed some cow's milk with formaldehyde. He obtained a shiny horn-like substance and thus came the second plastic. Its base was casein. It was used to make buttons or buckles. Again all was quiet on the plastic front, when in 1899 Dr. Leo Baekland made the third plastic out of carbolic acid and formaldehyde, and named it "bakelite." Since that day Dr. Baekland obtained over four hundred patents and an army of chemists throughout the country devoted their time and attention to the making of plastics. Today hundreds of articles made of this legion of plastics are as widely divergent as buttons, timing gears, radio cases, knobs, instrument dials, steering wheels, baby carriage frames, scales, linings of beer cans, etc. And those articles, made of plastics, are sold in immense quantities. It will be far beyond the space allotted the writer to give even a partial list of the chemicals and materials used today to produce plastics.

A word concerning quantities produced: Henry Ford manufactures a plastic of soy beans at the rate of one thousand pounds a day and the Bakelite Corporation produces many millions of pounds per annum. Of late new kinds of plastics have appeared in printing plants all over the United States. Plastics are moldable, many are composed in part of cellulose. Because of the fact that this quality and this raw material constitute part of dry mats, inventive minds in all parts of the world aware of these facts are increasingly occupied in trying to make mats of plastics. Here in the United States we already have had three such mats, namely the Williamson, the Bakelite and the duPont mats. These products did not make the final grade, principally due to the fact that they could not withstand heat of 600° F. Otherwise they produced some really good results and have, therefore, encouraged experimenting in many factories.

The plastic mat of the future will probably be very pliable when heated, mold easily and deeply, will be fusible and thus can be used over again. It probably will have no shrinkage and will resemble a sheet of wax which will be spread upon a paper base acting as carrier.

An interesting sidelight on the supply question is contained in an article which appeared recently, and of which a short excerpt is cited:

"A scientific solution to a surplus crop problem that has threatened the whole economy of Brazil will be put to its first real test in May. A five-story pilot plant, located in the center of a huge coffee warehouse in Sao Paulo, will begin the manufacture of plastics from unroasted coffee. The project is sponsored by the National Coffee Department of the Brazilian government.

"The Product: Coffee plastic, dubbed 'cafelite,' is produced from green coffee beans by a process which involves the extraction of certain chemical constituents, a relatively simple chemical treatment of these substances, and their reintroduction into the resultant coffee bean flour. Because the complex chemistry of the coffee bean provides the entire range of compounds necessary to the formation of plastic materials, including bulk material, plasticizers, and dyes, no extraneous materials need be added in manufacture.

"Cafelite is adaptable to a variety of uses, such as flooring materials, insulating and acoustical wallboard, roofing materials, and the whole wide range of molded products to which synthetic plastics have been adapted.

"Effect of Plastics: Cafelite as a finished plastic product, either thermoplastic or thermosetting, probably won't compete with established plastics in the United States. Instead, it will come into the picture here as an ingredient in the manufacture of other plastics."

In this recording details of a number of processes for rubber and plastic plate stereotyping will be given together with criticisms offered by actual users.

Plates made of rubber appeared on the American scene in 1846. In that year the first American patent on rubber stereotyping plates was granted to Josiah Warren, who sought to protect by these letters patent: "First, the mixture of shellac, tar and sand as a substitute for type metal. Second, the use of shellac as a basis to form a substitute for type metal, whether it be mixed with the substance I have mentioned or with other substances of a similar nature. Third, also the use of clay, clay mixed in sand in various preparations, also of gum arabic, beeswax, stearine, tallow and oil, for the purpose of engraving or forming matrices or molds in which to make casts for typographical purposes, of the material and in the manner substantially as herein set forth. Fourth, the use of clay as a basis from which to form matrices or molds as aforesaid, whether it be mixed with the materials mentioned or whether the substances be used instead of them are substantially of the same nature."

Several years later, in 1853, L. Westbrook was granted a patent on rubber stereotype plates. Westbrook invented a new and improved composition of matter as a substitute for type metal for the purposes of stereotyping. He explained not only his composition proper but also for the first time gave a description of a method of making such plates.

"He first takes shellac and plumbago or graphite, of each three parts, to which he adds one part of asphaltum, melts and mixes them thoroughly together. He then takes 13 parts gutta-percha in its crude state and cuts it into fine shreds with a cutting machine constructed for the purpose. He then puts the gutta-percha and the above described compound into a grinding apparatus constructed for the purpose. He then makes a solution of sulphate of copper in water in the proportions of one pound of sulphate of copper to one gallon of water. This solution, sufficient in quantity to cover the mass, is then heated to about 212° F. and passed through a tube or siphon into the mass in a regular stream while the grinding apparatus is set in motion and the whole passed through it, after which the new compound thus formed is passed between iron rollers that are immersed in the heated solution of sulphate of copper and water in the same proportions as described above. It is rolled out into thin sheets, and then, if found free from foreign substances, it is ready for use. The object of grinding and working the compound in the above described solution is to destroy its elasticity and ductility and to render it sufficiently and permanently hard and cohesive when formed into plates, casts, dies, molds or forms to withstand the necessary pressure or force requisite to produce the desired result. The new compound thus prepared, he immerses it in hot water, and when sufficiently soft he works it into the desired shape with his hands, being careful to keep a smooth and polished surface on one side by means of rubbing over it finely powdered ivory black or graphite. He then places the polished surface on the type, engraving or other form from which a facsimile is desired to be taken. He then puts them into a press with a smooth and level bed plate and platen, between which and on each side of the form to be taken, are placed two bearers of solid material ⅛″ thicker than the type or form. The platen of the press is then brought down until it presses firmly on the bearers, where it is retained until the composition becomes cool and hardened, which requires from five to ten minutes, when it is then taken out of the press and the composition is removed from the form, and it is then an exact matrix or mold of the form on which it has been impressed. He then places this matrix or mold on a block of mahogany or other hard wood of the desired length and breadth and ¼″ thinner than the bearers; and after preparing another portion of his composition in the same manner as described above he places it on the mold, puts it in the press, and brings the platen down to the bearers, as before, and retains it there until it is cool. Then it is taken out, the mold removed, and the plate, being an exact facsimile of the original, is ready for printing."

The next step was undertaken in 1864 by Alfred Leighton, a color printer of London. He claims in his patent that his modification of the stereotyping process in use at that time, consisted in the novelty that his plates were elastic, being made of India rubber compound. He also claimed that his discovery materially enlarged the capabilities of letterpress printing. Leighton's mold was formed from an ordinary font of type or engravings. A sunk copy was first made in gutta-percha, then a copy was made in plaster of Paris, and from

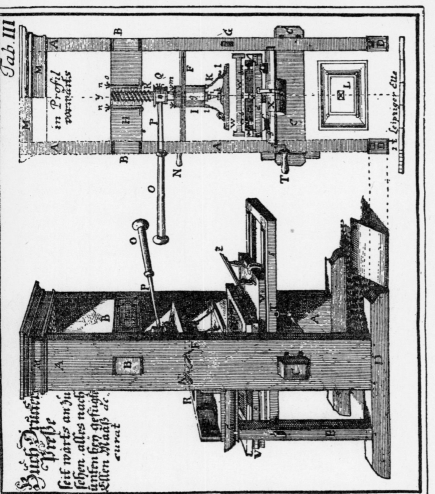

116. Printing Press (1720)

117. Stanhope Press (1800)

this the sunk matrix or mold in metal. The compound was pressed into the mold and at the back a plate was applied, formed with grooves and ridges on its surface. The effect of heat was to vulcanize the compound, and the ridges allowed the back of the surface to spread or give way with the pressure, and thus relieve and equalize the pressure on the face when the surface was in use. Leighton's invention was, after several minor improvements in the process of making these flexible stamps had been devised, quite a success in England, being very largely carried on in different parts of that country. The trade itself made various improvements, and it was universally claimed that an India rubber stereotype gave nearly as delicate an impression as ordinary type or a wood-block. However, it was not until quite recently that these so-called rubber stereotypes were improved to a degree that they were recognized by the trade as usable for certain printing work.

In 1905 a circular of the Skandinavisk Exprestypi Company of Copenhagen announced the production of a perfected process of making cuts from all descriptions of types and plates. The claims were that the work could be done in a few minutes by the printer without recourse to the stereotyper or electrotyper. A plastic mass was prepared, apparently of celluloid, and from this the first cut was made in about 15 minutes and each succeeding cut in 5 minutes. The material of which the cuts were made being a chemical substance, no planing or drilling was necessary, the edges only being required to be cut and they could then be fixed directly on the block by an adhesive substance the recipe for which was part of the process.

Comparatively recent developments in this art are: The *Paramats*. These are rubber stereos. A piece of mat is put on the form and beaten with a brush. The mat is dried and a sheet of uncured rubber is laid thereon. It is then pressed with a moderate application of heat, the rubber being dough-like. Then the cast is vulcanized. This paramat is praised as a substitute for plaster and lead molding.

The *Bakelite rubber stereotype*, which is made with a special Bakelite material. It is claimed that matrices produced from this material reproduce every detail in the original and that it is therefore possible to obtain rubber stereotypes which are exact replicas of the original. It is further claimed that such stereotypes are serviceable for much longer runs than those produced from a normal mat, as many as three quarter million copies having been printed from one rubber stereotype. Two grades of Bakelite rubber stereotypes are being produced, one of which is suitable for the reproduction of stereotypes or any solid matter, and the other for the reproduction of type. The Bakelite Corporation states that the time will come when this rubber can be used in general newspaper work.

The *Holite mats:* Holite is made of a patented plastic material by the Holite Press in London. Raw Holite exposed to heat and pressure becomes hard and remains hard. The method of making a mat by raw Holite is performed in the same manner as with a paper mat. The original is first cleaned with a paste consisting of graphite and olive oil or vaseline, then shoved under the press into position on top of the matrix, and left standing for about 5 minutes under the influence of pressure and heat. The back of the mat thus obtained is smooth while the face shows the picture. The mat thus made can again be placed under the press without change of its form through heat or pressure. It is then covered with another Holite plate and subjected to a second molding process. The result is a new plate true to the original and which takes the qualities of the mat made of Holite. The use of these plates is made in the same manner as with any "Druckstock" in the flat form press. Thin Holite plates can be used for printing on rotary presses. A dry mat can be finished in 5 minutes. To complete a Holite plate takes 9 minutes. A set of four-color plates can be made ready for use within 30 minutes and this shows, in comparison to electrotypes, a great saving in time. It is claimed that from one Holite plate millions of impressions can be made without any great wear and tear or deterioration. Holite plates are uninflammable; acids, alkalis, heat, cold and moisture do not affect them, and climatic changes are without harmful influence.

The finishing is done as with any other stereotype or electrotype plate. Holite plates withstand heat up to 302° F. It is maintained that in general the Holite, as soon as heat is applied, not only flows and requires little pressure, but that the resultant dot formation is excellent; in fact much better than in ordinary stereotype production. The point is stressed that complete newspaper pages with text, line and halftones, perfect in every detail, have been printed by the Holite stereotype plates, the latter having been curved for rotary newspaper printing. So much for the advantages claimed for Holite plates.

The critics state that Holite plates will not stay flat, that mailing costs may be cheaper than for electrotypes or stereotypes, but not as cheap as for mats, that one can cast a stereotype in 2 to 3 minutes whereas a Holite plate takes 15 minutes. In contrast to Holite material, stereotype metal is usable over and over again, and the price of paper mats is infinitesimal compared with that of Holite mats. Further, correcting and preparing presents a difficult job and Holite plates cannot be stored like stereotype mats as Holite bends and cracks.

The Palaplates: This printing plate is an invention of the Palatine Engraving Company of Liverpool, and is manufactured from specially selected synthetic materials.

For the duplication of color halftones, halftones, line blocks and type, the makers claim for the Palaplate perfect reproduction of the original. There is also the saving of wear on the inking rollers due to the smoothness of the plates. It is further claimed that being a pica in thickness these plates can be worked along with electrotypes and stereotypes if desired.

The make-ready is nil. A saving in ink consumption of from 15% to 20% is claimed for these plates. The peculiar warmth of the plate as against cold metal plates makes for better printing. Great wearing properties are claimed, and as Palaplates are about ⅛ the weight of stereotypes there is a material saving in mailing costs.

Indentically the same criticisms have been proffered concerning Palaplates as have been recorded in the paragraphs dealing with Holite stereotype plates.

The Glazier Process. This is an English invention using a plastic compound for the manufacture of its plates. It is claimed that plates made by this process are identical with plates made by Holite and Palaplate stereotyping. As an especial advantage it is claimed that stereotypers have been looking for a molding medium which will give perfect dot formation without excessive pressure, and that this advantage is supplied by the Glazier method, because immediately heat is applied it flows and requires little pressure and the resultant dot formation is far in advance of that attained in ordinary stereotype production. The Glazier stereotype is transparent and especially produced for stereotyping by newspapers and for use by printers on exceptionally long runs.

The criticisms levelled by stereotypers against the Glazier plate method are that corrections cannot be made, nor can the plates be pieced or made up; that after use they are valueless. Furthermore, that they are inflammable and irregular in thickness, that pressure produces defects, the plates wear, and that being resilient and nonconductors of heat the plates recede from contact. Many experts state that Glazier plates, as well as all of these new introductions in plastic stereotyping offer great difficulties to newspaper stereotypers. Success in flat stereotyping was not duplicated in newspaper stereotyping. With metal the paper mat casts down easily to the dot, which is not the case with all of these plastic stereotype plates. However, all critics agree that plastic plates mold satisfactorily by the cold process.

Cebotype Plastic Base Printing Plates: This new plate was invented by C. E. Boutwell of Birmingham, Ala. The plates are known as Cebotypes and are molded from a material known as Cebite. The plates are of an ivory color, slightly flexible and resistant to wear. For this process it is claimed that it attracts the ink film, is not porous, the same register is obtained as exists in the original forms, duplication of screens up to 150 line is effected, no squeeze is necessary to force the ink film out to the edges of the printing surface, no stretch occurs in curing, and that Cebotypes may be used for flatbed or rotary color register work. It is further claimed that they are not subject to corrosion or defacement from atmospheric conditions, and that they keep indefinitely.

The making of Cebotypes is as follows: These plates are duplicates of either type forms or photo-engravings, or a combination of both. The forms are locked with bearers. The form goes through a molding press and a mold is made in a period of 11-12 minutes. This mold may be used for making any number of duplicate Cebotype plates.

"Cebite" Sheeting is placed upon the mold, and both are put into a heated hydraulic press which is closed and the plates formed under heat and pressure. They are cooled before removing from the press, stripped from the mold and the surplus material is trimmed off. Then follow the shaving, routing and mounting operations.

A new plastic material called "Dermacell," made of a celluloid base, has been employed in the manufacture of a mat called "Vulkamat" by the most important dry mat factory in Germany. The claims for the Vulkamat are: no raveling, fuzzing or peeling; also no need of packing since the back of the mat is entirely smooth. When once molded, the depth is retained, the product does not curl up and is unbreakable. It is molded on a heated direct pressure molding press. This new mat has been used extensively in job shops and newspaper plants with signal success.

118. Columbia Press. Philadelphia 1813

119. Donkin Press

Machines for making plastic printing plates are manufactured by a number of European and American corporations. As examples: The American Evatype Corporation of Deerfield, Ill., has placed the Evatype precision rotary printing plate vulcanizing press on the market. The platens of the press are heat-treated and ground for extreme precision. The press is used for the molding and making of flatbed as well as cylinder rubber plates. The Lake Erie Engineering Corporation of Buffalo, N. Y., the American Type Founders Co., Elizabeth, N. J., and the H. H. Heinrich Co. of New York City, manufacture an extensive line of everything needed to make rubber plates. These corporations place special stress on the fact that very little equipment is necessary in the production of rubber plates, and that one single piece of equipment—a vulcanizing press—is almost wholly responsible for the finished accuracy of the work.

Geo. Washington, Jr., of Morristown, N. J., is the inventor of a photoelectric engraving device which he has adapted to making original cuts out of sheet celluloid.

While the use of celluloid cuts is not new, the present method of engraving the sheet is distinctly so. The heated stylus vibrating or oscillating at the rate of 360 cycles per second is operated by means of a photo-electric cell. As the photograph to be reproduced is scanned by the photo cell, the proper tone values of the copy are transferred to the celluloid sheet which is .016″ thick ($\frac{1}{64}$″). This is approximately one-quarter as thick as the usual engraver's zinc.

The oscillations of the engraving tool are controlled entirely by electricity so that the depth to which the stylus penetrates into the celluloid sheet as well as the spacing of the halftone dots is very accurately controlled.

Examination with a magnifying glass shows that the dots in adjacent vertical rolls are staggered. This is done to simulate or duplicate the appearance of a halftone made with the conventional halftone screen placed in the camera with the ruling at 45° to the vertical.

Of special interest to stereotypers is the fact that these halftone dots cannot be "undercut." The pyramidal shape of the tool assures that the dots are also pyramids. The mat cannot stick.

Tests have shown also that these celluloid cuts stand up well under the pressure required to mold dry mats. Whether mats can be dried on these celluloid cuts has not as yet been established.

If a transparent negative instead of a transparent positive were used for copy, the machine would make a reverse cut. It has been suggested that it may, therefore, have some possibilities in the production of rotogravure cylinders. No experiments along this line have yet been made.

Washington suggested that, inasmuch as the connection between the scanning system and the cutting tool is purely electrical, it is not necessary that they be mounted in proximity on the same machine. They might be separated by any distance. It appears, therefore, that it may be possible to adapt the machine to the long distance transmission of photographs and produce a celluloid cut at the receiving· end instead of a negative. It would be necessary, of course, that the scanning cylinder and receiving cylinder be synchronized, but that problem has already been solved for picture transmission.

Here in America controversies pro and con are being continually waged. Those experts who do not believe in any possible extended use of this kind of stereotyping agree on the following points: Starting with the beginning of the process, the first difficulty is that lead type cannot be molded in a plastic material with required heat from 300 to 320 degrees Fahrenheit without injury to the type. Type metal does not melt at temperatures up to 320 degrees Fahrenheit, but in addition to heat, pressure must be applied and held for periods of from six to twenty minutes. There are some operators who claim that they can mold regular type forms in the plastics used for matrices, but in most instances machine type is used and thrown into the hell box after serving for one mold, and no one is concerned over a few smashed characters.

Zinc and copper originals at times present problems in molding as the hard thermo setting plastic mat is solidified in contact with the original, and the latter if the least bit undercut cannot be separated from the mat without damage to the original. All originals must be removed from wood bases before molding, as wood will shrink and compress under heat and pressure required. Also every zinc and copper original must be examined carefully on the back, and precaution taken to fill up any acid holes as, at the pressure used in molding, these imperfections will be pushed through to the printing surface.

In closing this chapter a quotation in part is taken from an article written by Harold H. Cadmus, to wit: "Rubber plates, both hand engraved and molded, have become so popular for certain kinds of printing that one leading press manufacturer recently discovered that 60 percent of his presses have been adapted to their use. They are most popular in the West, and in Chicago four trade plants were kept busy making them. Approximately one-third less ink was required for rubber plates, and the cheaper analine inks can be used very satisfactorily with them. Other advantages of rubber plates are less time for make-ready, faster running, no need for impression beyond a "kiss," and their ability to print on materials often unsuitable for metal plates, such as glassine, glass, cloth, foil, etc. They are suitable for long runs on rule work and for the printing of tints on antique cover stock."

Development of synthetic rubber plates is proceeding rapidly and when they are perfected their use will eliminate the swelling that now occurs after the vulcanized rubber plates have been running on the press for several hours.

Rubber plates were unsuitable for the printing of halftones finer than 60 line, but for certain kinds of line and coarse screen printing, many printers had found them more satisfactory than either original line engravings (when hand engraved) or stereotypes and electrotypes.

Some paper bag and cellophane wrapper printers use these rubber and plastic plates because of the analine ink used, due to the high printing speed, necessitating rapid drying. Further, these plates have proven satisfactory in label and envelope work, on a number of paper box printing jobs, and also in the multigraph field.

120. Friedrich Koenig (1774-1833)

121. Koenig's Double Machine Built for the "Times." (London, 1814)

CHAPTER TEN

AUXILIARY NEWSPAPER OR SYNDICATE SERVICES

THE INVENTION and development of the so-called auxiliary newspaper or syndicate services increased the use of stereotyping to a
vast extent and served as a most effective propaganda for the adoption of stereotype matrices. Although there is no direct evidence
that the plants of these services produced any outstanding invention in stereotyping methods, the annual production of millions of
molded mats in these foundries have led to the discovery of a mass
of improvements in wet and dry mat methods, and in these plants
many defects and snags encountered not only in the primary stages
of mat use, but also ever since mats were introduced, were overcome
and in the end have made syndicate mat operations a routine matter, thus benefitting every phase of practical stereotyping.

This auxiliary service consisted in the making up of news matter
in a central office, taking casts and shipping the plates thus made,
known as "boiler plate" to various newspapers throughout the country. As time passed by, molded mats instead of metal plates were
shipped.

This idea of composing news matter in some central office and
taking casts to be sent to various newspapers who would thereby
save the expense of the original typesetting, appeared first in England about 1850. In 1858 Isaac Heyes of Sheffield and Samuel Har-
rison of the Sheffield "Times" started a partnership to conduct such
a business on a fairly large scale, and soon this firm did an important business supplying stereotyped columns all over England. In
1860 they formed a company known as the National Press Association of London, and further developed the system, sending out plates
cast in single columns (not yet in full pages) type high and of
metal.

The newspaper syndicate business in the United States was a
child of war. Conceived during an era of peace, its growth started
through an exigency which arose at the outbreak of the American
Civil War. The man who first syndicated newspaper material in the
United States later became one of the founders of the first American

Press Association, formed to gather the news and distribute it. He was Moses Y. Beach, owner and publisher of the New York "Sun." In December, 1841, Beach arranged to have a special messenger from Washington bring to New York a copy of President John Tyler's annual message to Congress. Thereupon he printed extra editions of one sheet containing it and sold them to a score of papers in the surrounding territory. He used the same type for the body of these editions, changing only the title head, so that it would be appropriate for the other papers. Their publishers were thus enabled to give their readers the whole text of the message without the delay and expense of setting it in type themselves.

The second attempt at syndicating news was made by Andrew Jackson Aikens of Barnard, Vermont. When President Polk's annual message to Congress was released, Aikens wrote to a Boston daily which already had the message in type and ordered several hundred impressions on one side of a sheet and filled the other side with local news, advertisements and editorials. He sent out this insert with his paper, "The Spirit of the Age." Meanwhile a new syndicated service was initiated in New York City by Moses Y. Beach and Alfred Eli Beach. One Staten Island paper began to buy printed "insides" from the Beaches.

In 1853 Ansel Nash Kellogg bought his "insides" from David Atwood and Horace E. Rublee, proprietors of the "Wisconsin State Journal" in Madison, Wisconsin. The first independent syndicate run by Atwood and Rublee made its appearance in 1861 in the form of an auxiliary service, the by-product of a daily newspaper. By the year 1863 they had a list of 30 weekly papers as customers. Kellogg foresaw the possibilities of the syndicate service growing into a profitable and important business, independent of any parent newspaper affiliation. He started his service in Chicago and hired as his foreman, James J. Schock. Schock set the type by hand, thereupon locked up the type he had set in a pair of forms (two 7 column pages) and carefully lowered them from the office on the second floor. Then he loaded them on a hand cart and trundled them through the dusty streets of Chicago to the customers' printing shops. There the forms were slid onto an old flatbed press, and on August 19th, 1865, the Kellogg Syndicate Service became the first to be printed from type set exclusively for country newspapers. Under such humble circumstances as these the first independent newspaper syndicate, the A. N. Kellogg Newspaper Company, began.

In 1860 James Wood patented improvements in making stereotype columns. Previously they had to be cast with a sort of bevel or shoulder at the sides. By the use of an improved casting box, Wood obviated this objection; the plates being flush with the type and ready for immediate use in a newspaper form alongside movable type matter.

B. B. Blackwell of New York also engaged in the business of manufacturing stereotype plates for the country press and in August, 1871, he invented a stereotype plate which could be made in two parts, consisting of a block or base and a thin surface plate, so arranged that they could be readily separated or locked together in the form. The advantage of this plate was that the bases could be kept permanently in the offices of the publishers, and after the first shipment the surface plates only required transportation. The saving thus effected in freight charges and in the quantity of metal required to conduct a business of this kind was very material. The utility of this form of plate was at once recognized, and other devices having the same object in view were patented in quick succession. Blackwell continued his business but a few months and was followed by M. J. Hughes of New York, who manufactured a plate of his own invention. It was in 1874 that Hughes patented a method of supplying auxiliary material in a cast-block plate without using any bases, beds or complicated furniture. All plates before being sent out were pressed down by level power machinery and run under the planing knife set exactly type high. In 1875 Hughes invented a reversible plate with different matter on each face. Inserted in each edge of the plate was a strong strip of combined paper and copper which held the plate firmly upon the wood base—which through being turned down or tacked in, threw the pressure of the quoins upon them. After one side had been used for printing the plate could be turned over and the matter on the other side printed.

Later on Hughes sold his patent to Damon and Peets of New York, who developed a successful business which they carried on for several years.

In 1875 Kellogg and Schock patented an important improvement in plates and their fastenings. Kellogg plates were drilled for screws or tacks with which to fasten them upon wood bases and could be cut to any desirable length by the publisher. When the publisher had printed from them and removed them from their bases which he kept for mounting other plates, he could ship them back to the supply house. The prime advantage of using these plates was the lower shipping charges since they were lighter than the old typehigh ready composition which had either solid metal bases or those with a thin core. Kellogg further improved his plates and fastenings in 1876 and 1878, and Schock perfected the "butterfly plate," one with a spring in the form of an "X" on the back. This spring was pinched together, inserted in a slot in the metal bases which were then being used, and upon expanding held the plate firmly to the base.

Kellogg sent an employee named Partridge to England to learn the "cold process" of stereotyping (not to be confused with the cold dry mat process). Partridge returned full of enthusiasm for the new process and Kellogg invested heavily in the necessary equipment, but the experiment proved a costly failure and was quickly abandoned.

The introduction of stereotype plates into the auxiliary plan met with some of the prejudice encountered by the Ready Print at its inception. Publishers, who had been suspicious of the use of Ready Print, were also opposed to plate matter for no reason apparently except a sense of consistency in opposing all innovations in their craft. For those with the "all-home-print" fetish it meant adding another word to their vocabulary of scorn for the users of auxiliary service. "Boiler plate" they called it, with the same derogatory imputation as they conveyed by the term "patent insides," and editors who filled their papers with plate matter cut to fit their needs were said to "edit their papers with a saw." Many years later the role played by this auxiliary service was eulogized with the statement: "It worked a revolution in the rural press of America, the far-reaching consequences of which defy measurement."

On June 11th, 1880, George J. Joslyn founded the Western Newspaper Union at Des Moines, Iowa. It was an amalgamation of the Omaha Newspaper Union, the Kansas City Newspaper Union and the Iowa Printing Company. (The term "Newspaper Union" was a misnomer in that it implied either some connection of ownership among the newspapers taking the service of these syndicate firms or a cooperative arrangement among those newspapers. In neither case was this true, but after 1870 most of the syndicates or auxiliary printing concerns called themselves "Newspaper Unions.")

The first of the Hearst syndicates was also started in 1895, and in 1906 Hearst organized his International News Service but disposed of it shortly after. In 1913 the Hearst organization started a new company called the Newspaper Feature Service, launched the

122. First Cylinder Press Made in America

123. The Bullock Press. First Machine to Print from a Continuous Web
of Paper. R. Hoe & Co.

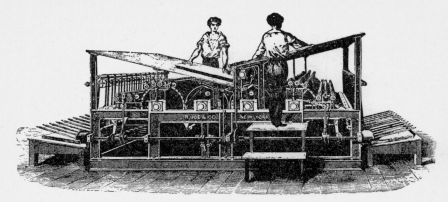

124. Patent Rotary Newspaper Perfecting Machine

125. Patent Rotary Newspaper Perfecting Press with from 4 to 8
Feeders

King Features Syndicate the next year, and soon afterwards the Premier Syndicate. All were merged with King Features Syndicate.

The King Features Syndicate acquired the Central Press Association, its subsidiary, the North American Printing Syndicate and the Editors Feature Service. Thus all four became the property of the Hearst chain. In charge was Joseph V. Connolly, one of the young leaders in the Syndicate field. Connolly was a reporter on the "New Haven (Conn.) Union" for six years before joining the editorial staff of the "New York Sun" in 1919. After serving in the World War he went over to the Hearst combine and managed the King Features Syndicate as president. He also is at the head of the International News Service, Universal Service, Central Press Association and International News Photos.

In 1909 the Scripps-McRae (later Scripps-Howard) chain of newspapers organized the NEA—"Newspaper Enterprise Association." It provides the large city dailies with everything they require except local and telegraph news. In 1910 the Central Press Association was founded by V. V. McNitt in Cleveland. This business was later taken over by the Hearst organization.

Other important syndicates are the George Matthew Adams Service, Inc., Wheeler Syndicate, McNaught Syndicate, United Features, Bell Syndicate, and North American Newspaper Alliance. News syndicates are the Associated Press, United Press Association, Ledger Syndicate and International Syndicate. In short, we have today in active business over 140 different syndicates.

Concerning the material sent out by these auxiliary services, at first it was confined to presidential messages. Shortly thereafter news items, feature material and advertisements were syndicated, and after a while non-political matter and some short stories followed. The services then enlarged their scope and included serial stories, agricultural information, children's reading, wit and humor, and general religious news. A momentous innovation was the syndicated sale of complete novels and stories from the "Century" and "St. Nicholas" magazines to country newspapers. In looking for further novel features to stereotype and sell to their customers, syndicates hit upon hiring special feature writers comparable to our present day columnists. Women's letters, travel letters were also included. Then comic strips for the Sunday editions followed, such as "Little Nemo." The Hearst combine presented articles by Dorothy Dix, Beatrice Fairfax and the well known "Mr. Dooley" stories by Dunne. Finally, sports news syndicates came into being and as a

[323]

culmination, a far cry from the one-sided page of yore, we have today 16 page weekly newspaper magazines of full color with great circulation, for example the "American Weekly" and "This Week."

One of the most important developments in the auxiliary news service is to be found in the "News Syndicates" and "Press Associations." Both furnish a newspaper with reading matter which members of its staff are enabled to supply. These associations sell state, national and international news. The foremost concerns in this particular field of supplying stereotype mats are the Associated Press and the United Press Association.

To recapitulate, up to 1850 syndicated services had to be limited to one medium of delivery to the publisher, namely printed sheets. Improvements in the art of stereotyping which came into general use in the United States about 1850 caused stereotype plates to be added to the printed sheet. From 1883 on, the printed sheet began to lose ground when the plate service was furnished. In 1895 for the first time stereotype mats instead of plates were sent to the newspapers. Today practically no plates whatsoever are shipped by syndicate services.

CHAPTER ELEVEN

PRESENT DAY DRY MATS

THESE ARE integral, homogeneous units delivered in sheet form of standard size, 20″ x 24″. They are made in any thickness between the limits of .020″ and .040″ to meet the preferences and needs of stereotypers under varying conditions and for use in all kinds of equipment. They are not laminated or pasted together and hence do not blister or blow up; neither do they deteriorate either before or after molding. They are delivered in standard cases containing 500 mats packed usually in water and air proof packages of 50 each.

During the course of the last decade demands made by the stereotyping foundries on performance of dry mats have been of a nature destined to improve the product to a great degree. In fact, present day dry mats are being used for plate work never before attempted. The demands made have forced dry mat manufacturers to devote all their inventive skill toward attaining signal improvements, and today's experimental work is being carried on in the most modern laboratories by chemists of great ability and experience.

Because of the prevalent opinion that the deeper the mold the better the printing, mats have been adapted to much greater depth of impression. The trend to effect savings in newspaper plants has resulted in the production of dry mats giving hitherto unheard of shrinkages, thus permitting of great savings in newsprint. As time has gone by the number of newspapers using illustrations has increased manifold, and with them the number of pictures in individual issues. The incessant demand for better halftones to produce better pictures has resulted in the making of so-called picture mats of supreme quality.

As a result of better picture mats finer screen work is being done throughout the industry; in fact, the work done by stereotyping with these mats is comparable to the best done by electrotyping methods. There is not only a possibility but a probability that in the not too far future we here in the United States will follow the example of the European plants, namely use stereotype plates for 75% of all letter press reproduction work, and the difference in cost between the electrotype and the stereotype has been found to be of paramount importance in the balance sheet of the purchasers and producers of printing. It may be confidently stated that no phase of the graphic art has developed more rapidly in recent years than stereotyping thru dry mats.

Stereotyping today offers a means of duplicating type matter and engravings with utmost fidelity to the original, and with a printing quality that cannot be distinguished from that of the original. Stereotyping in America is largely and increasingly employed in magazines and books where production standards are high. It is used for catalogue and commercial printing, for displays, wrappers, labels, containers—in fact in every phase of letter-press printing. No other reproductive plate making process has the economy of stereotyping. If only shipping and storage expenses are taken into consideration one needs only to compare the light, durable paper product to the heavy electrotype plate, the latter weighing approximately one ounce per square inch while it takes sixty square inches of dry mat to equal an ounce. The cost of packing electrotypes for shipping, including protection of the printing surface, is much greater than the equivalent steps in a stereotype mat. This should be borne in mind wherever the printed message is to be transported for publication elsewhere.

With the advent of these new dry mats plants have started to stereotype printed matter that is subject to rapid press runs, such as standard text forms and books of instruction.

But perhaps the most interesting evolution has taken place in the commercial job field. Originally all newspaper advertising matter went out on electros or wet mats. The cold molded dry mat cut in between, so to speak. Far superior to wet mats, particularly on halftone work, and much less expensive than electros, the dry mat presented a new problem of shrinkage as compared with electros and wet mats. Obviously the situation demanded an improved medium for those advertisers to whom the shrinkage was objectionable or whose copy demanded the utmost in faithful reproduction.

For such problems dry mats have been developed especially coated and processed, imparting to them all the necessary qualities for the work involved. By molding and baking such mats in a direct pressure machine, the resulting cast plate has the fidelity of the electro with the non-shrinking quality of the wet mat. Halftones sent out on such baked mats have proven themselves. They give

126. The Bullock Press Printing The New York "Weekly Sun" During The American
Institute Fair. 1869

127. Modern Newspaper Printing Press

newspaper reproductions that are at least as good as any other reproductions in the same newspaper. This has been borne out by usage and is not merely a matter of opinion.

The dry mat industry has indeed responded energetically to the new situation in the printing industry, as is evidenced by the manufacture of these new products. This article will by no means give a complete coverage of what has been achieved in the last few years, but these new dry mats that have proven their merit in hundreds of plants in the last few years are the following:

The Rapid Plastic Mat: This product is neither a wet nor a dry mat, as these two terms are generally understood today. It is delivered to the trade dry, coated with a chemical compound or facing, probably of the nature of the English wet mat coatings. In use the mat is well moistened, the coating becomes pliable and acts as in plaster of Paris molding. The claims made for this product are that through the application of the coating the grain or texture of the rough papier-mache mat is eliminated. It is dried under application of heat, does not warp since it is held on the form under pressure while drying.

The Blue Ribbon Mat: Blue Ribbon mats have been developed to meet the demand for a super-standard mat for newspaper advertising where conditions are unusually trying or the standards of excellence demanded are beyond the range of a standard price mat. Blue Ribbon mats have a specially treated surface which molds to unusual depth and retains the impression under all conditions. For large area solids, including halftone plates of unusual size, it molds uniformly throughout the whole area. Blue Ribbon mats are particularly intended for baking on the form.

The Electro Mat: It appears that this is a coated dry mat. The claims for this product are that it does away entirely with electrotypes for newspaper work and costs less than the cost of packing and shipping an electrotype of the same size.

The Silvertone Mat: Silvertones have been developed to bring out the ultimate possibilities of stereotyping in the finer fields of printing. They are invariably baked on the form. It is dependable in all the usual range of halftones from 110 to 150-line screens, and its rendering of type and line effects has a pleasing crispness. A distinctive quality of Silvertone mats is their dependable color register. Printing concerns specializing in color work are their steadiest users. They have done much to extend the field of stereotyping and to win it recognition as a process suited to fine magazine and commercial printing. The name "Silvertone" is derived from the peculiar sheen of the surface of plates cast from Silvertone mats.

Further illustration mats on the market are the Tonetex and the Wood-Hill mat. There has been one important argument against the baked quality mat. Users say the length of time involved in molding mats this way makes the price to the advertiser prohibitive.

However, this complaint calls for more effort on the part of the manufacturers. The solution of the problem may lay in developing a mat which would have the qualities of the baked mat, but the baking must be done in a separate steam table in order not to tie up the molding press. With such transfer mats one press could feed two or three steam tables, thus turning out a production which would enable advertisers to buy baked mats at a price they are more willing to pay.

The transfer mat may solve many problems of quality plus production. The quality will not be quite as high as that attained in direct pressure drying, but for some work will suffice. This entire phase of dry mat work is subject to rapid change in accordance with the demands of the trade.

An interesting fact: Although the mats are one of the most important and indispensable parts in the making of a newspaper, the cost of mats is approximately one-twelfth of one per cent of the total cost of operating a newspaper plant.

A contrast: The stereotype department of the United States Government Printing Office 50 years ago occupied two rooms and employed a superintendent, assistant, two experienced stereotypers and four laborers, who furnished all the stereotype plates required for the use of the office, and produced annually plates to the value of about $20,000. This department saved the Government annually more than $10,000, to say nothing of its marked convenience.

Today, bearing in mind that the Congressional Record, laws, many Congressional Reports and speeches are stereotyped, and electrotyped, it can be readily seen that a fairly good sized force is necessary and that a clean line has had to be established between the two processes and the work sent to each.

As a result of many years' experience definite rules have been established covering the length of time mats are to be held in storage in anticipation of recasting for reprints, although there are some classes of mats which are held indefinitely. For example, in the Plate Vault there are sections devoted to storage of large, tightly sealed metal boxes in which are kept stereotype mats of old laws. Very frequently there are compilations of these old laws. In that case a cast is made, folios and signatures are changed, and then new mats made from the corrected plates, the plates being then sent to press, the mats filed for future use.

Some of these old mats are over thirty years old and are still good for additional casts.

The stereotype work in the Government Printing Office can be divided into three classes: first, those jobs which are definitely assigned for plates; second, the jobs on which partial deliveries of printed copies are made from type, the forms being then sent to the foundry for plating; and third, jobs which have had short runs from type and the forms then sent to the foundry for what is called "Mat Only," the mats being stored for future use and the type destroyed.

All of this requires a filing system through which mats are available as needed, the value of which is difficult to estimate since very frequently calls are made for reprints which would require resetting of type were no mats in storage.

A recent survey showed that there are approximately 260,000 mats in the vaults of the Government Printing Office.

In answer to a frequent query by stereotypers: The question posed is whether used mats are of any value to mat manufacturers for re-pulping purposes, and what uses, if any, are made of old mats. The answer is that used mats are entirely unsuitable for re-pulping. Newspaper offices and job shops sell used mats to waste paper dealers, and they in turn dispose of them to paper mills to be utilized in the manufacture of low grade box paper and similar products.

Despite the fact that used mats are regarded as waste material by paper dealers, a number of uses are made of this material, such as for underlaying carpets, nailing on walls and ceilings for insulation against noise, for lining hen coops, for use instead of mulch paper for covering plants, and for one rather novel use as the following news item will show:

"A tomato grower in Australia found that old used mats made excellent protective collars for his plants against the depredations of cutworms. Other growers in the neighborhood immediately copied the idea."

David Atwood

Andrew Jackson Aikens

Ansel Nash Kellogg

Moses Yale Beach

James J. Schock

128.

V. V. McNitt

George A. Joslyn

Joseph V. Connolly

George Matthew Adams

H. H. Fish

129.

CHAPTER TWELVE

HISTORY OF STEREOTYPERS' UNIONS

In starting the compilation of historical data concerning stereo-typers' unions, a definition of the term "union" appears to be in order.

A union is a permanent alliance of employees for the protection and advancement of their rights and interests as peers or equals in rank, particularly with regard to working conditions. Unions in the present sense of the word were first formed under the designation of trade unions in England toward the end of the 18th century as a consequence of the enormous growth of the great industries, to protect the hitherto existing legal and customary working conditions, and particularly through the exploitation of juvenile and female workers which harmed the workmen who had learned their trade from the ground up.

Although the history of unions has been recorded since the beginning of the 17th century, and although this compilation covers only the origin and subsequent improvement of the art of stereotyping proper, yet undeniably the chapels, or unions, through the medium of their regular meetings and the exchange of experiences that doubtlessly took place at each such gathering of kindred spirits, have played a role in the development of stereotyping.

The designation "Chapel," given to the internal regulations of a printing office, originated in the great English printer, William Caxton who exercised the profession in 1474 in one of the Chapels in Westminster Abbey.

It is most probable that Caxton, after the manner observed in other monasteries, erected his press in one of the chapels attached to the aisles of the Abbey. His Printing Office might have super-seded the use of what was called the Scriptorium of the Abbey.

Eusebius, in his "Ecclesiastic History," relates that in every great Abbey, an apartment, called the Scriptorium, was expressly fitted up as a writing room, and here the Monks discharged their duty by copying manuscripts. Estates and legacies were often bequeathed for the support of the Scriptorium, and tithes appropriated for the express purpose of copying books.

The transcription of the Service books for the Choir was entrusted to boys and novices; but the missals and the Bible were ordered to be written by Monks of mature age and discretion. Persons qualified by experience and superior learning were appointed to revise every manuscript that came from the Scriptorium. The Monks of some monasteries were bitterly reproached for the extravagant sums they expended on their libraries.

The Monks, in these convential writing rooms, were enjoined to pursue their occupation in silence and cautiously to avoid mistakes in grammar, and spelling, and in certain instances authors prefixed to their works a solemn adjuration to the transcribers to copy them correctly. The following ancient one by Drenaeus has been preserved:

"I adjure thee, who shalt transcribe this book, by our Lord Jesus Christ, and by His glorious coming to judge the quick and the dead, that thou compare what thou transcribest, and correct it carefully, according to the copy from which thou transcribest; and that thou also annex a copy of this adjuration to what thou hast written."

In 1686 Joseph Maxon, an English letter cutter and mathematical instrument maker, Fellow of the Royal Society and Hydrographer to King Charles II, wrote a very interesting typographical work, entitled "Mechanical Exercises." At that time the demand for knowledge, and therefore for books, had become so general that in London twenty printers and four founders were quite inadequate for the supply.

A decree issued by Charles II restrained the number of master printers to twenty, and by this same act, the number of type founders to four. This decree was absurd and oppressive; the conditions imposed thereby were circumvented by dividing typography into the several trades of the master printer—the letter cutter, the letter caster, the letter dresser, the compositor, the corrector, the pressman, the ink-maker, besides several other trades which they took for their assistance, such as the smith, the joiner, etc.

In his "Mechanical Exercises" Maxon enumerates the following "Ancient Customs Used in a Printing House in 1650," and hands down the peculiar customs formerly observed with respect to that curious tribunal termed a "Chapel," as well as some other singularities in practice among the members of the art at this early period. We quote from Maxon:

"Every printing house is by the custom of times immemorial called a Chapel, and all the workmen that belong to it are members of the Chapel; and the oldest freeman is father of the Chapel. I suppose the style was originally conferred upon it by the courtesy of some great churchman, or men (doubtless when Chapels were in more veneration than of late years they have been here in England), who for the books of divinity that proceeded from the printing house, gave it the reverend title of Chapel.

"There have been formal customs and by-laws made and intended for the well and good government of the Chapel, and for the more civil and orderly deportment of all its members while in the Chapel; and the penalty for the breach of any of these laws and customs is, in printers' language, called a solace. The judges of these solaces and other controversies relating to the Chapel, or any of its members, were pluralities of votes in the Chapel, it being asserted as a maxim that the 'Chapel cannot err.' But when any controversy is thus decided, it always ends in the good of the Chapel.

"1. Swearing in the Chapel—a solace.

"2. Fighting in the Chapel—a solace.

"3. Abusive language, or giving the lie in the Chapel—a solace.

"4. To be drunk in the Chapel—a solace.

"5. For any of the workmen to leave his candle burning at night —a solace.

"6. If a compositor let fall his composing stick, and another take it up—a solace.

"7. Three letters and a space to lie under the compositor's case— a solace.

"8. If a pressman let fall his ball, or balls,* and another take it or them up—a solace." (* Ink daubers.)

These solaces were to be bought off, for the good of the Chapel; nor were the prices alike, for some were twelvepence, sixpence, fourpence, twopence, and one penny, according to the nature and quality of the solace. But if the delinquent proved obstinate or refractory and would not pay his solace at the price of the Chapel, they solaced him thus: "The workmen take him by force and lay him on his belly athwart the correcting stone, and hold him there, while another of the workmen, with a paperboard, gives him 10 pounds and a purse, viz., eleven blows on his buttocks, which he lays on according to his own mercy."

These nine solaces were all the solaces usually and generally accepted; yet in some particular Chapels the workmen did, by consent, make other solaces, viz:

"That it should be a solace for any of the workmen to mention joining their penny, or more, a price, to send for drink.

"To mention spending Chapel money till Saturday night, or any other before agreed time.

"To play at quadrats, or excite any of the Chapel to play at quadrats, either for money or drink. (This game was termed 'Jeffing,' and is always played with nine m quadrats, called 'Gods.')

"This solace is generally purchased by the master printer, as well because it hinders the workmen's works, as because it batters and spoils the quadrats, for the manner how they play with them is thus: They take five, or seven, or more m quadrats (generally of the English body) and holding their hand below the surface of the correcting stone, shake them in their hand and toss them upon the stone, and then count how many 'nicks' upwards each man throws in three times, or any number of times agreed upon; and he that throws most wins the bet of all the rest, and stands out free, till the rest have tried who throws fewest nicks upwards in so many throws, for all the rest are free, and he pays the bet.

"For any to take up a sheet, if he received copy-money; or if he received no copy-money, and did take up a sheet, and carried that sheet or sheets out of the printing house before the whole book was printed off and published.

"Any of the workmen may purchase a solace for any trivial matter, if the rest of the Chapel consents to it. As if any of the workmen sing in the Chapel, he that is offended at it may, with the Chapel's consent, purchase a penny or two-penny solace for any workman's singing after the solace is made. Or if a workman or a stranger salute a woman in the Chapel, after the making of the solace, it is a solace of such a value as is agreed upon.

"The price of all solaces to be purchased is wholly arbitrary in the chapel; and a penny solace may perhaps cost the purchaser six-pence, twelve-pence, or more, for the good of the Chapel.

"Yet sometimes solaces may cost double the purchase, or more; as if some compositor have (to affront a pressman) put a wisp of hay in the pressman's ball-racks; if the pressman cannot brook this affront, he will lay six-pence down on a correcting stone, to purchase of solace of twelve-pence upon him that did it; and the Chapel cannot in justice refuse to grant it, because it tends to the good of the Chapel; and being granted, it becomes every member's duty

[338]

[339]

130. Damon and Peets Advertisement. 1875

to make what discovery he can, because it tends to the further good of the Chapel; and by this means it seldom happens but the aggressor is found out."

Nor did solaces reach only the members of the Chapel, but also strangers that came into the Chapel and offered affronts or indignities to the Chapel, or any of its members; the Chapel would determine the solace: Example—it was a solace "for any to come to the King's Printing-house and ask for a ballad;

"For any to come and inquire of a compositor whether he had news of such a galley at sea;

"For any to bring a wisp of hay, directed to any of the pressmen."

And strangers were commonly sent by some who knew the customs of the Chapel, and had a mind to put a trick upon the stranger.

Other customs were used in the Chapel, which were not solaces, viz., "every new workman to pay half-a-crown, which is called his "bienvenue," or welcome. This being so constant a custom, is still looked upon by all workmen as the undoubted right of the Chapel, and therefore never disputed; he who has not paid his bienvenue is no member of the Chapel, nor enjoys any benefit of the Chapel money. If a journeyman wrought formerly in the same printing-house, and comes again to work in it, he pays but half a bienvenue. If a journeyman "smout" more or less in another printing-house, and any of the Chapel can prove it, he pays half a bienvenue.

"Using abusive language or giving the lie was a solace; but in discourse, when any of the workmen affirm anything that is not believed, the compositor knocks with the back corner of his composing-stick against the lower edge of his lower-case; and the pressman knocks the handles of his ball-stocks together, thereby signifying the discredit they give to his story.

"It is customary for all the journeymen to make every year new Paper-Windows, whether the old will serve again or no; because that day they make them, the master-printer gives them a "way-goose," that is, he makes them a good feast, and not only entertains them at his own house, but besides gives them money to spend at the ale-house, or tavern, at night; and to this feast they invite the corrector, founder, smith, joiner and ink-maker who all of them severally (except the corrector in his own civility) open their purse strings and add their benevolence (which workmen account their duty, because they generally choose these workmen) to the master-printers; but from the corrector they expect nothing, because the master-printer choosing him, the workmen can do him no kindness.

These "way-gooses" are always kept about Bartholomew-tide; and till the master-printer have given this "way-goose," the journeymen do not use to work by candle-light.

"If a journeyman marries he pays half-a-crown to the Chapel.

"When a wife comes to the Chapel, she pays six-pence, and then all the journeymen join their two-pence apiece to welcome her.

"If a journeyman have a son born, he pays one shilling; if a daughter, six-pence.

"The father of the Chapel drinks first of Chapel drink, except some other journeyman have a 'token,' viz., some agreed piece of coin or metal, marked by consent of the Chapel, for them, producing that token, he drinks first; this token is always given to him who in the round should have drank, had the last Chapel drink held out; therefore, when the Chapel drink comes in, they generally say, who has the token?

"Though these customs are no solaces, yet the Chapel excommunicates the delinquent; and he shall have no benefit of Chapel-money till he have paid.

"It is also customary in some printing-houses that if the compositor or pressman make either the other stand still through neglect of their contracted task, then that he who neglected shall pay him that stands still as much as if he had wrought.

"The compositors are jocosely called galley-slaves, because allusively they are, as it were, bound to their galleys; and the pressmen are jocosely called horses, because of the hard labour they go through all day long.

"An apprentice, when he is bound, pays half-a-crown to the Chapel, and when he is made free, another half-a-crown, but is yet no member of the Chapel; and if he continues to work journey-work in the same house, he pays another half-crown, and is then a member of the Chapel."

These were the Chapel customs of the year 1650 Anno Domine!

Almost two centuries later, in 1830, in important printing houses, where manly workmen were employed, the "calling of a Chapel" was a matter of great importance and generally it took place when a member of the plant had a complaint to prefer against any of his fellow-workmen. He made the first intimation of his grievance to the Father of the Chapel, usually the oldest printer in the printing-house, who, when he found the charge could be substantiated, and that the injury supposed to have been received was of such magnitude as to call for the interference of the law, summoned the members of the Chapel before him at the "imposing stone." There he received the allegations and the defense in solemn assembly, and dispensed justice with typographical rigor and impartiality.

The punishment generally consisted in the criminal providing a libation by which the offended workmen might wash away the stain that his misconduct left on the body at large. When the plaintiff was not able to substantiate his charge the fine then fell upon himself for having maliciously arraigned his companion, a practice which was marked with the features of sound policy, as it never loses sight of the "good of the Chapel."

This precise plan of a chapel was copied by members of the printing craft throughout Europe, and brought to America by immigrant printers. The preceding pages show that the "chapel" collected funds which were administered and used for the benefit of the chapel members. This basic idea of reciprocity and co-operation has been one of the most important objectives of all unions up to the present day. It should be noted that in the United States of America the International Typographical Union presents, with some modifications, the nearest approach to the English chapel. The designation "chapel" has been adopted to denote individual branches of American printing craft unions.

The earliest instance of co-operation among printers took place shortly before the outbreak of the Revolutionary War. Times were hard, especially for printers. Prices of provisions were high and steadily advancing; on account of the blockade the supply of firewood, the only fuel of the time, was greatly reduced and the price was beyond the reach of the printers. Taxes and rents were also increasing. The printers called a meeting for the express purpose of insisting upon an advance in their wages. They fixed what they considered a fair pay for their work and presented their demands to the newspapers of which they were employees. The papers consented to the increases except "The New York Gazette," owned by James Rivington. Upon his refusal to grant the increase the printers of his paper refused to work any longer at the old wage. Finding himself unable to print his newspaper Rivington yielded. The printers who had been receiving a wage of less than a dollar per day returned to their work.

The next instance of co-operation among printers in America occurred in Boston in 1786. The General Court of Massachusetts at its winter session of 1785 passed an act levying a duty of two-thirds of a penny on each copy of every newspaper and almanac printed within the state, to apply only to advertisements. Even in its altered form the law was not acceptable. In the issue dated July 27th, 1786 of "The Exchange Advertiser," published by Peter Edes in Boston, there appeared a notice signed by twelve Boston printers and their partners, as follows:

"To The Public"

"Monday next, the 31st instant, will complete one year since the Tax on News-Papers commenced. We have severely felt the injurious Restraint; and, respecting the size, in imitation of the diminutive Gazettes of Spain and other arbitrary governments in Europe, we must now reduce ours. Accordingly, after the last day of the present month, we shall be obliged to print our respective Gazettes on a smaller scale, excepting those published twice in the week, the prices of which will be enhanced proportionately. As Necessity alone is the cause, we hope for the sympathetick acquiesence of our good Customers. Those of them who are citizens of the neighbouring States, while they are enjoying the full exercise of the darling privilege of a free PRESS, will, it is humbly hoped, not suddenly withdraw the aid which their custom has hitherto afforded us. We are preparing, and shall soon publish, a respectful address to our fellow citizens, which will contain such observations on the act in question, and such a narration of the doings of the Legislature, as, we doubt not, will prove satisfactory to every honest friend of the revolution."

"BENJAMIN EDES & SON	PETER EDES	JAMES D. GRIFFITH
SAMUEL HALL	JOHN W. FOLSOM	BENJAMIN RUSSEL
JOHN MYCALL	ADAMS & NOURSE	STEBBINS & RUSSEL
EDWARD E. POWARS	THOMAS B. WAIT	ALLEN & CUSHING

"Boston, July, 1786."

Whether the signers of the protest were organized or whether they co-operated only when emergencies arose is not known. They probably remained in some sort of association in this particular instance until 1788, for it was not until that year that the objectionable stamp tax was repealed.

In 1788 the printers and booksellers of Philadelphia met to form regulations for the benefit of the trade. Isaiah Thomas of Worcester, Mass., attended, which indicates that the movement was national. Benjamin Franklin, although 82 years of age and not actively in business, was interested as always in matters connected with printing, and one of the meetings was held in his house. Thomas recorded the event, but neglected to give further particulars. Six years later, in 1794, the Company of Printers of Philadelphia was organized.

David Bruce and George Bruce were vice president and secretary respectively of the Franklin Typographical Association, formed in New York in 1799, the first printers' union in America. The first work of the union was to demand an increase in wages. Compositors and pressmen were getting $6.00 a week for 71 hours' work; they demanded $7.00 and obtained it.

The book publishers of that time were also printers and booksellers. In December, 1801 Mathew Carey of Philadelphia sent a circular to the leading booksellers throughout the country suggesting the formation of a co-operative association. The following March a committee of the booksellers of Baltimore issued a circular recommending a memorial to Congress requesting it to lay a duty on imported books. As a result of these two and probably other circulars there was held in New York in June, 1802 the first American Literary Fair, at which an association of booksellers and printers was formed, with Hugh Gains of New York as president and Mathew Carey as secretary.

The Society of Printers of Boston and Vicinity was formed in 1805 with Benjamin Russel as its first president. Its name was changed in 1808 to the Faustus Association. The New York Society of Printers was also formed in 1805.

Today there exists in the United States of America the International Stereotypers and Electrotypers Union. It comprises local unions spread all over the country. To record the historical development of each of these unions would, in so far as the essential facts are concerned, constitute a constant repetition. To afford a typical example of the arduous work encountered in the formation of such a union, and since it is the oldest union of the stereotyping craft in this country, a short historical sketch of New York Stereotypers Union No. 1 is offered on the following pages.

[It is to be greatly deplored that the men who were active in union work from the very inception of co-operative endeavor up to a few decades ago, failed almost entirely to keep a continuous record of events concerning proceedings of the union, events that today would constitute a history of great import. As it is, reference to meetings and minutes of such gatherings and many other vital matters are almost non-existent, or to say the least, exceedingly sparse and intermittent. Two descriptive articles have been written, one by James Pettiner and the other by M. A. Matthews, both of which shed light on the early history and proceedings of the New York Stereotypers Union, and of this material a restricted use has been made.]

It was between the years 1861 and 1862 that two finishers sitting next to each other discussing the signs of the times, concluded that the prospects of the trade were not very encouraging. There were only about half a dozen shops at that time, all using the plaster process of molding, and all but two independent in not being attached and belonging to any printing firm. Newspaper stereotyping had not been started, consequently the business required but a limited number of finishers. They became convinced that if the prevailing conditions continued, in a few years there would be a surplus of finishers and a consequent reduction in wages, for there were no restrictions of any kind on the employers, and as the shop in which they worked planned to take on as many boys, as apprentices, as they could use, and discharge them when they reached their majority, it was evident that that shop alone would in a few years duplicate the number of finishers employed at the trade.

This appeared to them to be a very serious matter, especially as the Civil War, then waging, the suspension of specie payment by the banks and the increasing premium on gold and silver lowered the purchasing power of the current money, increasing the cost of living, caused them to consider what prospect there would be to obtain an increase in wages, then $10 per week. A grave question was whether the finishers in the different shops would co-operate, especially as quite a number of them were of middle age and wedded to the old manner so long established. There was also very little intimacy between the different shops.

However, they concluded to write a request to the other shops to consider the condition of the trade and the advisability of endeavoring to obtain an increase in their wages from $10 to $12 per week. Having no authority, and also due to a subconscious fear of reprisal on the part of their employer, they signed the request "The Committee." The recipients of these letters were curious to know the object of such a meeting, and who were responsible for calling them together.

So on June 6th, 1863 a number of these artisans met in Tammany Hall, then located at the southwest corner of Park Row and Frankfort Street in New York City, and in that meeting there was

132. James Rivington

133. Reproduction of a Page from the Issue of the "Exchange Advertiser" of Boston, dated July 27, 1786. At the Top of the Fourth Column Appears a Notice of the Earliest Known Co-operative Action of American Printers

laid the foundation upon which the first stereotypers' union in the United States was reared.

In those days it took courage for workers to meet and discuss together their problems. The prevailing social system admitted little consideration for the workers of any class, and even less than that for those employed manually. Based primarily upon the theory that the less the wage the more amenable the worker, was rule with a rigid discipline, the effect of which manifested itself in many forms of injustices. Organizations of working men met with stern disapproval when they were allowed at all, and even the civil laws denied them the rights which are today firmly established and commonly enjoyed.

In this first meeting the finishers decided to make a request on their employers for an advance to $12 and to report at a future meeting. This meeting, the second, was held on June 13th, 1863, and it was reported that the workers of the largest shops, whose assistance was necessary, had accepted a compromise offer of $11 made to them by their employers. However, in this meeting a temporary chairman and a secretary were selected and a committee of three appointed to negotiate an increase in the wage scale to become effective three days later! The small attendance at the second meeting raised a doubt as to whether all the stereotype finishers would co-operate, and before the third meeting convened a written request was sent to each shop asking that conditions in the industry be studied with a view to eliminating some if not all of the hardships under which they worked, and appealing for support in the matter of the wage increase.

As a result of this wise action the third meeting, held on June 15th in the "Putter Mug" located on Frankfort Street, was attended by a majority of the finishers from all shops. Some were moved with a real desire to co-operate while others were moved more by curiosity to ascertain just who comprised the committee responsible for such an unprecedented step. However, a real organization was perfected, and before the assembly adjourned the action of the previous meeting in appointing a committee to negotiate a wage increase was approved. Thus was born the first scale committee. At that time the prevailing wage was $10 per week of 60 hours, and the demand was for a $2 increase. After a period of negotiation the committee reported back at a subsequent meeting that they had accepted a compromise of $1. This advantage was obtained before a formal organization existed; the men were eager to make use of this knowledge and meetings were held in July and August, 1863 for the purpose of creating a formal organization and consolidating the gains which had been procured.

It was at this time that stereotyping was begun on the newspapers, and those employed on them were inclined to form an organization independent of the finishers. For a time a confused situation existed because of this feeling, but the matter was finally settled to the satisfaction of all concerned. The two branches met on September 1st, 1863 and formally organized with a membership of 49 men. The president, vice president and secretary-treasurer were elected and the name "The Stereotypers Association" officially adopted. The constitution provided an initiation fee of $1 and dues of 25 cents per month. Admission to the union required "A candidate for membership must be a stereotype finisher or molder by the papier-mache method."

The new association had hardly begun to function when a new problem arose in the form of the electrotype. While this process was known as an adjunct to plate making, at that time it had a limited use. At the meeting of the "Stereotypers Association" on July 2nd, 1867 a communication was received from "The Electrotypers Union" proposing an amalgamation. A committee was appointed to pass upon the qualifications of electrotypers, as all of the latter except the molders were looked upon as unskilled laborers. There was a debate but no mention is made as to how the case was disposed of. This proves again what a regrettable circumstance it is that only very incomplete and desultory records of proceedings were kept in those historical years. In the years following many meetings and conferences in re wage adjustments were held, and such adjustments were effected, all accruing to the benefit of the stereotypers.

It was on June 6th, 1876 that the employers petitioned the association for a reduction of wages, omitting mention as to just how much this reduction was to be. Conferences were arranged and finally in October the representative of the employers declared that a reduction in the wage scale was an absolute necessity. He made the statement, repeated by employers many times since, that "the high wage rate was causing work to leave the city." He then asked for a $3 reduction in the scale, and in December the association acceded to the demand.

The benevolent activities of the union had for long been one of its outstanding characteristics, begun within five years of its organization. The first death recorded was in 1867, the entire union attending the funeral in addition to defraying the expenses. In the same year a donation was voted to the family of another deceased member, and in 1871 a permanent death benefit of $75 was established and made part of the constitution.

There is evidence that organizations of the stereotyping craft existed in Boston, Cincinnati and Philadelphia in 1863, as the minutes of the New York association record instructions to the secretary to notify the craft in those cities of its actions. Even though these organizations were active prior to the formation of the New York union there remains no record of their continuous existence. To the present New York Stereotypers Union No. 1 belongs the distinction of being the oldest in the stereotyping craft.

It was during the early '60's that the electrotype entered the field as an important factor in the printing industry. The electrotyping process was rapidly changing and reaching a stage of refinement that challenged the use of the stereotype for superior printing results.

The invention of the plating dynamo greatly reduced the time necessary for the deposition of the copper shell. Other improvements followed, and within a short time the electrotype displaced the stereotype in the commercial printing offices. The electrotypers and finishers became more conscious of their power now that their services were in greater demand, and at this opportune period "The Knights of Labor" appeared upon the scene. They first approached the Stereotypers Association in 1885, and a deputy of the Knights of Labor at that time proposed that the association make application for a charter. This demand was refused, whereupon the Knights of Labor issued a charter to the stereotype and electrotype finishers under the name of "The Good-Will Lodge" No. 4053. As an answer the old association joined the Central Labor Union and sent delegates in May, 1886 to the Trades Union Conference (this eventually became the American Federation of Labor) at Philadelphia. Meanwhile the members of the Good-Will Lodge of the Knights of Labor had not been idle. They applied for and received a charter from the International Typographical Union, adopting the name "Electrotypers and Stereotypers Union No. 1." The action of the International Typographical Union was bitterly assailed and enmity was rife until in 1888 delegates of the Good-Will Lodge and the Stereotypers Association met and, under a plan proposed two years before by James J. Freel, they combined and named the union "The New York Stereotypers Union;" however, the foundry men formed themselves into a separate unit. In 1889 the union was granted a charter by the International Typographical Union.

In 1893 an organization was formed within the International Typographical Union known as "The Trades District Union." Thru the extended power conferred upon the delegates by the stereotypers' and electrotypers' unions they were able to correct conditions which had in truth fostered many abuses, and eventually led to the formation of an international union. While the Trades District Union had been fairly successful in its meetings during the years of its existence, the idea of an international union had been continually discussed, but until 1900 no concerted action had been taken. In that year the resolution advocating withdrawal was first presented; it failed to pass because of lack of cohesive action. The following year, 1901, at the convention of the International Typographical Union held in Birmingham, Ala., the legislation was finally enacted and the stereotypers legally withdrew from the parent body, forming in 1902 "The International Stereotypers Union." With its organization the New York Stereotypers Union became the New York Stereotypers Union No. 1 of the International Stereotypers and Electrotypers Union of North America.

The further history of the union is a matter of record and concerns mainly, up to this date, decisions made to ameliorate the working conditions and to abolish abuses threatening those conditions. The first president of the New York Stereotypers Union was Edward Mills and the present incumbent is Michael J. P. Hogan.

Affiliated with the International Stereotypers and Electrotypers Union are 167 local unions, comprising in total 9,022 members. In all unions there exist Women's Auxiliaries, whose purpose is to further the purchasing of articles and goods American-made and Union-made. Also they render mutual aid and assistance to those members who are less fortunate.

From the time of the first strike in the office of Rivington's "Gazette" in the Revolutionary period to as late as 1850, labor conditions in newspaper offices were far from satisfactory. Most of the trouble was due to the fact that the compositors were paid for the amount of work they did and not for the amount of time they spent in the composing room.

The men who worked on the morning newspapers complained about the irregularity of their time. Local news and items clipped from the exchanges were usually in type by midnight. Sometimes ships bringing important news from abroad might dock at a wharf

134. Edward Mills, First President of the New York
Stereotypers Union

135. A Modern Stereotyping Plant. (1941)

late in the evening, and newspapers had to be prepared to meet just such an emergency. Printers could either hang around the office or they could go home, only to be aroused from their slumbers by the office devil who came with orders to hasten to the office in order that the latest news be put in the morning issue.

There was no uniformity in the price which individual papers paid their printers. These conditions were remedied thru the unions that were organized, and by the middle of the 19th century they did much to improve the conditions of the printers employed on city papers.

At the start editors were not debarred from membership in these unions. Horace Greeley was the first president of "The New York Printers Union" established in 1850, and he actively engaged in using his pen and his influence to improve working conditions among New York printers. When certain New York papers criticized the attempt to establish a union scale of wages throughout the city, it was Greeley who defended the cause of the printers to obtain "a fair day's pay for a fair day's work."

Other strikes of momentous importance to the newspaper pressmen, compositors and stereotypers were, first, the one instituted by the Typographical Union in 1883. The union started a weekly paper called "The Boycotter," to induce other trade unions to take up their strike against certain newspaper owners. This strike was not adjusted until 1892. Another important strike was the one fought out in the plant of "The New York Sun" in 1899. Hostilities did not cease until 1902 when a mutual agreement was reached.

A few remarks concerning schools and research work: A steadily increasing number of institutions and schools are performing the very commendable work of teaching practical stereotyping, and research work in the art is steadily increasing. In Europe there exist organizations associated with affiliates all through the different countries, which are engaged solely in the work of improving present printing methods, devoting special attention to newspaper problems. It is beyond the scope of this compilation to make mention of all centers of these activities.

Outstanding institutions of such a character abroad are: in England, the London School of Printing, which is an old established institution with day and evening classes for a five year training period in the art of stereotyping. At this school the rudiments of salesmanship applicable to the stereotyping industry also are taught. The Printing and Allied Trades Research Association (known as

Patra), in London, devotes a number of its monthly meetings to the study and advancement of stereotyping. For instance, one of its recent plenary meetings dealt solely with stereotyping problems. These meetings are attended by delegates from practically every important stereotype plant in England. The Liverpool School of Art has an important stereotype division. In the English colonies the Sydney Technical School in New South Wales has a practical stereotype department and conducts extensive research work.

The German Master Printers formed a research bureau in connection with the Technical High School in Charlottenburg. There also exist in that country a number of research laboratories and schools located throughout the country and run by the German Stereotypers Union, subsidized by the government.

The Association Générale Typographique of France is the head of all printing unions in that country. It maintains schools and research bureaus, located in different cities in France.

In France, the Printing Union subsidizes a number of schools of stereotyping and research is carried on in the polytechnical colleges.

In North America, the first cooperative research work on printing problems was undertaken in 1922 when George H. Carter established a testing section in the Government Printing Office in Washington. This department has been steadily developed and at present the testing section undertakes scientific research on problems which affect the whole of the printing trade, and naturally includes stereotyping. The American electrotypers conduct their research at the Bureau of Standards in Washington, and the American Lithographers have research laboratories in the University of Cincinnati. In the United States there also exist a large number of schools of journalism, and many trade schools in which theoretical and practical stereotyping is taught. Furthermore, the mechanical department of the American Newspaper Publishers Association publishes regularly exceedingly interesting bulletins covering every phase of the printing industry, and at their annual meetings which are attended by stereotypers from all over the country they have special stereotype symposia. There are also the Crafts Clubs with their research divisions located all over the United States; furthermore, the technical meetings of the International Stereotypers and Electrotypers Union with its school for stereotype apprentices. Finally the curriculum conducted yearly by the New York Times with its classes and exhibitions.

The Canadian printers have a research department for all branches of the printing art at the Government Library in Toronto.

In closing this compilation of historical data on stereotyping, the writer would like to repeat his often made statement that printers in America are more stereotype minded today than ever before. Present business conditions, increased competition, have forced producers and purchasers of printing work to look for substantial economies without sacrifice of quality. Of all reproducing mediums stereotyping is still the most economical. The ever increasing improvement and refinement of work done by stereotyping is attracting the purchasers of fine printing to that method. Letter-press printing has met all attacks and still maintains its predominant position in the printing art.

The wet paper pulp, clay and plaster of Paris methods of stereotyping dominated the field for over hundreds of years. The wet mat stereotyping process which celebrated its centenary in 1929, is still used in isolated cases. The infant among the matrices, the dry mat, is firmly implanted and has rapidly superseded its parent and grandparents.

The master stereotyper is well aware of the fact that stereotyping is an art as worthy of consideration and esteem as are the many other arts of the graphic industry, and he knows that the sum total of all of the above recited laborious experiments and the brilliant success achieved by his ancestors in the craft, have given to the art of printing an indispensable link without which a modern printing establishment cannot be imagined.

INDEX